30 YEARS BEHIND
BARS
KAREN GEDNEY, MD

To Rita,
please share it!

DEDICATION
TO MY HUSBAND.

TESTIMONIAL

"*30 Years Behind Bars* is a moving and ultimately uplifting recounting of a medical career spent behind the walls of prison, never sugarcoating the harshness of life behind bars, but affirming the shared humanity between caregiver and inmate. Dr. Gedney accurately captures the frustrations–and rewards–of providing care within a system that all too often favors retribution over rehabilitation and needlessly adds impediments to care that are at best capricious and–at worse–cruel, counterproductive, and dehumanizing. Through it all, her story affirms the best that exists within humanity and exemplifies what a force for emotional and physical healing a dedicated physician can be. In reminding us that all human beings deserve respect, Dr. Gedney reminds us that we can all choose to be forces for good. A fascinating read, and one I recommend to everyone."

- Richard Presnell, MD

GET IN TOUCH WITH KAREN GEDNEY, MD
www.DiscoverDrG.com

LIKE AND FOLLOW ON FACEBOOK
www.facebook.com/KarenGedneyMD

This is a work of nonfiction. In order to protect their identities, I changed the names and identifying details of colleagues, officers, and inmates — except for one name, which is a matter of public record. The events, timelines and conversations that took place were recounted from the journals I kept, from the writings of the inmates, from newspaper articles, and from my memory.

Karen Gedney, MD

First Edition

ISBN 978-0-9998809-0-6

Prologue

I looked at the phone in my hand, and thought: *So, I'm going to prison for the next four years.*

It was 1987, and the National Health Corps was placing me in an under-served area to pay back my medical school scholarship. I had known this day was coming, but it never occurred to me that I could be sent to a male medium-security prison.

Part of me was thrilled that they were sending me to a facility close by, so I didn't have to relocate to a different region. The other part of me wondered what it would be like to be a prison doctor.

I hung up the phone and went into the den to share the news with Coley, my husband of two months.

"Coley, do you want to hear where I'm going to be sent for the next four years?"

He turned toward me and shut off the television with an expectant, slightly worried look.

I sat down next to him. "We don't have to move, but they're placing me in the prison system."

Coley stood up and enveloped me in a bear hug. I knew he was relieved about not moving. "It's going to be a good opportunity for you," he murmured.

Coley was an optimist, even his business card displayed a Chinese phrase that was said to represent both crisis and opportunity. His attitude acted as my true north, and I valued that influence. I had grown up with a German mother, whose pessimism and anxieties were a byproduct of her experiences in World War II as a child. She had taught me to see every cloud; Coley taught me to see their silver linings.

We were still dating when I first told Coley about my commitment to the Corps. "When I get my placement, would you come with me?" I had asked.

His handsome brown face had broken into a sly smile. "Not if you get sent to some backwater in Mississippi."

Remembering that moment, I gave Coley another squeeze before letting go.

"You know," I said, "I just had the oddest memory. Remember how I told you that I decided to become a doctor when I was nine years old?"

He nodded his head and leaned back into the couch.

"Well, when I was a kid, I used to fantasize about healing wounds. You know, like the cowboy who got shot, the Indian who got stabbed, the spy who was poisoned. But they were always men, in my stories. I never thought of doctoring women. I find it a bit funny now that I'm going to be taking care of an all-male population for the next four years."

Coley cocked his head and studied me. A small smile turned up the corners of his mouth, "Well, you're a healer." He rubbed his chin. "So, when are you going to tell your mother?"

PART ONE

Karen Gedney, MD

1. First Day

Karen Gedney, MD

I drove over the rise and saw the sprawling, barren prison in the distance, surrounded by fields of green alfalfa. The road in front of me curved to the left, and to my right was a long straight road that led directly to a large parking lot. I slowed down and ran my eyes over a dozen grey buildings of varied sizes, surrounded by two chain-link fence systems with guard towers at each corner.

The prison was only twenty minutes from where I lived. I had seen its lights from the highway at night, but had never seen it in the day with the backdrop of the mountains. I turned onto the prison road, knowing I was entering a different world.

I found a parking spot and sat in my car, looking out at my new workplace. An officer walked out of the prison gatehouse and opened a large entrance gate. I noticed the glint of the summer sun off the curls of barbed wire running across the top of the fence. A small delivery truck pulled through the gate, and the officer closed and re-locked the metal fence behind it.

I could feel my heart beating behind my breastbone and my mouth starting to go dry as I opened the car door and stepped out. I had yet to find the courage to walk across the parking lot to the gatehouse. I breathed in and held it for a few seconds, then let it out slowly. *Is that the smell of manure?* I remembered that I would also be responsible for the adjacent prison camp, where the prisoners apparently took care of cows.

I took another slow breath and set my feet in motion, making my way to the light-grey building with GATEHOUSE stenciled in black above its door. The officer was still on his way back after closing the gate. I shifted my weight from one foot to the other and looked back at the parking lot, willing myself to stay calm. Suddenly a loud buzzer startled me, and it took me a moment to register that I had to pull open the door to enter.

The gate officer wore a tan uniform with one stripe on the shoulder and a heavy black belt with a large belly flowing over it. He stood in what looked like a cage to me. Sliding open the Plexiglas panel in front of him, he asked, "Are you here to see someone?"

3

I licked my dry lips and swallowed. "My name is Dr. G and I'm supposed to start work here today."

The officer brushed the sweat off his upper lip and ran his beefy hand across his bald head, then reached for a clipboard hanging on the wall. "Why the hell don't they tell me anything?" he muttered, leafing through the papers on the clipboard. After a moment, he glanced up at me again and asked, "You sure you weren't supposed to go to Central or the warden's office?"

I shook my head and mentally played back the conversation I'd had with Dr. Downing, the prison medical director who had hired me. He had told me to show up today at this place and this time. He had also informed me that the governor had petitioned the federal government to mandate the prison as a health manpower shortage area, so they could get a National Health Corps doctor like me. It seemed the prison was under federal lawsuits to give healthcare to the inmates, and since no doctor wanted to work behind prison walls, they had to requisition one.

The officer put the clipboard back on the wall and leaned forward on both his hands. "Was someone going to meet you up here to bring you in? Someone like the charge nurse?"

"Not that I know of." I took a small step back, intimidated by his body language.

He snorted, picked up the black phone in front of him and punched three buttons.

"Hey Lieutenant, it's Jones in the gatehouse. Do you know anything about a doctor who's supposed to start working here today? ...No, she's standing right in front of me and doesn't seem to know anything." He paused, sighed, and looked me up and down. I felt the heat start in my neck and travel up to my face. Finally, he looked back at his papers. "Yeah, okay," he said, and hung up the phone.

Officer Jones pointed at a clipboard on the counter with the heading "Visitors" on it. "Sign in. I need to see your driver's license."

4

I handed him my license, and he tossed a visitor's badge onto the counter. "When you leave, give the officer your visitor's badge, and he'll give you back your license." Then he pointed at my black bag, which held my stethoscope and lunch. "I need to check your bag, and you need to walk through the metal detector."

Finally, the officer seemed satisfied that I wasn't his problem anymore, and buzzed open the door in front of me. Inside, I turned and saw that he had another opening in his cage on this side, and had put my black bag on the counter.

Officer Jones nudged the bag in my direction. "Just go through that door and you'll see an iron gate. Take a right and you'll be in Operations. Then the lieutenant will show you where Medical is."

"Thanks," I muttered. He turned his back on me before I could ask anything else.

I was glad I could see the gate he was talking about, just fifty feet beyond the door as I stepped out of the gatehouse and onto the prison campus. There was a little grass on each side of the concrete walkway. I could see inmates dressed in blue in the distance through the metal fence.

Feeling conspicuous, I walked to the gate and looked at the white door to my right. *This must be Operations.* The door was propped open with a grey cement block, and the smell of burnt coffee greeted me when I peeked inside. I could see another pair of iron bars ten feet past this door, with three officers standing at desks behind a counter. As I timidly stepped inside, one of the officers spied me and hit a button on his desk, and the barred door clattered open. I tried to look authoritative as I walked through to the area where the officers were seated. The heavy door closed behind me with a harsh clang that reverberated off the concrete walls. I cringed.

The officer laughed and pointed at another iron door twenty feet ahead. "You'll get used to it. Go through that one, and the officer in the infirmary will let you in."

5

I glanced at the cement wall behind him, which was covered in bulletin boards featuring names followed by numbers. He ignored me and turned to the officer sitting at the other desk. "Hey, do we have bed changes and movements today?"

I choked back a giggle. *Sounds like bowel movements. Oh, get a grip on yourself, Karen.* I bit the inside of my cheek and walked through the second iron door, making sure I held onto it when it closed so it didn't make that horrible sound.

This door was the exit from Operations, and the entrance to the prison itself. Inside, the first thing I saw was an open jail cell, followed by yet another iron door. *All these gates and doors. This is going to add half an hour to my day just getting in and out of the building.*

An officer with fading red hair pulled the next door open from the other side and gave me a tired smile. "My name's Fred. I'm the infirmary officer."

I smiled and put out my hand, "I'm Dr. G. and this is my first day in prison."

He shook my hand and cocked his head toward a large fan in the corner. "I hope you like the heat because we don't have air conditioning back here." Looking down the long hallway, he added, "There's Hannah. Maybe she can fill you in before we have to do the meds." I sure hoped so.

Hannah was wearing a white nurse's uniform and white nurse's shoes and had white starched hair to match. The only color she had on was a startling, dark red lipstick accentuating her thin, wrinkled lips. When she shook my hand, I noticed that her fingernails were painted the same shade of red. Her hands were thin, and the weak handshake did not match the shrill tone in her voice.

"Hello. So you're the new doctor."

"Yes, I'm Dr. G."

"I know." She gestured at a portly, kind-faced man in a blue scrub, who

6

had followed a few paces behind her. "I'm going to have Tom show you around, because I've got to pass out meds now and I'm the only one here now. I'll talk to you later."

Hannah pivoted with military precision and marched into a small room, where I could see shelves filled with bottles of pills.

The man put out his hand and gave me a kind smile. "Hi, my name's Tom. It would be my pleasure to show you your office and give you a tour of the infirmary."

Finally, somebody polite. Tom's interest in me helped decrease the rate at which my heart was pounding. He showed me the treatment room and X-ray room, then we walked down a long dark hallway. "I hope you like your new office," Tom said, standing back so I could open the door.

The room had white walls and a grey floor. One wall had a line of windows made of security glass with wire woven through it. *At least I have windows, so some light can come in. Why is this place so dark and cramped?* I walked over to the windows and felt relieved when I saw a small patch of green lawn next to the outside wall. On the other side of the green was a tall metal fence and the parched brown dirt of the prison yard.

We continued our tour, into another dark hallway lined with doors. My nose wrinkled at the distinctive smell of urine that had been sitting around too long. Tom stopped and pointed down the hallway.

"We've got a total of ten rooms back here. We can house twenty guys in here if we have to. Right now, we have fifteen. Most of them are probably sleeping now, and I doubt Hannah wants me to bring you into their cells. She'll let you know what she wants you to do."

He looked at his wristwatch. "She'll be wrapping up pretty soon. I should get you back there."

We walked back toward the infirmary offices, but I felt Tom slow his pace when we turned the corner. A large man in dark green scrubs was walking toward us. I slowed my pace to match Tom's, as the man in front of us

7

stopped and put his hand on his hip.

Tom stopped too and cleared his throat. "Hannah asked me to show the new doctor around." He turned to me. "Dr. G., this is Gordy. He's one of the PAs here." Then Tom turned quickly and strode away without another word.

I extended my hand to Gordy, but he didn't seem to notice it, because he was glaring at Tom.

"Do you know who he is?" Gordy asked me. "He's a cho-mo." My puzzled look must have irritated him because he said in a voice that my retreating guide must have heard: "You know. He's a child molester."

I felt my jaw go slack. I didn't know if I was shocked because I had no idea that I was being led around by an inmate—or was I more shocked by the unprofessional behavior of the staff for not telling me?

I sensed that I was being tested, but by whom, and for what reason?

2. Prison Life

I survived my first two weeks in prison, in a whirlwind of new routines, medical consults, and confusing interactions. At least I had grown accustomed to being surrounded by inmates. Their medical complaints were like any other patient and doing my job as professionally as I could made me feel less like a fish out of water. Sometimes, the inmates seemed to be easier to talk to than the officers and nurses—but maybe I just needed to get my bearings.

Entering the clinic on Monday morning of my third week, I was greeted by Gordy, the physician assistant. He was a couple of inches over six feet, but his girth and his large, meaty hands made him seem bigger.

Gordy pulled the collar of his shirt away from his neck. "Doc, I hear it's going to be over a hundred today, and when it's that hot you can expect some excitement." He twirled the end of his handlebar mustache, appearing almost happy about the prospect. He had been an Army medic in Vietnam, and seemed to be at home working in the prison.

"What kind of excitement do you mean?" I asked, not wanting to make the mistake of assuming that I knew what the staff or the inmates were talking about.

He laughed and the jowls above his large neck quivered. His bright brown eyes looked down at me. "The heat makes them irritated," he said. "Anything can set them off. You'll see for yourself today, because I'm heading over to the women's prison."

There were two other prisons within five miles of this one, but the medical director still had not briefed me on the hierarchy in the medical department, or who was responsible for what Gordy did. He seemed to do what he wanted and go where he pleased.

"Gordy, is the medical director your supervising physician?" I asked. "He hasn't talked to me since he hired me, and I was told he went on vacation the week I started working here. I called his secretary yesterday and she said she wasn't sure when he would be back. Do you know him? What's going on?"

10

Gordy shrugged his shoulders and pulled his white shirt off his sweaty chest. "Yeah, he's one of those political types and supervises me in name only."

"What does that mean?" I asked.

"He's a buddy of the governor. He came out of retirement to help them get a doctor for this place and one for Max." He chuckled. "A blonde here, and a black female at Max. You've gotta love it."

Gordy turned and walked away before I could formulate a response. All I knew was that my list of questions was getting longer every minute. Nobody seemed to give straight answers around here. Gordy called me "Doc," but considered himself in charge and just laughed at me when I asked him questions.

I flashed back to what my husband Coley had told me about surviving Vietnam as a platoon leader and lieutenant: he had asked his sergeant, an experienced combat leader, to keep him out of trouble. *Should I ask Gordy to keep me out of trouble? Or should I just wait until I can talk to the director?* I wondered if he would keep me out of trouble anyway; I had my doubts. My paranoia was increasing with each passing day. *How could the medical director go on vacation the day I started, and not leave anyone else in charge to help me navigate this system?*

My thoughts were interrupted by the sound of officers yelling. I looked down the hallway to see two officers dragging a muscular, sweaty black inmate who was cuffed behind his back. They had him by the arms and were trying to avoid being kicked as they dragged him.

I could see the inmate was bleeding from a wound over his eye. One of his kicks connected with the shin of one of the officers, who stopped and yelled, "God dammit, lay the fucker down so we can shackle his legs."

The other officer kicked the inmate in the back of his knee, and they slammed him into the floor face-first and held him down. By this time, an officer from Operations had come through the gate. He hog-tied the inmate's legs to his hands.

The inmate was fighting and yelling. "I'm gonna fuckin' kill you when I get out of these chains!" he screamed.

The officers weren't looking at me, and I hoped the inmate would tire himself out with all his yelling and thrashing before anyone asked me to do anything. Then I heard barking. The inmate jerked his head around and his eyes widened in fear. A big German Shepherd was pulling hard on its leash, and the thin officer at the other end was having a hard time holding the dog back. Its claws were scraping on the concrete floor and saliva dripped from its mouth.

The inmate started to shake and whimper, which seemed to make the dog harder to control. One of the officers started laughing. "So look who's scared of dogs. Ya gonna quit kickin' us or what?"

Suddenly the inmate convulsed and went into a seizure. The dog lunged with such force that the officer couldn't control it, and its jaws closed on the seizing inmate's thigh. Two officers began pulling the dog off the inmate's leg, and the officer still holding down the inmate screamed "What the fuck?" as he continued to seize.

I have to do something, but what? I looked down the hall toward the treatment room, and saw Rodney standing in the doorway. He was the X-ray tech, and also an inmate. His eyes locked on mine, and then he went back into the room and reappeared with gloves and supplies. My hand was shaking when I took them, but steadied when I put the gloves on.

I walked over to the inmate, who was bleeding from the thigh and still convulsing. The dog was being dragged out of the room. I knelt next to the inmate's head. "We need to roll him to his side so he doesn't choke," I said to the officers holding him.

But the officers didn't do anything. Instead, they turned toward Hannah, who was standing behind the med counter, watching with her arms crossed and fists clenched.

Hannah scoffed. "She's the new doctor."

The officers looked back at me, and I added in a stronger voice, "Can you also take the cuffs off him? One of his wrists looks really swollen and I'm worried it's broken."

"Take the cuffs off his wrists, but leave his leg irons on," said one of the officers. The others did what he said, and we rolled him to his side. The inmate had stopped convulsing, and his breathing seemed to be improving. I felt his pulse at his wrist; it was hammering at a rate over a hundred. I wrapped gauze around his thigh to stop the bleeding, then looked up to see Rodney standing nearby.

"Doc, do you want to take him to X-ray and check his wrist before we bring him to the treatment room?" Rodney asked.

I looked down the hallway and nodded. "Makes sense. Let's get him on the board. I need two strong officers, one on each end. Rodney and I will be on the sides to make sure he doesn't roll off. One, two, three, lift."

Fortunately, the inmate didn't regain full consciousness until after we completed the X-ray and the treatment for his wounds. After we had finished and he was safely inside a locked cell, I asked Rodney to come into my office to talk. He had helped me get through my first little emergency, and I felt I had found a potential ally.

Rodney stood in the doorway and looked nervously down the hall. He was in his early thirties and had intelligent blue eyes and sandy hair.

I pointed to the chair in front of my desk. "Why don't you come in and sit down. I wanted to tell you how much I appreciated your help this morning... and I wanted to ask you some questions."

Rodney shifted his weight and looked down at the floor, shaking his head. Then he looked up and gave me a little smile. "It's better if I stay out here."

"Okay. Well, the X-ray you took today was great, but I don't understand why an inmate is taking X-rays. Don't they have an X-ray tech here?"

"No, they haven't been able to hire one and I've been doing it up here for the last four years. I actually was an X-ray and nuclear medicine tech on the outside." He looked down the hall again and rocked forward on his feet.

"Rodney, do you help Gordy and the nurses as well in this department when they need it?"

He put his hands in his pockets and the smallest smile touched his eyes. "Some don't think they need any help."

"Well, I appreciate any help when it comes to taking care of my patients."

I wanted to ask him what he thought about Hannah, but held my tongue. I couldn't imagine her ever doing anything that would get her white nurse's dress dirty. I had only seen her pass out pills and give orders to the other nurses, who were not fond of her mood swings.

Instead I asked, "Rodney, have you ever seen them bring in a dog when an inmate is already tied up on the ground?"

His eyes darted to me and then down the hall. He replied, "Not in the clinic," before he pushed himself off the door he was leaning on and walked back to the X-ray room.

I watched Rodney leave and threw my empty yogurt container in the wastebasket next to my desk with more force than was necessary. I looked around at the empty white walls of my office. *Am I allowed to bring anything into my office to brighten it up?* My hands clenched and I felt a wave of frustration roll over me. *Who would I ask? Why didn't the medical director at least give me some orientation before he left on vacation? It's been over two weeks since I started in this place. Something has to be wrong.*

I picked up the phone and dialed.

"Medical Director's office, this is Mary speaking."

"Mary, this is Dr. G. We talked last week. I wanted to know if Dr. Downing is back from his vacation yet."

She hesitated. "No... He isn't, can I take a message?"

"Can you tell me when he'll be back?"

Her hesitation was longer this time. "Uh... I don't know when he'll be back."

I could feel my eyebrows raising as my pulse accelerated. "Is there something wrong? He *is* coming back, right?"

Silence. Then I heard her clear her throat. "I'm, ahh... not at liberty to say."

I held the black phone receiver away from my body and stared at it, thinking. Then I put it back to my ear. "Okay. Who can tell me what's going on and what's expected of me? This is my first time working in a prison and I've been given no orientation or training or anything."

I could hear the pitch in my voice going up, and told myself to stay calm. *Calm? What, am I crazy? I don't know any of the rules of the game here and the only people who seem to have been kind and helpful to me have been inmates.*

"I'm sorry," Mary said, "but I don't know anything about your orientation or who is supposed to be responsible for that. Have you talked to the Director of Nursing, Sylvia Ignin?"

Ignin. Why does that name sound familiar to me? Oh, I remember, the Associate Warden here is named Ignin too.

"No, no one has really talked to me. What does she do?"

"Sylvia is in charge of all the nurses. She has an office at Central. Would you like me to call her and ask if she could see you today?"

"Yes, please do." Some of the tension left my body with the prospect of finally speaking to someone who could shed some light on my duties in the prison.

Twenty minutes later, Mary called back. "Sylvia can see you today at

4:45."

I had been to Central once before, when Dr. Downing interviewed me. I knew that the prison director and other major administrators had offices in that old stone building, a mile down the road from my facility. The Central building looked like it had been built in the late 1800s. At least it would be easy to find. I grabbed a pen and started a list of questions I needed answers for.

- Where is Dr. Downing, and when is he coming back?
- Who is responsible for giving me orientation?
- Who do I talk to in security? Is it the warden, the captain, the assistant warden, or someone else?
- Am I Gordy's supervisor? If not, am I responsible for what he does?
- Who is Hannah's supervisor and why does she seem to have an issue with me?
- Who supervises the inmates that are working in the medical department?

Over the past two weeks, I had tried to get my questions answered, but I was still in the dark. I hoped that Sylvia Ignin, who was in charge of all the prison nurses in the state, would give me some answers and help me feel that I was needed and welcome in the medical department. I had worked in various challenging medical settings over the years, but I had never before experienced paranoia over my own job and wellbeing. *Why? Is it just this place, or is it my imagination?*

I arrived at Sylvia's office ten minutes early. She glanced at the large circular clock behind her on the wall, and motioned me to sit in the chair in front of her desk. The desk was covered in paper, with a large ashtray overflowing with cigarette butts next to her right hand.

I put out my hand and introduced myself before sitting. Sylvia's short, light brown hair added to the pinched look on her face, and when she nodded, her wire-rimmed glasses slipped down her nose.

16

She pushed them back with a tobacco-stained index finger. "What can I do for you? Mary said you wanted to talk to me."

"Well, first, thank you for taking the time to speak with me. I was hoping you could tell me when Dr. Downing would be back. I haven't gone through any orientation yet and I don't know who I should report to if I need to talk to someone about medical issues or what happens in the clinic." I could still see the teeth of the German Shepherd latched onto the inmate's thigh.

Sylvia looked at the clock again and sighed. "I'm not responsible for Dr. Downing or the docs, only the nurses. The nurses are the ones who've always run the medical department."

"Dr. Downing informed me in my interview that the prison was having a hard time getting a doctor to work in the prison. When was the last time the nurses at my facility worked with a doctor?"

"Hmph—if you would even call the last guy a doctor. He used to talk to an imaginary parrot on his shoulder for advice, and he left two years ago anyway."

I didn't know how to respond to that, and Sylvia filled in the silence. "Look, the only docs who've ever worked here are the type that can't work anywhere else. If they could, they wouldn't be here. The nurses and physician assistants have run this place for years, and I expect we'll just keep running it in the future." She pushed her chair back, its feet grating on the floor, and stood up.

I felt foolish sitting there, so I stood up as well. "Ms. Ignin, since you don't know when Dr. Downing will return, could you please tell me who I should consider my supervisor? Who would be able to help me with my orientation to the prison system?"

Her eyes narrowed behind her glasses. "Like I told you, the nurses are in charge. Hannah will tell you what you need to know."

I was taken back by her hostility. *What did I ever do to you?* I decided to avoid aggravating her further. "Thank you for taking the time to talk to me.

17

If you have any new information regarding Dr. Downing, please let me know."

"If there's any news, it will come from his secretary, not me. If you'll excuse me, I have important things to do." Sylvia walked out of her office without looking back at me.

I felt the heat rise in my face and in the roots of my hair. *What is that woman's problem? Does she think I'm an impaired physician, like the last doctor who was talking to an imaginary parrot? Does she have an issue with doctors for some other reason I don't know about? Is it me, or does she treat everyone like that? And she's married to the assistant warden at my facility. Wonderful.*

Walking out of Central, I started imagining the conversation I would try to initiate tomorrow with Hannah, but stopped myself. *Not now, it will just ruin my dinner with Coley tonight.*

The next morning, I saw a pretty nurse with red hair walk into the clinic, followed by Rodney carrying a large medical bag. She stopped at the counter in front of the med room and smiled at me. "You must be the new doctor here. I'm Lucy. And that was my first time on the prison yard."

"Nice to meet you, I'm Dr. G. I haven't even been on the yard yet. What was it like?"

She laughed. "Well, thank God Rodney went with me, otherwise I wouldn't have known where to go or what to do when I finally got out there. He knew the guy and told me he had a history of panic attacks. Sure enough, when we got him breathing in a bag, he calmed down and his vitals went back to normal."

"I know what you mean. Rodney was very helpful to me yesterday as well. Lucy, I've only been here for two weeks and haven't really been shown around. Has Hannah helped you get oriented here?"

Lucy lifted her well-shaped red eyebrows. "You've got to be kidding. I don't know what her story is. I'm not sure from day to day whether I'll be dealing with Dr. Jekyll or Mr. Hyde. She started me on the night shift, and all she seemed to care about was passing out nighttime meds. If it wasn't for

Rodney, I would have quit. He showed me where everything was, helped me with the patients in the back and…" She looked down at her grey sneakers, which matched her scrubs. "It's crazy, isn't it?"

"I know what you mean." We both heard Hannah's shrill voice at the end of the hallway, yelling at the inmate she was wheeling into the clinic, and our eyes met.

Lucy's brows arched again. "Good luck," she whispered. "I'm heading home now, but I hope to see you in the future."

"Me too," I said, and I walked down the hallway toward the treatment room.

As I approached, I heard a shout: "Stop yelling at me! It's not my fault it got worse, I told you I needed a better bed."

I stepped into the room. Hannah looked up and took a step back from the man in the wheelchair.

"I told him not to sit on that bedsore, but does he listen to me?" She threw her arms in the air. "See if you can do something with him," she snarled, and stomped out of the room.

I had met the patient, Mr. Nerelli, only briefly the week before. He was a thirty-two-year-old who had been shot in the back at twenty-nine and was paralyzed from the waist down. He did his own self-care. I was told he couldn't live on the yard, because it was not built to accommodate wheelchairs or a person who had to take extra measures every day to pass urine and stool—measures that the other inmates found offensive.

Nerelli rubbed the front of his neck while he watched Hannah leave. "She's a witch, isn't she?"

"Um… She seemed concerned about your bed sore. How long have you had it?"

He turned his wheelchair around to face me and pushed up on his strong hands to sit straighter. "I'm not sure, because I can't feel anything be-

19

low my nipples, but I noticed blood on my underwear a week ago. The mattress on my bed is for shit, and I told Hannah I needed a special cushion for my chair. I know what to do to keep my skin from breaking down, but I can't lie in a metal bed and sit all day in this shitty chair without getting into trouble."

Nerelli pointed at the small wheel at the base of his chair. "You see that? It's about to come off. All I need is to fall over and break a leg." He touched his thin thigh. "They're like matchsticks now."

"What are the nurses dressing it with?"

"The new nurse Lucy was the first one who took care of it, but that witch Hannah chewed her out and said I need to change the dressing myself. I would if I could see or feel it, but I can't do either. I don't want Lucy to get in trouble with Hannah, but... I don't want it to get worse either."

I examined him and re-dressed his large bedsore, which would be considered a stage two decubitus. Then I went back to his cell to evaluate his bed and mattress. The bed was a sheet of metal, and the lumpy mattress was less than an inch thick.

"Mr. Nerelli, I'm new here and I'm not sure how things are done, but I will see what I can do to help you get some pressure off that open sore you're sitting on all day long."

He put his hands on the side of his wheelchair and pushed his body up, holding himself above his chair. "I really do what I can to keep the pressure off. It would be great, though, if you could just get me a thick cushion for the chair. A double mattress would be a godsend."

"Keep doing as much as you can to keep the pressure off that area, and I'll talk to Hannah about the supplies you need. I'll also write an order in your chart to have a nurse measure the decubitus and do your dressing changes every day, so I know if it's healing."

"That would be great, Doc," Nerelli said as I turned to go, "but watch out for Cruella, she's the type that eats puppies."

20

I smiled as I walked down the hallway. Cruella, the Disney villain. There was a bit of a resemblance. The white hair, the startling red lips, the shrieking. Cruella wanted to kill all the puppies to make herself a coat, if I remembered correctly. What did Hannah want?

3. Dr. Downing

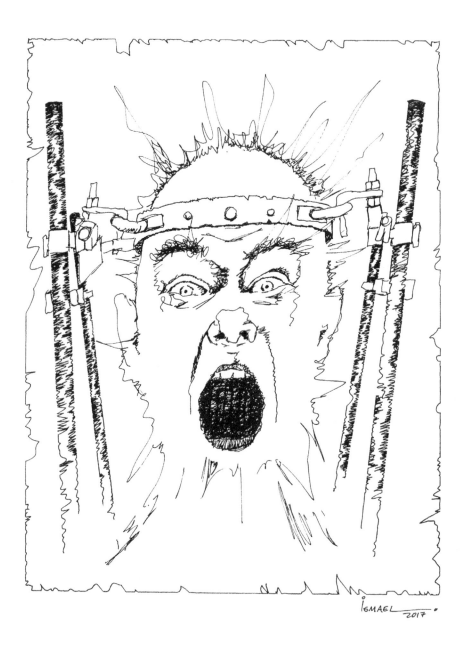

Karen Gedney, MD

I opened the car door and immediately regretted that I had forgotten to crack the windows of my little white Escort to keep it from turning into an oven. The July sun was still broiling the top of my steering wheel at five o'clock, and I decided to open the doors of the car to let the light breeze off the alfalfa fields see what it could do.

As I drove out of the parking lot, I looked at the half-mile road leading into the prison and noticed green vans coming back into the adjacent prison camp. They would be carrying the inmates who had been doing work for the Division of Forestry that day. I smiled, thinking about the inmate I saw today from the Forestry camp. He had twisted his ankle after working on a fire. The whites of his eyes stood out in his expressive dark face when he told me about sleeping outside on the side of a mountain, "with all those nasty crawly things." It had never occurred to me that the Forestry Service used prison inmates to climb up and down the mountains and fight fires.

I glanced back at the main prison yard, and wondered what an officer did all day in one of those towers at each corner of the prison fence. *Over eight hours just sitting there, looking at one fence line. I'd go nuts.* It was Friday, the end of my third week in prison—and at least I wasn't bored. Frustrated and irritated, yes, but not bored.

When I got home that night, Coley hugged me longer than usual. I took a step back from him and his eyes travelled down my body. "How's my beautiful wife holding up?"

I pulled my blouse away from my sweaty chest. "Surviving, but I'll feel better once I get out of these clothes. All I really want to do right now is drink something cold."

"You'll feel like eating when you see this shrimp and crab salad I brought you from the store."

He was right; I did feel hungry when I sat down across from him, gulping down another glass of ice tea.

"Coley," I said, "what would you do if you were in my position and the

23

guy that hired you took off for three weeks and didn't put anything in place to orient you when you started, and everyone you asked said they didn't know when he was coming back?"

Coley stopped with his forkful of crab halfway to his mouth. "I'd think there was something fishy going on," he said, and popped his food in his mouth. Seeing me roll my eyes, he added, "Who's his boss?"

I bit my lower lip and looked down at my plate, spearing a plump shrimp with my fork. "No one's above him in the medical department, but I guess the prison director for the entire state would be considered his boss."

"Have you asked him?"

"No… not yet. But why do you think no one I've talked to in the medical department has given me any information? I don't know what or who to believe. Today, one of the inmates who works in the clinic basically told me to watch my back if I was around the assistant warden or his wife. Remember I told you I met Sylvia, the director of nursing, the other day, and how rude she was?"

"She probably just had a bad day—or she was jealous."

"Jealous of what?"

"Your youth and beauty, my dear," Coley said and raised his glass.

"No, I don't think that was the reason, but I'm glad you think I'm cute. Seriously, Coley, why would an inmate tell me such a thing? Do you think he was telling the truth?"

Coley finished chewing and took a sip of his iced tea. I could see he was considering what to say. We had lived together for a year, but had only been married for a few months, and he was still unsure whether I wanted an answer or just wanted to vent.

He took the easy way out and asked, "What do *you* think?"

"I'm not sure, but when I asked the inmate why he told me that, he said the Ignins were dangerous and considered me a threat. He told me it had to do with the power they could wield between the two of them to control the inmates and the budget."

Coley's thick black eyebrows raised. "What would an inmate know about budgets?"

"I don't know, but the inmate who warned me today had worked for years as a clerk to the captain. That's the officer in charge of all of the security. And it's the weirdest thing. The inmates tell me all sorts of things, but the people who are in charge basically brush me off and don't tell me anything."

Coley rubbed his stubbled cheeks and looked up at the ceiling. "Yeah, you'd think the people in charge would want you to know about your role and prison security. I'd be careful, though, around the inmates. You're a very attractive, fit blonde and I'm sure they want to get on your good side."

"Well, if I'm so attractive, why haven't the security officers tried to get on my good side?"

Coley laughed and leaned back in his chair. "You probably intimidate them. Think about it. You're a doctor, and how many of them do you think have even gone to college?" He stood and picked up his plate. "So do you want to watch a movie tonight? "

The movie did take my mind off the prison, and when I curled up with Coley that night, I felt safe and was able to fall asleep quickly. That weekend brought temperatures over a hundred degrees, and I was glad we had air conditioning in the house and could stay inside. I wondered how the inmates and staff were faring in the heat, and hoped it would cool off before I headed back to work on Monday.

I didn't start to feel anxious again until I walked into the clinic Monday morning. I jumped when the phone rang, but then breathed a sigh of relief: it was Dr. Downing's secretary, and he wanted to see me in his office at noon.

I was so relieved and distracted that I almost didn't notice the inmate sitting outside Gordy's office on a bench. He was leaning forward with his right fist clenched over his left chest.

25

I stopped and squatted down to see his face. "Are you all right? Has anyone seen you yet?"

The inmate's face was pale and his sandy brown hair was balding, but he didn't look over thirty-five to me. He said through clenched teeth, "The doc says it's just gas and the nurse went to get me some Mylanta."

I stood up and noticed that Gordy wasn't in his room. Down the hall, Hannah was marching toward me holding a small plastic cup filled with Mylanta.

She waved her hand at me. "He's already been seen. Once he takes this, he can go."

I looked at the inmate and thought, *If he wasn't so young, I'd think he was having a heart attack.*

"Hannah, I'm going to see how he does with the antacid."

"Hmph, well, I've got to pass the meds and you have patients waiting." She took the empty medicine cup from the inmate and held it between two fingers as she walked back to her meds room.

I sat down next to the inmate. "Did the Mylanta help?"

He shook his head and bent further over.

"Did Gordy examine you and do an EKG?"

He shook his head again, and I could see him grimace.

"Look, my name is Dr. G. and I'd like to do an EKG on you and examine you. Is that okay with you?"

He turned his head to look at me. His grey eyes were starting to tear up as he grunted, "Can you stop this pain in my chest?"

"On a scale of one to ten, where ten is the worst pain ever, how bad is it?"

He gulped. "Nine I guess." Then he bent over further and exhaled, "Maybe ten."

The treatment room with the EKG machine was fifteen feet away. I put my hand under his left arm. "If I help you, can you walk to that room?"

He nodded, stood up, and walked without straightening up all the way. When I entered the room, I was relieved to see Rodney cleaning the sink in the room. He looked at me, then grabbed the EKG machine and wheeled it over to the exam table. I started to unbutton the inmate's blue shirt, and had him lie on the table.

As I helped Rodney attach the leads, I eyed the old EKG machine and prayed it worked. Indeed, it did: we saw the EKG come out with tombstone T-waves across his anterior leads. He was having a heart attack, and it was a big one.

"Rodney, how do I get him shipped out to an ER? Do we have any nitro, or an IV setup in here?" I tried to pull open the drawer of the crash cart and found it was locked. No one had thought to give me a key.

The inmate on the table rolled to his left side and clenched his fist. "Why does it hurt so bad?" he groaned. "What's the matter with me?"

I patted him on the shoulder and told Rodney to get Hannah to call 911, then bring me what I needed.

"What's your name?" I asked, feeling his pulse at his wrist. *Where do they keep the blood pressure cuff in this room?* I checked my watch. Eight-fifteen in the morning.

"Robbins. Andy Robbins."

"Mr. Robbins, I'm concerned that the pain is coming from your heart. I'm going to send you to the hospital so they can take care of you. When my nurse gets here, I'm going to give you something that should help with the pain. Have you ever had problems with your heart before?"

He shook his head.

"Are you taking any medications or any drugs off the yard?"

"No," he moaned.

I didn't have to ask him if he was a smoker, because I could see the nicotine stains on his fingers and smell the cheap Bugler tobacco the inmates used in their rolled cigarettes.

"Did you use drugs in the past, like cocaine or meth?"

He nodded. I knew those drugs constricted blood vessels, and had seen addicts ruin their hearts.

Rodney returned to the room. "The ambulance has been called, and Hannah is bringing what you need. I told her to bring you some morphine too."

I touched Mr. Robbins on the shoulder. "Are you allergic to any medications?"

He shook his head.

"What were you doing when the pain started?"

"I just was reading the letter my fiancée sent me and... she's leaving me," Robbins whimpered.

Hannah walked through the door with a tray and placed it on the counter. I picked up the little brown glass bottle of nitroglycerin pills, and placed one of the tiny white pills under Mr. Robbins' tongue.

"Hannah, can you put in an IV?"

Her shoulders drew back. "I don't do IVs anymore, I just pass out meds. That's your job."

I glanced at Rodney, who looked down at his faded blue tennis shoes. I put in the IV and picked up the vial of morphine.

"That's the only one we have, and the ambulance will be here soon," Hannah said, with an edge to her voice.

"He needs it, and I'm giving him three milligrams now. Rodney, what's his BP?"

"It's 152 over 100 and his rate is 82." *A little high, but that's probably due to his pain.*

"Mr. Robbins, what's the number on your pain now? The medicine I've given you should be starting to help you."

"Maybe an eight. I need some more morphine."

Hannah sniffed, but stopped the roll of her eyes when she saw my look.

A few minutes later, the paramedics arrived. When they left with the inmate and his EKG, I breathed a sigh of relief. I had dodged a bullet.

I needed to find out what medical supplies we actually had, and where everything was kept. Also, where was Gordy, and what was I going to say to him?

By eleven o'clock I had seen ten patients, but not Gordy. The inmates didn't know where he was, and when I asked Hannah and told her that I had a meeting at Central with Dr. Downing, her mouth tightened into a red line.

The wrinkles deepened above her lips when she answered. "I expect Gordy is at the women's prison. If I need you I'll call you."

Why doesn't Gordy let me know when he isn't going to be in the clinic, let alone where he's going? Maybe Dr. Downing could fill in the pieces for me, because Gordy and Hannah certainly were not doing it.

I pulled into the parking lot at Central and stepped out of the car. An inmate was mowing the grass in front of the stone building. He touched the brim of his blue baseball hat and gave me a quick nod and smile. Another inmate was at the end of the building pruning a tall green bush with large shears. He stopped when he saw me and put the shears across his shoulders, arching his back and straining the faded blue shirt across his chest as he grinned at me. I looked down and inhaled the smell of freshly mowed grass, and pulled open the door to the building. *Finally, I'm going to get some answers.*

I took two steps into the medical director's office and froze. Dr. Down-

29

ing was sitting in a wheelchair, with a halo around his head that was bolted into his skull. The device was attached to a brace that pulled his shoulders back.

I had only met him once during the interview process, and I wouldn't have recognized him except for his light blue eyes; even they seemed a different shade.

"Take a seat," he said. "It's hard for me to look up."

I could feel myself blush as my slack jaw came back into a neutral position and I sat down on the edge of the faded gold couch.

Dr. Downing turned his wheelchair to look at me, and his eyes softened. "I didn't know this was going to happen to me when I went on vacation." The skin on his face sagged even more when he sighed. "I thought the cancer was gone. Last year I was two years out from the surgery and the chemo and radiation, and wouldn't you know…" His smile was weak. "It metastasized to my bones and a vertebra in my neck collapsed."

He looked at the wall where his medical plaques hung. His eyes drifted back to me, like he had almost forgotten that I was there. "I'm going to keep on going till I can't anymore. I'm so sorry this happened, and that I can't really help you much." His eyes wandered again to the plaques on his wall. "I was going to tell you about some of the staff, but maybe it's better you decide for yourself. Right?"

Dr. Downing's pupils were pinpoint in the dim room. I knew he was on opiates, and who knew what else, for his pain. My mouth was dry and I wanted to say *no, please tell me everything that I need to know.* But instead I said, "Dr. Downing, I'm so sorry that this happened to you. Are you sure you wouldn't feel better if you were home? Is there anything I can do for you?"

He was looking at his wall again and I followed his eyes to the plaque that said he was a board-certified pulmonologist. He didn't look at me as he murmured, "Maybe you could write me a prescription for Ritalin, that could keep me going for a while."

I didn't know what to say, and when he looked back at me it appeared that he had already forgotten what he had asked. He turned his wheelchair toward his desk and pointed with a shaky hand at the paperwork on his desk. "I've got to take care of some of the paperwork before I go home tonight, so if you need anything more, just ask my secretary."

I stood up and my knees felt weak. "Okay, thanks for seeing me today. I hope you feel better tomorrow."

God, couldn't you come up with something better than that? I asked myself as I stepped out of the office and closed the door.

I stopped at his secretary's desk. "Mary, is Dr. Downing going to be okay in there all alone?"

Mary picked up a tissue and sniffled. "It's so hard to see him like this, but he wants to get things in order." Her eyes were reddened. She lifted up her glasses and dabbed the corners of her eyes. "Damn, I shouldn't have worn mascara today. I must look like a raccoon."

"I wanted to ask him some questions, but seeing him like that, I didn't want to bother him. If Dr. Downing isn't able to work, who is in charge of the medical department for the state?"

Mary looked a bit startled. 'That would be you, wouldn't it?"

The room seemed to get smaller and compress the air out of my lungs. "That can't be right. Isn't there a more senior doctor in the prison system than me? I've only been here three weeks."

Mary picked up her pencil and chewed on the eraser. "Well, down south there's a PA. We had to let the doctor go, because he kept showing up drunk on the job. At Max prison, we have a PA, and the new doc there is supposed to start in two weeks. I hear she's like you, I mean not really like you, you know, she's black. I mean she's got a four-year payback like you. And of course there's Gordy, and he's been helping us out at the women's prison and your place."

Karen Gedney, MD

"Mary, I met the director of nursing, but besides the nurses is there anyone else who knows what is going on in the medical department? Like an administrator or coordinator or something?"

Mary snapped her fingers. "Oh, I forgot about Christine, she works on the budget and Dr. Downing's wife has been helping her out. I bet she can help fill in some of the gaps for you."

"How do I get in touch with Christine?"

Mary lifted up the phone and punched in three numbers. "Let me see if she's in."

Christine had bags under her eyes and her brown hair was starting to grey. I introduced myself, but before I could ask her any questions she said, "I don't know what Dr. Downing told you, but now that you're here, I hope you can help him out. On Wednesday he's supposed to give a talk in the warden's conference room. It's about what the medical department is going to do about AIDS, and I don't know if he's up for it. Can you be there at nine o'clock just in case?"

"Um, sure, but what *is* the medical department going to do about AIDS in the prison? I've taken care of a few patients with AIDS when I was a resident, but I haven't seen any AIDS patients yet in the prison. Do you know how many we have?"

"I don't know *now*, but two years ago they decided to test every inmate in the system. One hundred and twenty came up positive."

I felt like I was hit in the stomach. My mind flashed back to 1982, when I was a medical student in Cincinnati taking care of a gay man visiting from San Francisco who was dying from a variety of rare cancers and infections. The doctors knew he was dying of the dread disease that they called AIDS, and put him in isolation. I would always remember his wasted body with blue skin lesions from Kaposi's sarcoma. I had accidentally stuck my finger with his infected blood when I drew his blood. I didn't tell anyone, and at that time there were no tests to determine if I had become infected. It was now 1987, I was

32

healthy... not positive for HIV and chose to push any thoughts about it out of my mind.

Still, my voice cracked when I asked, "Why did they do that? How many inmates do we have in the system?"

"We've got about 4,500 inmates now. I think it was probably some homophobic legislator who pushed the prison to find out how many inmates we had that were infected. But now that we know, what are we going to do with that information? The good old boy network is good at reacting, but not so great on thinking about the consequences." Christine took a sip of her coffee. "Look, I don't know what else to tell you. Maybe when you're at the meeting on Wednesday you'll find out more information, but I have to go now, okay?" She looked at her wristwatch for emphasis, and stood up to leave.

"Thank you for taking the time to talk to me, Christine."

She nodded and was already heading down the hallway when I stood up to go, suddenly realizing I hadn't been able to ask her any of my questions.

On the drive back to the prison, I started counting up the number of HIV-positive patients I had seen in the six years since it had been recognized as a disease. *Maybe twenty-five. If Christine's numbers are right, that would mean that two to three percent of the inmates are infected.*

It was 1987, and the medical world knew that the virus could be spread sexually and by blood, but not how infectious it was. We still had so many unanswered questions. If you were stuck with an infected needle, like I had been, what were your chances of converting? We really didn't know. We could identify the virus in the blood, but did that mean every person who had it was going to die from it? How long would it take them to die? When would they develop a drug that would work? And how would the prison deal with the inmates that were positive?

My hands tightened on the steering wheel. I could feel the sweat running down my neck as I turned into the parking lot and looked at the warden's building, wondering what would happen on Wednesday.

33

Wednesday morning came soon, and I found myself standing in the back of the warden's air-conditioned conference room. I was surprised to see a camera from a local TV station in the crowd, with a petite blonde reporter.

The physician assistant from Max introduced himself to me as Rudy, and pointed out a few of the key players in the room. I immediately liked his smile and banter. Then Christine rolled Dr. Downing in, and the room quieted as he was introduced.

Dr. Downing answered some questions from the audience, but soon he started to ramble. "Yes, we know how many inmates have HIV at this time and ahh, no they don't need to be isolated and ahh, I know some places do that, but ahh, no I don't, ahh well, I don't know for sure, and ahh, well...." He looked at the long, dark wooden conference table in front of him and the people sitting around it, starting to squirm in their seats. A few of them glanced at the TV camera. The silence was uncomfortable.

The blonde reporter cleared her throat and asked, "Dr. Downing, what measures will you take to make sure the prison staff and the other inmates won't be infected?"

Dr. Downing looked up, but he clearly didn't know who had spoken. His eyes scanned the faces around the conference table. Many felt too uncomfortable to meet his gaze; others were trying to cock their head toward the reporter, who stood off to the side of the room. A few people knew I was a doctor, and they were starting to glance at me with looks of concern.

"Dr. Downing, are you all right?" the reporter asked.

He looked at her then. "Oh sure, and what did you want?"

She repeated the question and he looked down at his thin hands lying on the arms of his wheelchair and said, "Well, you know that the virus is in the blood, and ahh when it's in the blood, ahh it's in there and..."

Rudy nudged my shoulder and whispered, "You've got to do something."

34

More people were now looking at me. My legs started to shake as I walked toward Dr. Downing and squatted down near his wheelchair.

"Dr. Downing, I see you're tired, would you like me to take over?"

He looked at me like I was a pet dog and patted me on my head. "That's okay," he said. "I'll be dead soon enough."

I froze and heard gasps in the room over the roaring in my ears. I couldn't look at anyone. All I wanted to do was wheel Dr. Downing out of that room, so that is what I did. He was now muttering incoherently. I wondered what I should do next.

Rudy came up behind me. "I know how to get hold of his wife," he said. "We can get him sent over to the ER. Do you think it's the meds he's on, or the cancer?"

"Probably both, but why in the world did they let him try to give a presentation, and with the media there as well?"

"I hear he was okay yesterday and it was important to him. I just hope the media doesn't run with it and make him look like an idiot. He was a great doctor and as sharp as they come." Rudy shook his head, and bent down and took Dr. Downing's hand. "Everything's going to be all right, Doc."

How could anything in this place be all right?

35

4. Early Days of HIV

Karen Gedney, MD

Six months had passed since I watched the ambulance take Dr. Downing away. He never returned to the prison, and died shortly after that incident.

I wanted to know when a new medical director would be hired. I asked my new friend Rudy, the PA to keep me informed of any developments, but he didn't know what was happening either. He seemed more interested in updating me with the gossip at Central. It seemed that the prison director, Guy Sumtin, had not yet found a replacement for Dr. Downing. Instead, he was using Dr. Downing's widow, Annie, to help him make sense of the medical paperwork left behind by her husband. Rudy enjoyed hinting that there was relationship developing between Annie and Director Sumtin, who was married.

According to Rudy, Sumtin was known as "the Italian stallion" at Central, and he acted in a way that would have gotten him in trouble if he hadn't been everyone's boss. If a woman wanted to complain, there was no one above Sumtin to complain to, except for the state governor who appointed him.

It made me think about some of the middle-aged doctors I had worked with in the past. They were attracted to me because I was young and listened to the problems they were having with their wives and children. I knew some of them had wanted more than my listening skills, but I had not yet had to deal with a male superior who actually tried to abuse that power and sexually harass me. As Rudy educated me on the intricacies of prison politics, I realized that I never wanted to be in a political position. I could only defend myself if I stayed in my field where I had expertise, and that was medicine.

It was not long before I got a chance to test my defenses.

"Hello, Dr. G. speaking."

"Hey, how are you? This is Director Sumtin. Sorry I haven't talked to you since the medical director died, but I need you to fly with me next week to Las Vegas."

"Oh? What for?"

"They're holding some big conference about HIV and AIDS and how

37

the state health departments and prisons are going to deal with it. So since I haven't been able to get a medical director yet, you're going to come with me. I'm not going to deal with all those yahoos down there without a doctor next to me. They will all be asking about what we're going to do with the inmates who have AIDS."

"Well, I can help, but what are we going to—"

"My secretary will handle your plane reservation and we'll leave early in the morning next Monday. I'll pick you up at your house to make it easy on you. Where do you live?"

I told him, and he hung up before I could even ask him who the yahoos were.

I had only met Director Sumtin briefly, and the variety of rumors now circulating about him did not paint a pretty picture. *Wonderful, I'm now going on a trip to Las Vegas with the Italian stallion.* I looked at the phone and wished there was someone in the chain of command between me and Sumtin, anyone that I could feel comfortable talking to. My only confidant was Rudy, and I wasn't going to give him any additional fuel for gossip. I might listen to what he said, but that was it.

The next day, the clink of chains and female voices coming down the hallway interrupted my lunch break. I got up and looked around the corner to see a dozen women in ill-fitting orange jumpsuits sitting on the bench outside the X-ray room. They were chattering away at top volume. A young male officer was trying to quiet them, but was having no success.

I walked up to the officer, introduced myself, and asked him why female inmates had been brought over to the male prison.

"Well, the doc over there told me to bring them here because the X-ray machine is broken. He told me they all needed chest X-rays." He turned back to the female inmates and yelled, "Hey, I told all of you to keep it down!"

"Did that 'doc' have a large handlebar mustache by any chance?" I asked.

"So you know Gordy?"

Yes, I did. *Why didn't Gordy let me know he would be sending over all these women?* Not one of them looked at me. They were all yelling and laughing, trying to get the attention of the male inmates who were being escorted out of the clinic.

"I said shut the fuck up," the officer yelled in a loud voice. The women stopped for a split second, and then resumed talking as if nothing had happened.

The officer looked at me and then down the hallway. Not knowing what he should do next, he crossed his arms in front of him and gave them a stern look. *He must be new,* I thought. *Should I leave him alone with a dozen women so I can find another officer to help him out? Or should I stay with him?*

One of my infirmary patients chose this moment to come out and chat with the women. Mr. Green was thin, black, and effeminate. He had full-blown AIDS and dementia. He also considered himself a lady in every way, and loved talking to—and being one of—the girls. In his last conversation with me, he had explained how he made his own mascara to make his eyes look big. "Girlfriend, you got to wear some makeup," he had said to me. "And those eyebrows… mm-mm-mm, you *need* to pluck 'em."

The new officer saw Mr. Green approaching and started yelling. "What the fuck are you doing out here? Get back behind those doors and stay there."

Mr. Green turned around, but he waved at the ladies and me and sashayed as he went behind the doors. I decided to see if I could find my clinic officer Fred to help the new guy. But I only made it halfway down the hall when I heard the officer yelling and cursing again. When I turned, I was stunned to see Mr. Green and the officer rolling around on the floor as the female prisoners laughed and jeered at them.

"Fred!" I yelled down the hallway. "Get in here!"

Luckily, Fred was in earshot. He rounded the corner and ran down the hall to pull a scratching, biting, crazed Mr. Green off of the rookie officer.

39

Reinforcements came close behind him, and when things calmed down, it was my turn to examine the parties involved in the altercation.

Fred ran his hand through his red hair and sighed. "God, I'm sorry Doc. I should have been back here with the new guy. He doesn't know anything about our procedures." He shrugged. "And he sure as hell doesn't know our patients."

Nurse Hannah was trying to calm down Mr. Green, who was now handcuffed and crying. I felt guilty as well. How would a new officer know that Mr. Green had dementia and couldn't remember what was told to him from one moment to the next?

I walked into the treatment room, where the new officer was trying to explain to the lieutenant what had happened.

The lieutenant looked up and nodded to me. "Doc, just check him out and then I need to take some pictures of the scratches on his hands."

The officer was still breathing hard, and his hands trembled.

"How are you doing?" I asked as I examined the superficial scratches on the back of his hand.

"That God damn nut tried to bite me," he hissed, and pointed to a reddened area on his forearm. His voice cracked. "The nurse told me he has AIDS."

I heard the lieutenant behind me murmur, "Oh, shit."

"He didn't break the skin when he tried to bite you. I'm going to clean up your scratches, so you won't get an infection. You're going to be fine. You're not going to get AIDS."

His voice went up an octave. "How the hell do you know? Spit might have gotten on my hand. Oh my God, I have a wife and kids."

"I know you're scared and have heard all sorts of things about AIDS, but I've taken care of AIDS patients and have studied this disease. I know a lot about it. It's transmitted sexually and through blood. There's no need for you

40

to worry."

His mouth dropped open and he pulled his hand away. "I want to talk to my own doctor. Someone I can trust."

"I understand, and I encourage you to do whatever makes you feel comfortable." I wanted to add that it was doubtful his doctor had ever seen a patient with AIDS in this small rural city, but decided that comment wouldn't help.

The lieutenant shifted his weight. "You know, Doc, he could go to the urgent care clinic for state workers who get hurt on the job."

"Yeah, that's where I want to go," the officer said, standing up.

I looked at both of them. "I don't know anything about the clinic, and I've never been told about my responsibility for officer injuries, so Lieutenant, it's your decision."

When the officers left, I asked Hannah what had happened with Mr. Green.

"Oh, don't worry about him. He was fine once he stopped crying. I cleaned him up, calmed him down, and told him everything was going to be all right. Poor baby. He was scared when the officer pushed him and started yelling at him. He thought he was being attacked." She snickered. "He fought just like a little girl."

"Where is he now?"

"Didn't I tell you not to worry? He's up in the holding cell, and they're trying to figure out what to do with him. He's too sick to be on the yard, so they'll probably just put him back in the infirmary and write him up for assault." Hannah turned sharply on her heel and said over her shoulder, "Like that's going to do any good. He'll be dead before the summer's over."

She's probably only off by six months, I thought, and went back to my office.

I leaned back in my chair, and as I closed my eyes, I saw the faces of

41

the men I had treated who had died of AIDS. AZT, the only drug available, didn't seem to help—and most of my black patients wouldn't take it, because of rumors that it was a plot by whites to hasten their death.

I sat up and looked through the paperwork on my desk, but my mind was wandering to my upcoming trip to Las Vegas. *What do I need to get across to the director?* I knew the meeting in Las Vegas would only last one day, so the only time I had to speak with Director Sumtin would be on the plane. I needed to find out whether he had thought about any of those issues, and what he wanted to do in regard to policy.

Monday morning found me on the curb outside my house, pacing and looking at my watch every two minutes, convinced that if Sumtin didn't pick me up in the next minute, there was no way we'd make the plane. Finally, his black sedan screeched to a halt and I jumped in. The car reeked of tobacco and made my contacts sting.

"We're probably going to miss the plane," I said, and pulled the seat belt snug around me as he accelerated.

Sumtin gripped the steering wheel tighter. "We'll make it. We're just going to have to run when we get there."

I glanced at his stomach bulging over his seatbelt and the grey tinge of his skin, and wondered whether he could even run a block.

Sumtin didn't say anything during the twenty minutes it took to get to the airport and I didn't want to distract him, because he was speeding.

We made the plane, but only because it was delayed. As he sat down in the window seat, Sumtin patted the seat next to him and smiled. "You see, Doc? Things always work out for me."

"What type of meeting are we going to, Director?"

"Hey, we're out of the office now, just call me Guy."

"Ah, well… I was hoping that you would tell me more about this meeting we're attending, and what you need from me as a doctor."

The left side of his mouth curled in a partial smile. "You're new at this game. It's all about politics, what the legislators and governor want, what the press decides to print, and how we're going to get sued." He put his elbow on the armrest between us and leaned over.

"Look, all of a sudden we have all these AIDS patients, because the legislators wanted to know how many cases we had in the system. Well, now they know, but no one ever thought about what we were going to do with that information. This is the first state meeting on AIDS. There's no way I was going to show up without a doctor who knows something about it." He put his hand on my leg for a moment and winked. "You just follow my lead, and don't talk to anyone on your own."

"Can I ask you some specific questions?"

He leaned back into his seat and stretched his neck. "Shoot."

"Is the prison going to institute any training on HIV and AIDS for the officers? They need to know what the real risks are and how to protect themselves from exposure."

Sumtin rubbed his chin. "Yeah, we need it and I'll talk to the training officer. But we'll have to have someone teach it, and there isn't any extra money in the budget." He looked at me and smirked. "I guess you just volunteered for that one. I'll have him call you."

Great, I thought. *I better be careful what I ask next.* "Okay. How do you want the medical department to classify the inmates with HIV and AIDS? The officers in the culinary don't want them to work in that area even as porters, but I see no medical reason why they can't."

"Shit. I can't have any of them work in the culinary. All I need is for one of them to bleed or spit in someone's food and there would be a riot." He shifted in his seat to look at me. "You know, I was hired because I'm tough. I've turned around violent systems in the past, but you make one mistake that becomes an embarrassment to the governor, and you're out. Do you know the average tenure of a prison director before something happens and you have to

43

find a new job?"

I shook my head.

"About three and a half years." He leaned back. "That's why I've got something else in place. When I step down as director, I'll become the warden of the new Supermax."

I had heard they were building a new maximum-security prison in the northern part of the state. "When is that going to be built?"

"They say a year, so it'll probably be more like two." He rubbed his hands together. "The timing will be perfect, and the guy I recommend to re-place me will owe me one."

"How many beds does the Supermax have? Will it be able to take care of inmates that are really ill? I hear there isn't a hospital up there or anything."

He laughed. "That's the way it goes with prisons now. No one wants a prison in their backyard, so they're built out in the sticks where land is cheap and people are hard up for a job. The only problem is getting a doctor up there." He grinned. "You want to join me up there in the sticks?"

"Ehh, that would be a no."

Sumtin laughed and patted me on the thigh again. "You don't know what you'd be missing."

That was the end of our discussion. Upon landing in Vegas, we took a taxi to the meeting. It was in a large, bland conference room where over two hundred people were milling around drinking coffee and munching on donuts.

Sumtin pushed me toward the table with the coffee. "God, I need some caffeine. Do you want a cup, Doc?"

"No, thanks. When does the meeting start?" I looked around the room; people were starting to sit down at the tables.

"Soon." He pointed at a table in the corner. "Let's sit in the back, so I can sneak out for a smoke."

44

As we sat, a woman with grey hair tapped a spoon on her glass to get people to quiet down. She introduced herself as the head of the state health department.

"I'd like to welcome all of you to our first AIDS task force meeting. Especially the people in our community who have been affected by this disease."

A table of men and older women at the front of the room erupted in a little cheer. *Oh, it can't be,* I thought. I recognized one of the inmates who had left my prison a month ago. Sure enough. The dark hair, the gaunt cheeks, and the way he kept tugging at his shirt brought back his last words to me. "Doc, I'm not going to die in this shithole. I'm going to parole to my mother next week."

At the break, Sumtin informed me he was going out for a smoke. Before he could ask me to accompany him, I told him I was going to the restroom. When he had left, I wandered around the room until a middle-aged man in a blue suit introduced himself as one of the state legislators.

"How do you know Director Sumtin?" he asked.

I was just about to tell him that I was the prison doctor, when someone grabbed my right arm and pulled me around.

The inmate I had recognized was shifting his weight from one foot to another. "I know you. You're... uhh..." He started scratching his forehead, and dandruff drifted down his face.

The legislator was looking at me curiously as an older woman walked over and put her hand on the inmate's shoulder.

"Johnny, let's not bother these people," the woman said. "Why don't we go over there and get another donut."

Johnny looked at his mother and me. "Mom, I know this lady." He started bouncing up and down and pointed his finger at me. "Oh yeah, you had your finger up my butt."

Johnny's mother gasped, the legislator's mouth dropped, and I couldn't breathe.

"Oh, I'm so sorry," Johnny's mother said as she pulled her son away from us.

My face was on fire. The legislator bit his lower lip and murmured, "The meeting's going to start soon," as he backed away.

I didn't look at anyone until I got back to my seat and felt the redness leave my face. Sumtin slid in next to me. "Did you miss me? Are you having fun yet?"

No, I thought.

The meeting seemed to have no true leader to direct the agenda or its purpose, and it dissolved into special-interest groups and politicians campaigning for their own issues. As the day wore on, my desire for it to end escalated; I breathed a sigh of relief when we were finally on the plane back home.

"Director Sumtin," I said, "thank you for taking me to the meeting, but I saw no reason for me to be there. Unless it was to teach me not to get involved with the politics of state agencies."

Sumtin scoffed. "Didn't have fun, did you?"

"I'm a clinician, not a politician. I hope you'll find a medical director soon to help you with policy decisions. I have a lot of work to do in the clinic, and I hope you won't need me for any more trips."

He leaned toward me and his heavy-lidded brown eyes twinkled. "Aren't you going to miss me?"

"Does that actually work on women?"

Sumtin's head rocked back and he laughed in earnest. "Well, usually, yeah." He smiled and was about to pat me on the thigh again, but instead leaned back in his seat, and closed his eyes. "You know, I like you, Doc. You have balls."

The next day, I was back at work and happy to be there. But that after-

46

noon, I found myself initialing a lab sheet showing that one of the new inmates was HIV-positive. I sighed, and looked at his date of birth. *Oh brother, he's only nineteen. He probably doesn't know.* I scheduled an appointment right away with the inmate, a Mr. Washington.

Soon afterward, he was standing in my doorway. He looked healthy, a muscular young man with his hair in cornrows. "Um, why did the officers say I needed to see you?" he said. "I'm not sick. I didn't do anything."

"Mr. Washington, my name's Dr. G. Why don't you sit down so we can talk?"

I could see the whites of his eyes become more pronounced as he eyed the chair.

"Please sit down," I said, and pointed to the chair again.

He sat slowly, and his orange jumpsuit tightened around his broad shoulders. His right hand started patting his braids. I knew he was scared, but I had to give him his diagnosis.

"I asked Custody to bring you over because I needed to talk to you about your blood test. When you came into the prison as a new inmate, your blood was checked for syphilis and HIV." I paused a few seconds to see if he understood. "And I'm sorry to inform you that your test came back positive for HIV."

He stopped patting his head, and his mouth sagged. He swallowed, shaking his head.

"Mr. Washington, have you ever had a blood transfusion, shot up drugs, or had sex without a condom?"

He started to pat his head again. "I ain't got that shit. I feel fine, nothing's wrong with me."

"Many people who have HIV don't know it until they start feeling sick. Since your blood test shows that you do have it, we had to inform you. I know it's a shock. I also wanted you to know that someone from the state health de-

47

partment will be seeing you, because HIV is a sexually transmitted disease." I studied his face to see if he understood what I was saying, and wasn't sure. "Have you ever had a sexually transmitted disease, like gonorrhea or chlamydia?"

A crease developed between his brows. "You mean like the clap?"

"Yes, like the clap."

He rubbed the back of his neck. "Well, I had it a couple of times, but they said the shot and pills would take care of it." He pushed himself further back in his chair and stiffened. "I don't have to take those damn shots again, do I?"

"No, and shots won't help HIV. I know this is a lot to take in today, but I need to do some more blood work on you and get a urine sample as well. Do you understand that you have HIV? I know it's a shock, but you do have it. For many people, it takes a while to accept it. So I'll also see you again in a week with the results from the other tests, and I will give you information on how to stay healthy. Do you have any questions you'd like to ask me before I examine you?"

He looked down at his thighs, rubbed them, and murmured, "I ain't got that shit."

His exam was only remarkable for some swollen nodes in his neck, and I decided to wait until next time to tell him about the new drug on the market, AZT. I had read the studies that showed it helped patients live a little longer, but it had significant side effects. I wondered whether it was worth the risk.

While Hannah drew Mr. Washington's blood, the officer who brought him over from the intake unit stepped into my office and jerked his thumb toward the treatment room. "Hey, the nurse told me that guy has AIDS. Are you going to keep him in the infirmary and away from us?"

"He's currently healthy. I see no need for him to be in an infirmary. He has a positive blood test for HIV, that doesn't mean he has AIDS."

48

He scratched his bulbous, blue-veined nose. "Well, if it's in his blood, he's a security risk to all of us. If someone in the unit finds out that he has it, there'll be hell to pay."

"That's why medical things should be kept confidential. Hannah shouldn't have told you."

He pulled up his belt, which sagged under his protuberant gut. "Us officers need to know so we can protect ourselves. I mean, what if he bleeds or spits on us or something?"

"All the officers should consider blood from anyone to be infectious. You should wear gloves if you are handling it. Blood can be infected with different viruses, like the ones that cause hepatitis, and you don't know whose blood is infectious."

"Yeah, well that AIDS kills you, and they did it to themselves. We should just keep them locked up in here so they don't give it to anyone else." He started to get red in the face. "I hear you're giving them expensive medication, too. You should just let them die."

I felt my jaw tighten. I couldn't help myself when I turned back to the officer and said, "I can understand how you feel about individuals having a lifestyle that puts them at risk for a disease. Do you feel the same way about someone who has a heart attack from smoking, drinking, and eating too much?"

He stiffened and glared at me, then stomped out of the room, followed by his stench of cigarettes.

As I sat down, I realized I had taken out my irritation on the wrong person. The officer was just afraid. My issue was with Hannah. She was the charge nurse, and she supervised the other nurses. She set the tone, but she seemed to value only one skill, and that was passing out medications. I had never seen her give true comfort to a patient, or communicate with a patient in a way that implied she cared. What was worse, she was mean and rude to the nurses who did give good nursing care, and punished them by putting

49

them on the worst shifts.

Lucy, the redheaded nurse who had become a confidant, had told me that she was considering getting another job because of the way she was treated by Hannah and Sylvia. I urged her to stay, telling her it would be a great loss if she left. Lucy had skills that the department needed. She had been a chemotherapy nurse in the past and was highly skilled in drawing blood, as well as placing IV lines. She also had diagnostic skills, and knew what she was doing with dressings and trauma. Hannah had none of those skills, and seemed to resent Lucy for having them.

I had never in the past had problems working with nurses, and I found Hannah's thinly veiled contempt of me unsettling. It wasn't what she said; it was how she said it and the way she looked at me. I had tried to confront her about her behavior, but had only been scolded by Sylvia Ignin, her supervisor. She had told me the nurses were not in my chain of command. *If only there was a medical director here who could reprimand Hannah and stand up to Sylvia. Maybe when Director Sumtin finally hires somebody, things will improve. Until then, I'm on my own.*

5. Cho-Mo

"You're needed in the treatment room, Dr. G," Gordy said as he dropped a large stack of medical charts on my desk.

"What's up?"

"Some old guy, needs a lot of stitches."

"Is he stable?" I asked, and reached for my stethoscope.

"He'll live. He looks like he was on the short end of a lock-in-a-sock party."

I stopped and turned. "A what?"

He tilted his head and squinted at me. "Haven't you heard about that one yet? Well, the inmates have these combination locks they use to keep their property safe. They collect a few, put them in a sock, and wail on the poor slob they don't like." He winked at me. "It sure saves their knuckles though."

I walked across the hallway and entered the treatment room, where two officers in green uniforms flanked an elderly male. Blood had seeped through the bandages wrapped around his head; it was running down his face, saturating his white t-shirt. He tried to peer out of his left eye, which was not entirely swollen like his right.

An officer glanced up. "Hey Doc, we need to take pictures of his wounds. Can you get that bandage thing off his head?"

"Let me examine him first." I turned to the inmate. "How are you doing?"

"I'm shaky." He put out this trembling hand, and then wrapped both arms around himself in an attempt to stop it.

"What's your name?"

"Sam Chester."

"Where else did they hit you besides your head?"

He shook his head and rocked back and forth. His vitals were stable.

52

He was neurologically intact and had not lost consciousness; what I needed to do next was to see what other injuries he had sustained.

"Let's take off your shirt and pants and take a look."

Thin extremities with sparse grey hair were covered with multiple dusky red contusions. Urine-stained, too-large blue boxers accentuated his bony hips.

"Mr. Chester, I'm going to take the bandages off your head so the officers can take their pictures, and then I'll see what I can do for you."

Eight pictures of each laceration and goose-egg lump on Chester's bald head were taken and placed on the counter top. It was standard procedure for the officers to take pictures of the injuries in altercations, because assault charges could be levied against the perpetrators.

"How bad is it, Doc?" Mr. Chester asked, and gingerly touched the lumps on his head.

"You'll be fine. Just lie back and relax. I'm going to suture you back together."

Sixty-eight sutures later, his head resembled a sparsely quilled porcupine.

"When will I see you again, Doc?"

"I'm going to put you in the infirmary for observation and see you tomorrow. Is there something you want discuss with me now?"

His head rotated and his swollen-shut eyes faced the direction where he thought the officers were standing.

"Naw, I'll be fine."

When the officers had taken the inmate to his cell, Gordy motioned me over to the nurse's counter. "Don't you think it's a riot that his name is Chester?"

My blank stare made him laugh. "Oh, come on now. You know! Chester the molester."

Now it clicked. He was a child molester. In the prison hierarchy, he was on the lowest rung and the most likely to be attacked.

Gordy scratched the back of his head. "Those guys deserve whatever they've got comin'."

A week passed before I could remove Mr. Chester's sutures. He now had dark purple bruising below both eyes, which gave him the appearance of a scrawny, tired raccoon.

"How are you doing today, Mr. Chester?"

He touched the blue sutures running the entire length of his left eyebrow.

"Why can't they just leave me alone?" He looked at me and I noted the scleral hemorrhages around his grey eyes. He sighed and looked down at his hands. "They think they're better than me. We all did something wrong and we're paying for it. My punishment was prison, why do they have the right to..." His voice cracked and he put his head in his hand.

"Why do they think they are better than you?"

"You see, I had these two step-daughters..." he started to chew the nail on his index finger.

"And you were convicted of child molestation," I added.

He nodded.

"Do you want to tell me what happened?"

He put his hands together like he was going to pray and exhaled. "My wife worked swing shift and I had to take care of her two little girls. They were only three and five years old and I had to feed and take care of them in the evening. They always wanted me to read to them in bed and tuck them in. Both of them were terrified of the dark like you wouldn't believe. I started to stay in bed with them until they would fall asleep. They were always crawling all over me and cuddling. They wanted me to hold them and kiss them. You know, I was with them every night."

He looked up at me to see my reaction and then looked back down at his hands. "Their mother was a cold fish." He shook his head. "My oldest wanted the attention. When my youngest turned fifteen, she made it clear she didn't want it anymore and I left her alone."

"Who ultimately pressed charges?"

"That nosy social worker in the church. She made friends with my youngest daughter and brought charges against me."

"What happened to your daughters?"

He scratched one of the scabs on his head. "The oldest is still in touch with me. The youngest never wanted anything to do with me again."

There was a long pause before he placed his chin on his clasped hands and gazed at the wall behind me. "Do you know, I'm supposed to attend a sexual offender group every week? Twenty of us guys rehashing the past. Don't know what the psychologist thinks he's going to accomplish. Most of us go, though, because we know we'll never pass the psych panel without it."

"You have to pass a psych panel before you can be considered for parole, is that right? Have you ever been before the psych panel?" I asked.

"Once. What do they know? They want to see remorse, as if that's going to change anything. I can't change the past, can I?" He put his head in his hands again and closed his eyes. The silence made me uncomfortable.

"Talking about it doesn't help, does it?" he muttered after a while.

"It doesn't change the past. It only helps if it will change the future. Do you think a different future is possible?"

He shrugged. "Doc, do you want to take the sutures out?"

Yes, I thought, *and thank you for ending the discussion.*

It was lunchtime, and the smell of pizza permeated the little kitchen

55

room. I was searching for my salad in the refrigerator when Gordy asked, "Hey Doc, I hear you took the sutures out of that cho-mo. Is he any prettier now?"

Hannah piped in. "Those guys make me sick. They deserve what's coming to them."

She turned to Fred, the custody officer, who had smelled the pizza and joined the nurses. "Fred, what do you think? You've seen those perverts go to psych groups, do you think any of them ever change?"

Fred swallowed and dabbed the grease off the corner of his mouth with a small paper napkin. "I've dealt with them for years, and I know the parole board requires them to go to it, but in my opinion they'll never change."

"Do they have to go to a group to pass their psych panel?" I asked.

"Most never pass the psych panel, no matter what they do." Fred said, and reached for another slice of pizza.

"So Doc, what do you think makes them tick?" Gordy asked.

"I don't really know, but I do feel that if we don't understand why the behavior occurs, we will never have much success in preventing or changing it."

Fred put down his pizza and looked at me. "The psychologists say some of them were abused as children themselves. But that's no excuse. I had a cousin who was abused and he never molested anybody."

I shrugged. "Many times it's not the event in a person's life that affects them, but rather their interpretation of it."

Hannah snorted. "Yeah, well they're sick and should never get out. I wouldn't want to see one of those vermin out in my neighborhood with all the young kids running around."

After lunch, I decided to visit one of my infirmary patients. Mr. Dodsen was sitting on his bed, writing in a small black-and-white notebook. His roommate, a man in his nineties, was sleeping in the bed next to him still wearing his glasses and baseball hat. Sporadic snorts disrupted his loud snor-

56

ing.

"How's your stomach, Mr. Dodsen? Do you need anything?"

He carefully laid down his notebook open on the bedside table next to him. "It was really bothering me this morning, but now I feel fine." He looked over his glasses and smiled. "Must be the food we get back here." He clasped his hands behind his head and stretched backward. "After all these years in here, I don't eat the crap in the culinary anymore. I buy my stuff out of the store and canteen. I have some chips waiting for me."

"So, what else do you eat that you can buy from the store?"

He took his hands from behind his head and started to rub them together. "Well, I start off with Ramen soup and I throw in any vegetable or decent scrap of meat I can find." He shook a finger at me. "Plus hot sauce. The hotter the better."

Sounds like a recipe for indigestion, I thought. I nodded at his thick notebook, which was crammed with tiny print. "How is your book coming along?"

Within the prison population, Dodsen was known for his communication skills, and if anyone wanted to find him he could usually be found in the library. After being here for thirty-three years, he had decided to write a book about the prison hierarchy.

"It's good, Doc. Making progress."

"Can I ask you something? In the prison hierarchy, who do you think is on the bottom?"

"The cho-mos, of course. You know, Doc. The baby rapers, the Chesters."

"Why do you call them Chesters?" I asked, thinking back to my new patient's unfortunate name.

"Think about it, Doc. It's a contraction of "child" and "molester." But to the old cons like me, they'll always be cho-mos."

57

Dodsen studied me for a few moments and continued. "You know, every group needs a group to hate. Whether you're white, black or Latino, it doesn't matter. But what we all agree on is hating the cho-mos. It's a sick offense and we can't relate to it. Doc, do you know what the cho-mos hate?"

I shook my head.

"They hate not having a rock to crawl under and hide. They try. The very first thing you see them do is look for a Bible and a group of Christians they can hide in."

"Do you think there is any possibility in rehabilitating them?" I asked.

"I've lived with a lot of cho-mos over the years. They have something fundamentally wrong with them. It influences everything they do. For example, once I had one of them testify against me at a disciplinary hearing, and he had nothing to gain by doing it. So why do it?" He pointed at his head. "Because something's not right up there."

Dodsen tapped his open book with his pen, and looked up, thinking. "You know, the investigator let me hear that guy's name on the tape. They did nothing to protect his identity, which is what they're supposed to do. Let me tell you, no one likes a cho-mo. I don't think I ever met one who liked himself either. And one other thing, if a custody officer wants to do harm to an inmate, all what he has to do is label him a child molester. Tell the right convict and..." He tilted his head to the side and drew his index finger across his throat.

I looked at my watch and realized I didn't have enough time to find out who was on the top of the hierarchy. "Well, I'm glad you're feeling better, Mr. Dodsen. I've got to go and see my next patient."

Next on my list was a frail, elderly white male who was oxygen-dependent. I wondered where he was on the prison hierarchy. I had been told that he had been the shot caller for the AWs: the Aryan Warriors. That meant that he had been a powerful figure in a white supremacist gang, a man who could make anyone miserable, or order that person to be killed.

Mr. Weiss did not look powerful now. He had been a chain smoker all his life, and now he had emphysema to the point that it took all his energy to just breathe. He couldn't hold a conversation, because he could barely say yes or no. His labored breathing made me feel short of breath myself, and the fear in his eyes was palpable in the room. The officers kept him in a room by himself. I wasn't sure if it was because they didn't want anyone to take retribution on him for his past transgressions, or because they were expecting him to die and didn't want to do the extra paperwork from someone else being in the room.

Slow suffocation over a long period of time. What a horrible way to die, I thought. Mr. Weiss was on all the medications that were available, and if I sent him to the hospital he would only end up on a ventilator. Last week, I had talked to him about that possibility; he made it clear that he didn't want to end up on a machine. If he did, they would never be able to get him off it.

"Mr. Weiss, is there anything I can do for you today?"

He couldn't talk. He was just gasping like a fish that had been pulled out of the water and tossed on the deck of a boat.

"Would you like a sip of water?"

He shook his head no, but his eyes never left mine.

I had seen that look in the eyes of other patients. They just wanted their suffering to end. They wanted to die.

"Mr. Weiss, do you want me to give you something that will make you more comfortable, but would put you at some risk because it would decrease the rate of your breathing?"

His eyes started to tear up, and he nodded a yes.

"Are you sure, Mr. Weiss?"

He gasped, "Yes."

"Do you want to see a chaplain first?"

He shook his head, and kept gasping.

59

I looked at my watch. *Lucy will be on duty now. I'll get her to put in an IV, and I'll write the meds to keep him comfortable. She'll watch over him tonight.*

I went back to my office to write the orders, and thought about how different all the inmates were—and what in their lives could have made each of them go down the path he was on. I knew many on the yard hated the child molesters, but what about an AW shot caller? White supremacists were certainly hated by the non-white inmates they preyed on. *Instead of hating and fearing those groups, wouldn't it make more sense to try to understand why they had chosen to live their life in that way?*

Maybe I was naive, but it seemed to me that many of the people in both groups shared similar traits. They had been victims themselves, and then became victimizers. That was a cycle that needed to be broken. Either there needed to be fewer victims, or we had to help victims to avoid becoming victimizers.

I wondered if there was any way to do that in a prison.

6. Investigations

Karen Gedney, MD

Next month would mark my one-year anniversary in the prison. At some point, Director Sumtin had hired a medical director, but this one only lasted a month and was gone without saying goodbye. The gossip at Central was that he left for a personal reason, but I wondered what actually happened. The rumors at Central in no way made me feel comfortable; I had to consciously ignore them so I wouldn't get paranoid.

I felt more comfortable in the clinic. I had accepted that I could not change Hannah's behavior, and I tried to work around her. Gordy spent most of his time now at the women's prison, and as I became more comfortable with the routine in the clinic, I didn't miss him. I enjoyed my interactions with the inmate porters and clerks the most, because they seemed to enjoy working in the clinic and helping me with the patients.

I lengthened my stride, rushing down the dim hallway to get to my phone before it stopped ringing.

"Dr. G. speaking."

"Hey girl friend, isn't this weather crazy? That wind has just gone all out and messed up my hair. And now the yard is covered with hailstones, of all things. It's the first week in June, for heaven's sake."

"Hi, Marla," I laughed. "You might get lucky, it could start snowing over there at Max and they might even shut down the yard and let you go home early."

"Yeah, like that would happen. These officers over here will write me up for anything."

I smiled, thinking back to the first time I had met my counterpart at the other prison. Marla was the Max doctor, and had started working a few months after I did. An African-American doctor from Georgia with striking amber eyes and a full figure. She wore long, fashionable skirts with boots, and was incensed when she was told she had to wear pants in her clinic. On Marla's first day at work, they wouldn't let her inside the prison until she put pants on. Marla didn't own pants; she only wore loose, flowing skirts that suited her ample hips. When she told the Max officers this, they told her to go to the local Kmart and buy some stretch pants. She was not amused, and her story always made me think how the literal interpretation of rules could be so stupid. Custody didn't want women working in the prison to show off their figures, but putting stretch pants on Dr. Marla wasn't the way to go.

"So, Marla, what can I do for you today?"

"Well, I wanted to tell you that over the weekend they called me about an inmate at your place who was sick as a dog with jaundice. I wasn't just going to sit on him over the weekend, so I told Custody they had to ship him to the ER. His name is Ramsey. You haven't heard anything about him yet, have you?"

"No. What do you think was his problem? Hepatitis? Or something like biliary obstruction?"

"Couldn't really tell talking to Gordy, that PA of yours. Worst assessment I've ever heard. I guess the inmate couldn't give a history because he was so out of it. When Gordy called, he hadn't even pulled the guy's medical record or done the basics on him like check his temp, or pupils, or anything. It's scary to think we have to rely on someone like that to give us information. Can't you teach him or something?"

"I only see him at the end of the week, and when I ask him to do something, he ignores me. I don't know why he has such an issue with me. I think it's Hannah's influence."

"Girl, you're the doctor over there and you need to set them straight before they really get you into trouble. I don't know what's really going on, but Rudy tells me that there are rumors over at Central that you're being investigated."

"What? Investigated? What would I be investigated for? And who would be investigating me?"

"I don't really know, but Rudy is friends with some of the people over at Central and there are rumors that an investigation is being done on you."

63

Rudy. He had always been friendly to me, and Marla was always letting me know how much she liked him as her physician assistant. He was a gossip, but could he be telling the truth?

My heart picked up its pace and my thoughts started jumping around. *Could an inmate have made up some story about me for some reason? If I'm doing something wrong, then someone should tell me.* My mind jumped to Hannah as well as the Director of Nursing, Sylvia Ignin. Both of them seemed to dislike me—and Sylvia had influence at Central. *Maybe it's Sylvia and her husband, Assistant Warden Ignin. What did that inmate tell me about the Ignins? Something about me affecting their power.*

My chest started getting tighter. I had to let out a deep breath before I could ask, "What did he tell you exactly?"

"You know me, I pumped him for information, but it seems it's all rumors. Rudy told me that there's an Inspector General's office at Central, and they do the investigations on staff and inmates. Seems if anyone just drops an anonymous note accusing someone of doing something, that office looks into it. He also told me they listen to the phone calls the inmates make, and ours as well. I'd watch your back. I don't trust those old rednecks. I'd make sure you lock your car and search your office everyday so they don't plant something on you."

My eyes widened in shock and I looked around my office. "You can't be serious."

"Maybe I'm just paranoid, and maybe I shouldn't be really saying anything on the phone either, but... Hell, maybe it's better if we talk later. Like I said, watch your back."

After she hung up, I stared at the black phone, rubbing my forehead. *Did I say anything on the phone that could be misinterpreted?* If it was true that you could be accused of something anonymously, anyone who didn't like you or had an issue with you could make your life miserable. *What kind of place is this? This is nuts. Why am I reacting like this? If I was doing something wrong, who would tell me? Hannah? Gordy? The assistant warden? A non-existent medical director?*

My mind started to race and for the first time, I started to understand how an inmate must feel when they were being investigated. If anyone could just anonymously drop a note and start an investigation, your life could be hell.

I didn't feel like eating lunch. I was staring out the window, watching the wind whirling the dry dirt into a sandstorm, when I heard officers opening the iron clinic gate. I stood up and looked down the hall to see them wheel in a young man whose skin was the color of a pumpkin, in a green hospital gown with a grey blanket wrapped around his shoulders. Hannah was walking behind the wheelchair, shaking her head as she pulled surgical gloves over her red manicured nails.

This must be Mr. Ramsey. He looks barely conscious. "Hannah, have them put him in the treatment room first so I can examine him. Did the hospital send back any information on him?" I asked as I walked toward the group.

"No, they never do. You'll have to wait a few weeks for the discharge note."

I doubted Ramsey had a few weeks. "Hannah, have we ever tried calling the hospital to get more information?"

"Hmph, that's not my job. If you want it, why don't *you* call."

I wanted to lash out, but restrained myself. "That's what I'm going to do right now. Can you please do a set of vitals on him, and get me his chart?"

"All right, Doctor," she said and her nostrils flared. She would have to make the officers turn the wheelchair around, instead of following her apparent plan of putting him in a bed in the back of the infirmary.

I got through to the doctor who had discharged Ramsey from the hospital, and he was relieved to talk to a prison medical representative. The doctor informed me that Mr. Ramsey was dying of liver failure from fulminant hepatitis B, and that there was nothing the hospital could do. They had sent him back to the prison to die. I thanked him, but as I hung up, I realized I had forgotten to ask whether Mr. Ramsey was aware of his prognosis.

Hannah put his thin, light green chart on my desk. It had a yellow sticky note on it with his vitals. "So, does he have hepatitis?"

"Yes, and the doctor says he's in complete liver failure and was sent back here to die." I watched her stripping off her surgical gloves and dropping them one at a time in my waste basket. "Hannah, how does the prison handle cases like this?"

She sighed and made little *tsk tsk* sounds, then started counting on her fingers. "First, I'll isolate him, second, I'll tell the lieutenant, third I'll get Classification to tell his family, fourth I'll tell the chaplain. The only thing *you* have to do is write a no-code order on him."

"Okay, thank you," I said to Hannah's back as she turned quickly and left my office.

I walked into the treatment room and was glad to see Rodney, the inmate. He was wearing gloves, making sure Mr. Ramsey didn't roll off the treatment table as he moaned and picked at his grey blanket. I had never seen skin that orange or eyes that glowed a shade of neon orange-red.

Rodney looked up. "He isn't going to make it, is he?"

I shook my head.

"Hep B?"

I looked at Rodney and nodded. I trusted his judgment in the medical area. "Do you know Mr. Ramsey?"

He nodded and sighed. "He's a dope fiend." He glanced up and then out the clinic door, lowering his voice. "He shared his rig with a lot of guys."

Oh no. An active hepatitis B patient's blood was infectious. "How many?" I asked.

He shrugged. "Maybe a dozen."

"Do you think they'll come in to be tested?"

Rodney looked at the ceiling and then back at me. "Well, they're scared. They saw him turn orange. But they won't do it if they think they can get in trouble over it."

"They need to know that they have to get rid of that rig, and not to shoot up with anyone else because they could pass it on. Tell them that no amount of bleach or boiling water will make that rig safe." I looked down at Mr. Ramsey's swollen limbs, which were beginning to mottle. "We don't want any more of them to end up like this."

"Yep, I know," Rodney said.

"Rodney, please let the guys who shot up with Mr. Ramsey know that they should come in and be tested. Tell them I will not tell Custody that they were shooting up. I consider it medically confidential and I don't get involved with security issues. Mr. Ramsey probably got it from one of them. Someone may be a chronic carrier of the virus. He might feel healthy, but can transmit it to others. Do you think they will understand how serious this situation is? They may have a one in three chance of getting hepatitis B just from having shot up with Mr. Ramsey."

Rodney pointed at Mr. Ramsey's swollen belly. "How often do they get like that?"

"I was taught that the risk of dying from fulminant hepatitis was one in two hundred. Did you get vaccinated for hepatitis B?"

"Yeah, three times. How effective do you think the vaccine is for protecting us from that?" He looked down at Mr. Ramsey, and I could see the sadness in his eyes.

"Pretty good, but not as good as avoiding being exposed to his blood. Make sure the porters who clean back there really take precautions. I've seen guys like this bleed out. It's a mess."

Mr. Ramsey died alone in the back a few days later, in a pool of blood. A week after his death, I had two inmates who came in sick with hepatitis B. I used the opportunity to educate them on all the diseases and complications they could get from their IV drug use. Losing their friend and worrying that they might suffer a similar fate seemed to make them receptive to the information. I didn't know if it would change their behavior, but I wanted them to know that I cared what happened to them and I would keep the medical information that they told me confidential.

If I told Custody that the inmates had shot up, Custody would write them up on charges and put them in isolation. I also knew from talking to the inmates that they sometimes were transferred to a higher security prison, or given more time on their sentence. I had heard there were certain officers who, on being alerted that there was contraband in an area, would tear apart the unit looking for it. I didn't want anyone searching for a rig to accidentally get stuck.

Most importantly, I was trained to keep medical issues confidential. A doctor wants a patient to feel comfortable telling them about any behavior that caused the medical problem. In the medical world, it would be unheard-of to treat a patient that was involved in IV drug use, and then turn them over to the cops. A doctor wants to help people get treatment, not punishment. Medical confidentiality is important.

Still, I had started to wonder if it was possible to maintain doctor-patient confidentiality in a prison. I thought back to what Marla had said about my actions being under investigation. *What are Custody's expectations of me regarding medical confidentiality?* I started to get anxious. *I need a second opinion. Who do I trust that understands confidentiality?*

The obvious choice was Marla, and the next day I called her.

"Marla, how's the weather at Max today?"

She laughed. She knew I wasn't talking about the temperature, seeing as the two prisons were only a few miles apart. "Well, it's a lot cooler here today than yesterday, when a couple of the inmates went at it at the weight pile."

"Anyone really hurt?"

"Nah. Fortunately this time the officers didn't hit anybody when they fired off warning shots. So how are you doing over at your place?"

"Surviving," I said. *But for how much longer?* "Marla, did anyone over there talk to you about the subject of medical confidentiality and how the prison looks at it?"

"Hmph, I bet they think about it differently than we do. But as far as I'm concerned, I'm the doctor and that license means more to me than any job. If they don't like it, I expect they can take it up with the Feds who put us here." She laughed. "I'd love to see them do that."

"So you don't feel any pressure to break confidentiality because we're in a prison instead of a clinic?"

"The only reason we're both sitting in prison now is that they're under that big lawsuit. You know, I saw the inmate named in that suit for pneumonia last week. He's this skinny schizophrenic with scary eyes. When I looked at his X-ray and other films done on him in the past, you wouldn't believe the amount of buckshot in his body. He's probably carrying around a half-pound of lead in him. Rudy told me that when he acted up in the past—before they had any provider to give him an anti-psychotic—the officers would just shoot him in order to control him."

I didn't like lawsuits, but I knew that sometimes it was the only way something could be brought to attention that needed to be done. The lawsuit against the prison had enabled the system to be given two federal doctors for four years: myself, and Marla.

"Yeah, I heard about that lawsuit. Taking care of the mentally ill, especially violent paranoid schizophrenics, would be difficult for a mental institution with a psychiatrist. Let alone a prison with no real doctors. I never knew there were so many mentally ill patients in a prison. For some reason I

69

thought they would be in mental institutions."

"Wake up, honey! When Reagan was president, he gutted those mental health clinics and asylums. Why do you think we have so many more homeless people now?"

"I knew about that, but seeing it up close is different. It's not only the mentally ill, it's all the addicts. I don't see how sticking a guy in a cage and making his life miserable is going to address the things that caused him to be an addict in the first place."

Maybe I was being made to feel that I was not wanted because I really *wasn't*. Maybe the prison administration didn't want things to change.

"Who brought the suit against the prison?" I asked. "I can't imagine that anyone I've seen in this place would ever take that on."

"Rudy told me it was an inmate who worked in the law library, and after he filed it, they shipped him off to another prison."

"Well, it sounds like your PA is an asset to you."

"Rudy is a blast, and he actually knows some medicine. How are you doing with your PA?"

"I never see Gordy. He spends almost all his time over at the women's prison now."

"Rudy tells me that Gordy likes playing the big cheese, and it's easier for him to do it there. So how you holding up?"

"I don't know and I hate this feeling of not knowing what's going on, it's making me crazy." I took a sip of my tepid coffee to see if it would help the tightness in my throat.

"Well, find a way to figure it out! I've gotta go."

Two days later, Lucy confided in me that my staff had been called over to the Inspector General's office, one by one, to answer questions about my behavior in the clinic. "It's a witch hunt," Lucy said. "I could lose my job for telling you, but I don't care. I'm looking for another job anyway."

After she left, I stared into my coffee cup looking for an answer. *I can't go on worrying about everything I did or didn't do, in an environment where I don't know who to trust. I'll be facing another sleepless night if I don't do something.* I steadied my hand as I reached for the phone. *You might as well go right to the top*, I told myself as I punched in his number.

"Doc, what can I do for you?" Director Sumtin's voice boomed.

"I hate to bother you, but I understand there is an investigation going on regarding me and.... no one has told me what's going on and I don't know what I'm supposed to do." I winced. My voice sounded so pathetic.

There was an uncomfortable silence. I found myself holding my breath. Finally he asked, "Are you telling me that no one has talked to you yet?"

I bit my lower lip. "No one has told me why I'm being investigated."

I heard a loud exhale and the scraping sound of a chair being pushed back. "Come over to my office today at noon," he said, and hung up.

My body slumped. *How am I going to distract myself until then?* I checked the time: 10:20. I had enough time to see Mr. Camey, my metastatic lung cancer patient. He had been treated by an oncologist I knew from my residency, and when I told the doctor I had a nurse trained in chemotherapy, he decided that I could give the chemo treatments in the prison. Lucy was a godsend, not just because of her training, but because of her caring and competence. I was relieved to see her, exiting Mr. Camey's room with a box of dressings.

"Lucy, how's Mr. Camey doing today? Do you think he'll tolerate another course of chemo next week?"

She stopped and placed the box of dressings on the small white table outside his room. "He'll tolerate it, but he's in a fair amount of pain. He tells me that when he asks for his pain meds, Hannah reads him the riot act." Lucy's hazel eyes told me how she felt about the way Hannah treated the inmates. "Maybe you could give him something long-acting, so he wouldn't have to ask for it that often."

"That's a good idea, but I'll have to be careful so I don't give him too much. What else do you think he needs?"

She leaned back against the grey wall. "Well, if you go up on his narcotics he'll need something to make sure he doesn't get constipated. He isn't eating much, but he asked for some jello. I asked Hannah if we could keep some for him in the refrigerator, and she said there was no order for it."

I shook my head. "When do you think she stopped being a real nurse?"

Lucy studied her sneakers, which were light pink to match her scrubs. "Maybe she's always been a witch," she murmured.

"How are you doing here, Lucy?"

Her head came up, and she brushed a strand of red hair back behind her right ear. "Probably as good as you are. I've never worked in this type of ugly setting before."

"Well, I keep reminding myself that I was hired to be a doctor here, and these are my patients. I can't control what other staff think and feel, but I expect all of them to act like professionals. Like you."

Lucy smiled tearfully and turned to pick up the dressings on the table so I couldn't see the emotion in her face.

"See you later," I said, and walked into Mr. Camey's room. He was snoring and his sunken grey cheeks expanded a little with his exhale. I didn't wake him. I decided to leave the infirmary, before something could interfere with my meeting with Director Sumtin.

When the director's secretary tapped on his door, he looked up from his paperwork and motioned for me to enter. "Shut the door, Doc, and take a seat over here." He pointed to a black padded chair in front of his large shiny wood desk. I sat down, glad he couldn't see my legs shaking as my foot tapped nervously.

Sumtin leaned across his desk and put his large right palm on a file that stood about six inches tall. "Do you know what this is?" he asked.

I stared at it. *Is that the information about the investigation on me? I've barely even worked for the prison a year.*

"Look," the director went on, "I never do this, but I need a doctor in this system. If you're going to survive, you're going to need to know who your enemies are so you can get them before they get you."

He leaned back and rested his chin on his fist. His dark eyes studied me. "Go ahead and read it, while I finish up my paperwork."

He picked up his pen, rolled his shoulders back, and started signing the documents in front of him.

I looked at the first page and saw the Inspector General's office stamp and a list of the people they had interviewed. I didn't even recognize half the names, but the name Ignin stood out and I flipped to the assistant warden's interview.

> *Dr. G. is felt to be a security risk to the institution. She is at high risk of being compromised. She is often found acting unprofessionally when she interacts with the inmates. She takes the side of inmates over Custody and can not be trusted.*

I bristled, thinking back to the incident where Custody had brought a dog into the infirmary and created a situation that led to a bound inmate being bitten. Assistant Warden Ignin had not appreciated it when I brought the incident to his attention.

Instead of anxiety, I was now feeling a new emotion: anger.

I flipped next to the Director of Nursing, Sylvia Ignin.

> *Dr. G. has an unprofessional appearance and dresses to get attention. She is friendly to the inmates, and will be compromised by them. She is a threat to institutional security because she is writing more narcotics*

73

than any other doctor in the system.

Now I was starting to see red. How were white pants, sneakers, and a jacket unprofessional? I didn't wear makeup at all, let alone bright red lipstick and nails like Hannah. And narcotics? *Give me a break. I'm the one taking care of the sickest patients, because none of the other prisons take care of cancer patients or have infirmary beds.*

Next, I flipped to Hannah's interview.

Dr. G. doesn't respect security or the officers. She is naive and believes what the inmates tell her. She coddles the inmates and has even ordered soft beds and cushions for them."

Soft beds and cushions? I was treating that inmate's bedsore!

Up next were Gordy's comments.

Dr. G. does not have good judgment. She gives preferential treatment to blacks because she's married to one.

What kind of witch hunt was this? How could they say such things? Did they actually believe what they were saying?

Then I saw the name of the pharmacist, whom I had only met in passing. What could he possibly have to say about me?

Dr. G. will affect the budget adversely. Her choice to prescribe a chemotherapy drug and narcotics shows that she does not realize that she is working in a prison.

Was that about Mr. Camey? He has a horrible cancer and is suffering! I slammed the folder shut.

"Seen enough?" the Director asked. His brown eyes looked concerned.

I could feel the prick of tears start. I looked down at my lap. *Don't you dare cry, don't you dare.*

Over the roaring in my ears, I heard Sumtin say, "You know what I'm going to do with this?"

74

I looked up again and saw him toss the entire file into the large wastebasket next to him. He leaned forward and looked me in the eyes. "The Ignins think you're going to be a problem for them. They tried to get the Inspector General's office to do their dirty work. I'm telling you, you've got to get down in the mud and get them before they get you first."

"Did they really say all those things about me?"

"Yep, the I.G.'s office tapes everything."

"Why do they have such an issue with me? If they're concerned about my behavior, why don't they tell me?"

'The Ignins have controlled your facility for a long time, and when they look at you, the only thing they see is a threat to their power. It's as simple as that. They were hoping the investigation would turn up something, so they could get rid of you before your probation was over. In a few weeks, you'll have worked for the department a year. Then it'll be harder for them to get rid of you."

"I'm not interested in disrupting their power, Director Sumtin. All I want is to be a doctor."

"I know, but just by being a doctor who cares and acts professionally, you'll become a threat to them. I'm telling you, you need to get them before they get you."

"Thank you for telling me what has been going on, but I try to avoid confrontations. I wouldn't even know how to get them. If they are such a problem, why don't *you* do something?"

An imperceptible smile almost reached his lips. "They've got something on me."

I wasn't sure what he meant, but his face hardened and I decided not to ask. Instead, I asked another question. "Before I go, can you tell me what the prison's stand is on medical confidentiality?"

"What do you mean?"

"Well, if a patient in the outside world told us they got sick by shooting up or fighting, it would be considered medically confidential. I'm following the guidelines I was taught as a doctor. I'm just wondering if there's any behavior or act that I have to report to Custody. If there is, I'll tell the inmate not to talk to me about it."

He smiled, stood up and pushed his chair back. "Yeah, tell them not to tell you they're going to escape or kill somebody, and you'll be in the clear."

7. Martin Luther King Jr. Day

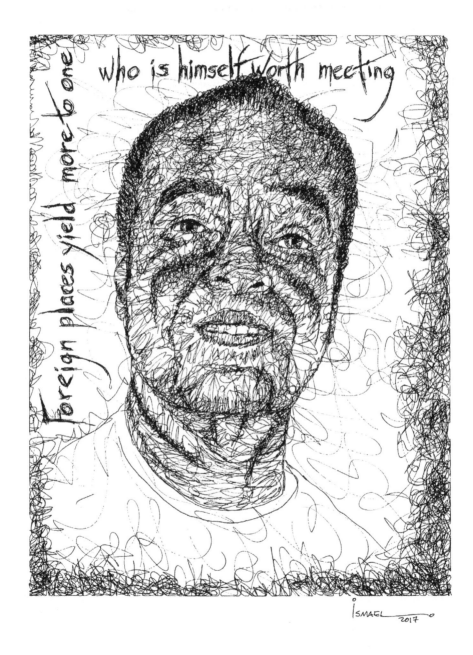

Miraculously, I survived my first year in prison and my probation period was over. Knowing that Director Sumtin wanted me to continue working in the prison, and that he was willing to protect me from the Ignins of the world, made me feel a little safer. I still wondered what he meant when he said the Ignins "had something" on him. What could that possibly mean?

Sumtin's advice to me about getting in the mud and fighting had unsettled me at first. When I asked Coley for his advice, he said, "Don't fight a battle unless you can win the war." I preferred to avoid situations where I would be involved in conflict, but was uncertain if pacifism was possible in a hostile environment.

Perhaps we were picking up bad lessons from the inmates we were meant to be rehabilitating. On the yard, fighting was common; every week or two I would be taking care of injuries. Shortly after my one-year anniversary date on campus, I walked through the gatehouse that morning in August with Lucy at my side, and was not surprised to hear shots on the yard.

Lucy cringed and looked at me. "God, I was hoping for a quiet day today."

"So was I. Yesterday I had to suture an inmate's scalp back together, after another inmate bashed his head into a window. Those windows have wire running through them, and that really did a number on his scalp. He looked like a jigsaw after I finished. I'm not sure all those pieces I put back together will take."

"Last weekend when you weren't here, they brought in an inmate who got hit with buckshot. It was the first time I ever had to dig little pellets out of somebody's legs. He was in his underwear and if the shots had been a little higher..."

I winced. "Yeah, that would have been a problem, but I'm more worried if it hits them in their eyes. I know the officers are supposed to skip the buckshot off the ground, but if those pellets hit a hard surface they can go anywhere."

78

Lucy and I entered the clinic and found Hannah standing at the med counter tapping her foot. She turned and pointed her thin, red-tipped index finger at Lucy. "If Custody needs Medical out there, you go. Doctor, there's a patient in the treatment room waiting for you…" Hannah barely looked at me as she turned and went back into her med room. "Damn, now my med pass will be delayed," she was muttering.

I sighed and winked at Lucy, who shook her head. We both headed down the hall to the treatment room. Fred, the clinic officer was in the treatment room listening to crackling voices on his walkie-talkie. He nodded to Lucy. "They need Medical out there. Take Rodney. I'll stay here with Dr. G."

Lucy left. I put on my gloves and walked around to look at the bloody face of a thin, short black man sitting on the treatment table with his arms cuffed behind him. Blood was dripping down his face from a gash through his left eyebrow, and pooling in the collar of his blue shirt.

"Fred, did Hannah examine him yet?"

Fred adjusted his thick leather belt, which was strained with the weight of a large flashlight hanging from one side. "Nah, she said you needed to see him because he needs stitches."

The inmate's left eye was already starting to swell, but I could tell he was sizing me up with his right.

"Hi. My name's Dr. G. Can you tell me what happened?"

"That no good punk-ass white rat just hit me out of nowhere. I don't even know the piece of shit, but if I ever get my hands on him…"

"Did you pass out when you were hit?"

"Nah, it sort of stunned me. But if I see his pimply white face again…"

His hands clenched and his shoulders drew back.

"Did you get hit anywhere else?"

He shook his head.

"I'd like to examine you now and take care of your face, is that okay with you?"

He nodded, and after I sutured his eyebrow, Fred led him away. I was about to start filling out an incident report when Lucy came into my office and sat down.

"So what happened out there?" I asked, and leaned back in my chair.

"When I got out there with Rodney, they already had both of the inmates cuffed on the ground. A white guy and a black guy. I don't know why they were fighting, but they were still calling each other all sorts of choice words when Custody hauled them off. Neither one of them had any injuries that we had to deal with. Custody just wanted me to check them out medically."

"Hmm, I've heard from some of the inmates that racial tension has been heating up. Have you heard anything?"

"No," Lucy said, "but I've seen how some of the officers talk about the black prisoners, and how they deal with them, and it's not pretty. I mean, it's 1988. I know racism exists, but we're not in the Deep South or anything."

"No we're not, but how many black people have you seen living in this area since you moved here?"

She brushed back her red hair and looked down. "Yeah, I see what you mean."

"You know, when Coley and I moved here, I teased him that he was the only black man in this town. And there must be over thirty thousand people here."

Lucy blushed. "What is that like? I mean... does anyone give you a problem?"

"Well, sometimes we get some odd stares, and one time a police officer stopped us and asked for Coley's parole papers."

Lucy's hazel eyes widened. "He didn't."

80

"Yes he did, and I enjoyed showing him my state prison ID and telling him I was married to Coley and that he was a financial investment advisor."

Lucy put her hand over her mouth and laughed.

"For the most part people are nice," I went on. "At least to my face. I think they are disarmed when Coley interacts with them. Coley doesn't have a chip on his shoulder like a lot of the men here."

"What do you mean?"

"Well, how many times have you heard inmates talk about someone who dissed them, and how it led to a fight? Many of the men in here get all worked up if someone looks at them a certain way, or says something they don't like. That hypersensitivity is like carrying a chip on your shoulder. When people see it, they take a swing at it."

"So if Coley has to deal with racism just like other black men, why doesn't he have a chip on his shoulder?"

I smiled. "I'll tell you what I think sometime, but we need to get back to work."

When I finished the incident report, I gave it to Fred. "Fred," I asked, "who in Custody reads these reports, and what do they actually do with them?"

"Well, the captain sees them, and I guess he informs the warden if he thinks things are brewing on the yard."

"So...what do you think? Are things brewing?"

Fred shrugged and leaned against the wall. "I've seen it worse. Before you came, they even had to pull in the National Guard to handle a race riot over at Max. That's when they hired Director Sumtin."

"What do you think about Sumtin? Is he making things better?"

Fred put his hands on his hips and shook his head. "I learned a long time ago not to think. I just follow orders and collect my check at the end of

81

the week."

I nodded and felt the corners' of my mouth turn down as I walked back to my office. I remembered my German mother's stories about the Second World War, and how many people "just followed orders."

There were no more shots or altercations that day, but I felt uneasy on the ride home. Fred's words kept bubbling up. "I don't think, I just follow orders." He seemed so tired and beaten when he said those words. I wondered when he had decided to give up thinking. *To not think... to not question... to not wonder if something could be done in a better way...* it scared me.

I felt uneasy until I walked into the house, and smelled the aroma of something Italian. It made my mouth water.

Coley was stirring the sauce. He smiled. "Glad you're home early. You hungry? Why don't you grab the salad and some plates, and we can start eating."

I felt much better after eating. As we started to wash the dishes, I told Coley a little of what had transpired. It was not the first conversation we had had on the subject, but today Coley stopped drying dishes and turned to face me.

"You remember me telling you about coming back from Vietnam?" he said.

How could I forget? Coley had been a platoon leader. He had been shot through the chest on Christmas Eve 1969, and spent over a year in a hospital recovering from his wounds (as well as malaria). He told me that his first wife, who had been his high school sweetheart, visited every day until the doctors told her that he wouldn't recover. She couldn't handle it and she left him.

But he proved the doctors wrong. Coley was forty-four years old now, and physically strong. He could easily hike up mountains with me until we reached 7,000 feet or so, at which point he would start calling me a mountain goat.

I also remembered one of our first hikes, when I was in the lead. I was about to step over a fishing line that was on the trail, when I suddenly ended up in a bush ten feet away. Coley had tackled me. After I dusted myself off, he explained to me that it was a reflex. Stepping over the line, to him, meant that I had tripped an explosive device.

I nodded, and Coley continued. "Well, after I started to feel a bit normal again I became involved in the support groups for the vets. Today, a guy in town contacted me and asked me to join the veterans group here. Would you believe he's an officer at your place?"

"Really? What's his name?"

"Harold Green. He's president of the vets group here, and I met him for coffee this afternoon. Do you know him?"

"I don't think so. What does he look like?"

"He looks like me, just not as young and handsome."

I laughed. "You've got to be kidding. I haven't seen any black officers at my place."

"Harold said he works at the camp next to your place. I thought you might have seen him."

"No, and I would have definitely remembered him. What is he like?"

Coley shrugged. "He's comfortable in his own skin, and seems like he really wants to help the vets. He's a leader. I like him."

"Does he have a chip on his shoulder?"

He snorted. "What gave you that idea?"

"Well, I've been dealing with a lot of the inmates who seem to have a chip on their shoulder, and I was telling Lucy that you didn't have one."

"Since when are you comparing me to inmates?"

"Coley, you know what I mean. You grew up in a rich, educated world, with a good family. You have never seen yourself as a victim. That is not how the majority of the inmates have experienced life. You grew up with a platinum spoon in your mouth, admit it." I waved the spoon at him before putting it away.

Coley laughed and snapped the dishtowel at me. "Well I don't have that spoon now. I have my beautiful wife, and I am happier for it."

Nothing stays the same for anyone or any system. Two months later, Director Sumtin got his wish to become the warden of the newly-built Supermax prison. Just like he told me he would do, he recommended his own replacement. The new Director Frye was an unknown to me, and I was worried about losing my ally. What did Frye think of the Ignins? What would become of me now?

Just be glad that you are through your probation period, and that the investigation on you was thrown out, I told myself. *Don't start getting a chip on your shoulder.*

A couple of weeks later, I finally met Harold Green. He was a robust custody officer, who strode into the infirmary with one of the inmates from the minimum-security camp and gave me a big smile and a bear hug.

"Hey Doc, did your husband tell you what we're up to?" Harold asked me.

"Not exactly. I understand it's something to do with Vietnam veterans, right?"

Harold watched the nurse lead the inmate into the treatment room, and positioned himself at the door." We're going to start a VVA chapter for incarcerated vets in the camp, and your husband is going to be our outside sponsor."

"What exactly is a VVA chapter?"

"Vietnam Veterans of America. The vets in camp asked me whether they could form a support group and get help with their PTSD, alcoholism, and addictions. You know, on the outside there are counseling centers, outreach programs, and support for them, but there's nothing on the inside."

"How do you start something like that in the prison? Don't you have to get approval or something?"

He started laughing. "Well, it helps when the lieutenant and the prison director are both combat vets like me."

"I would have never thought that about Director Frye," I said. I had only met the new director once, and he had not struck me as a soldier.

"Why not?" Harold asked.

"I'm not sure. It's probably because I'm thinking of the vets I took care of when I did my residency in a VA hospital. He doesn't remind me of them."

"Well he's a survivor of Hamburger Hill. You ever hear of that battle?"

"Oh yes," I said. Hamburger Hill was one of the early battles, where the leadership on both sides was testing the resolve of each other. Neither side backed down, and the soldiers were turned into hamburger. *I'm lucky I never applied for a military scholarship*, I thought to myself. *I would have made a lousy soldier. I was never good at following orders that did not make sense to me.*

Harold nodded and looked up as Hannah brought the inmate out of the treatment room. "Nice chattin' with you, Doc. Remind your husband I'll see him next week."

I watched Harold walk down the hallway with the assurance of a lion strolling through his pride. Coley had told me that Harold had served in Korea as well as Vietnam. He was the first African American to be part of an underwater demolition team, which later became known as the Navy Seals.

My mind started to wander to thoughts of the higher-ups. I felt I could trust Harold, and so did Coley, but what about the lieutenant in the camp— and what about Director Frye? Did I trust them? I had seen the lieutenant in passing. He seemed gruff, but I had never really talked to him. Director Frye seemed like an energetic politician. I didn't know if I could trust either of

85

them. *Are they friends of the Ignins? If they are, that could be a problem.* I shook off the thought. *I have no reason to be paranoid. If I let these thoughts slip in all the time, I'll never trust anyone.*

Not long after, I encountered Mr. Grindy. He was a large man who was wheezing from asthma. He sat down in my office and unbuttoned a few of the top buttons on his faded blue shirt, so his large chest could fill up with more air.

"Did you use your inhaler today?" I asked.

He shook his head and squeaked, "Ran out last week."

"Okay, let's go to the treatment room and give you a breathing treatment. Slow down your breathing and breathe through pursed lips like this." I puckered up and showed him how to do it, then led him to the treatment room and handed him the breathing tube for the nebulizer machine. The machine would fill his lungs with a medicine that reduced bronchiole spasms.

Grindy's vitals improved in a few minutes, and he was able to talk without gasping. "Thanks, Doc. It wouldn't have got this bad, but my new cellie does nothing but just sit around the cell, whining and smoking. If I have to live in that cell for years with that asshole, the smoke will probably kill me. It could even give me cancer, couldn't it?" His voice was returning to a rich baritone.

"It mainly puts people at risk for cancer if they smoke themselves, but secondhand smoke can also increase your risk. You know how I feel about smoking. I don't think anyone should smoke or be subjected to it."

"Why don't you get Custody to take it off the yard? I heard some states don't allow inmates to smoke at all."

"That's true, and I hear the inmates didn't riot over it like they expected. It seems that the ones who complained the most about it were the officers." I looked at Mr. Grindy's sweaty face and handed him a paper towel. "I've done everything I can to make them realize what a problem it is and how much money it costs the medical department, but the current director and the

86

majority of the custody officers smoke. So..."

He handed me back the nebulizer tube. "I bet this system is just making too much money off selling tobacco to inmates, and they don't care what it does to guys like me. Maybe I should just sue their asses."

I wanted to add that lawsuits could prompt other states to make the decision to ban smoking in their own prison systems—but I held my tongue. "Mr. Grindy, if you want, I can ask the caseworker whether it's possible for you to get a cellie that doesn't smoke. I can't promise you it will happen, because that's up to the caseworker, but is that something you would like me to do?"

He buttoned his shirt and swallowed. "I'll let you know, Doc. Some of the caseworkers are haters. If they think you're trying to get something over on them, they make your life harder. Instead of moving my cellie, they could move me to the hole or another unit to punish me."

"I hadn't thought about that." I bit my lip. "I'll get you a rescue inhaler, and add a steroid inhaler which I want you to use every day. It will hopefully help you have fewer attacks."

"There's one more thing I wanted to ask you about," Grindy said.

"What is it?" I said.

"You may not know this, but I'm the president of the NAACP chapter on the yard. I was wondering if your husband could come in and be a speaker for Martin Luther King Jr. Day. I hear he has a visitor's badge already."

"Who did you hear that from?" I asked. *The inmate grapevine is more impressive than I realized. Coley only got that badge last week.*

Grindy shrugged. "The clerk who takes the pictures for the badges is a friend of mine. He says your husband is intelligent and that he's going to sponsor a group in the camp. We need a speaker like him, and the guy who was going to do it bailed on us. Do you think he'd be willing to come in?"

"I can ask him tonight. How long do you want him to speak, and what day are you thinking about?"

Mr. Grindy wrote down the information for me, and had a bounce in his step when he left with his inhalers.

When I got home that night, I made sure my husband had enjoyed his dinner before I started talking about the prison. Coley had a tremendous number of wonderful qualities, but being able to think about new challenges when he was hungry was not one of them.

"Guess who I saw recently?" I asked, putting dirty plates in the sink.

"You're going to tell me," he said, and started packing up the leftovers.

"I saw Harold. He told me you are going to be the outside sponsor for the VVA group in the camp."

His smile transformed his face like a happy child's. "Harold is one of the best. What else did he say?"

"He explained how it started, and that the higher-ups gave him approval. But he didn't explain why he needed an outside sponsor like you."

"If the group is going to need contacts on the outside, or if any money is involved, they have to have someone who is not employed by the prison."

"Yeah, I can see how that would make sense. I just find it interesting that Harold would take on such a project, when he's already running a VVA chapter in town."

Coley picked up a towel and started to dry the dishes I had washed. "Well, he feels that he could have been in their spot, if things had gone differently in his life."

"What do you mean?"

"Harold told me that when he was young he was a petty criminal and in and out of juvenile detention. He was facing a prison term when he turned eighteen. The way he tells it, he was standing before the judge and the judge gave him a choice. He could enlist in the military and if he kept his nose clean

88

for four years his juvenile record would be closed—or he could go to prison."

"Wow, and he turned military service into a career."

Coley put the last plate away. "Judges could do that in those days, but it doesn't happen now. You know, the military doesn't want problem children now. Not until we're in a really serious war and they have no other options."

"By the way, Coley, one of the black inmates asked me for a favor. He's the president of the NAACP on the yard and heard about you. He wanted me to ask you, if you would come in and be a speaker for Martin Luther King Jr. Day."

Coley took a step back. A line appeared between his brows. "Why me?"

"Coley, because you're black."

Coley leaned back on the counter. "I'm a finance guy, not a historian. What could I offer?"

Coley's ancestry was black, white, and Cherokee. He grew up in a rarified atmosphere of wealth, culture, and education, and didn't truly experience racism until his teenage years, when his father lost the family's fortune in real estate. I liked to tease him that he had grown up with a silver spoon in his mouth, while I had grown up in the countryside without any spoon at all.

"Coley, you're a bright, eloquent guy. I'm sure you would give them a great speech. The NAACP said their speaker couldn't do it. Who else do you think they can ask? You and I both know that there are basically no other people that look like you in this town."

Coley hugged me and started laughing. "Okay. I'll do it, but it may not be the type of speech they want to hear."

Great. I pushed down the anxiety and tried to avoid visions of the speech ending in a riot.

I tried to sleep that night, but my dreams and memories became twisted. I remembered the day I heard that Martin Luther King Jr. had been assassinated. My mother had cried, just like she cried when President Kennedy was assassinated. I thought of her telling me she had never seen a black person in Germany, until an African-American MP gave her a roll of crackers when she was starving after the war. She went into great detail, telling me how each cracker tasted and how she made them last for two weeks. She also told me how upset she was when she found the little container of butter on the bottom that had gone rancid. She said she ate it anyway, with no crackers.

I woke up and heard Coley snoring softly next to me. *What was that dream all about?* I didn't know, but decided that it wasn't good for me to get sucked down into the negativism and paranoia of the prison. *Coley will protect me. Maybe the prison would think twice about going after me, if they really knew him.* I rolled to my side and curled up next to him, and felt safe.

Two weeks later, Coley gave the talk in the gym. I was able to catch the last few minutes. I stood in the back and scanned the inmates' faces. *That's interesting, there are two white guys sitting in the front row.* I leaned over to get a better look and recognized both of them. Mr. Alario was a middle-aged man from France, and Mr. Sandina was a young Hispanic guy who I knew was exceptionally bright, and known on the yard for his artwork.

The acoustics weren't the best, but the guys were attentive and sitting on the bleachers without jostling or talking. Coley had on black pants and a white polo shirt, and his stance implied power. I didn't know if his upbringing or his time in Vietnam as a platoon leader caused him to have such presence, but it was unmistakable even from the back of the gym.

He was wrapping up, and I leaned forward to hear him speak.

"Martin Luther King Jr. would want all of you to understand that if you want your lives to be different from when you entered prison, you need to be of service to others. Regardless of their race. If you want to solve the problems of the black community, you also have to solve the problems facing other groups that are poor and uneducated, including white Americans." He paused to let that thought sink in and continued a little louder.

"He would also want you to understand that this country has moved

90

into an era very different from when he was a child. We are in a period where there are not enough good black male role models for young people. Young children of all races just want a hero to look up to, someone they can model their behavior on. You can be those heroes. That is what Martin Luther King Jr. would want from you today."

There was silence... and then the inmates all stood up and started clapping. I glanced at the two custody officers, and they were clapping as well. The inmates started to disperse then, and their voices filled the gym. Coley had a bunch of them around him, asking him questions and shaking his hand. I decided to talk to him when I saw him at home.

"What did the guys say to you after the speech?" I asked him, back in our kitchen several hours later. "Did they like it?"

"They must have, because they asked me to teach a black history course out there."

"Really? What did you tell them?"

"I told them that if I taught it, it would be a course on the ethnic history of America and they would have to set it up with the college. They said they'd do it." He shrugged and smiled. "We'll see. You're turning me into a good person, Karen. I don't know if that's such a smart idea."

It was a smart idea. Coley started his course on the ethnic history of America, which was attended by many of the black inmates and Mr. Alario, the Frenchman. After a few classes, Alario asked permission to bring his friend, Mr. Jensen, who happened to be the Aryan Warrior shot caller and head of the whites on the yard. Jensen was bald and covered in swastika tattoos, and Coley told me that he sat in the back and watched the class quietly. When the semester was over, Mr. Jensen came up and told Coley that if he'd had a father or an uncle like him, he would never have gone to prison.

Coley considered that one of the best compliments he ever received. He went on to teach accounting, finance, and human resources—not only in the prison I worked at, but at the maximum-security prison and women's prison as well.

8. Moth

The gatehouse door leading into the prison buzzed open and I walked in. I was surprised to see my infirmary officer, Fred, in the control room. I had seen Fred almost every day since my first day in the prison. As the infirmary officer, he controlled the inmates coming into the clinic and provided the security the medical staff needed in the clinic and in the infirmary. I had worked with him for one and a half years, and I felt comfortable with his laid-back demeanor. He was a calming influence when Hannah or the inmates started overreacting.

Now I wondered why he was stationed in the gatehouse.

I handed Fred my briefcase. "What are you doing out here? Who's going to protect me in the infirmary today?"

He pushed my briefcase back to me without searching through it, and gave me a little smile. "I've watched out for you ever since you came in, and I think you'll be fine with the new officer. Every year or two we get rotated to a new position, so we don't get too comfortable in one spot."

Fred brushed a hand through his faded reddish hair and sighed. "I just wish we had some overlap with the prior officer. I've been in the gatehouse before, so I know the routine, but the infirmary isn't like any other unit. It takes a while to get used to." He cocked his head and raised his bushy ginger eyebrows. "Especially if they have a run-in with Hannah."

Hannah was still the charge nurse, and even though her starched white uniform and curly white hair did not change from day to day, her mood swings were becoming entirely unpredictable. It was unsettling to see her go from saccharine sweet to outright scary, and I was always waiting for her to turn on me. *Is she going through menopause? She seems past that age.*

"It seems you knew how to handle Hannah," I said. "What do you think I should tell the new officer if she goes off on him?"

Fred laughed. "She tried that shit with me once and I let her know who really called the shots in the infirmary, and that was you."

I looked up, surprised. "I thought you were going to say it was you,

93

Fred!"

He put both hands on the counter and peered through the opening that separated us. "I call the shots when it comes to security, but you call the shots in the medical department. And that includes the nurses."

I wanted to tell him that I wished that was true, but someone else was knocking on the door to come in.

"I'll keep that in mind, Fred," I said, and waved as I walked through the metal detector.

I strolled past the mailroom where an officer was sifting through letters and packages, and opened the swinging doors to the outside where I breathed in the welcome smell of the clean morning air. I stepped over the long green hoses littering the walkway, and pushed the button to alert the officer in the control room to let me in. The lieutenant and two officers were sitting at their desks. One officer was smoking, and the other officer was leaning back in his chair drinking coffee. The coffee drinker nodded to me, and grabbed a chocolate glazed donut from the pink box in front of him as he swung forward to push the button and buzz me in.

Like every day, I passed through a large iron gate that separated the infirmary from the officers' area, called Operations. I knew there were other rooms in the Operations wing, down the hallway where the assistant wardens and caseworkers had offices, but I had never been down that way. The hallway was still dark at this hour: they started work at eight, and I started my day at six-thirty. I sometimes wondered if the clinic sat right next to their area so they could eavesdrop on my patients.

Entering the infirmary, I smelled biscuits. The inmate clerks and porters were gathered in the small kitchen, all sitting around one side of a long table that was pushed next to the wall. They were enjoying their breakfast and laughing about some funny story.

Mr. Carter, one of my favorite inmate porters, saw me out of the corner of his eye. "Hey, Dr. G!" he yelled, and hit the shoulder of the inmate next

94

to him. "Do you want a biscuit before this doughboy eats them all?"

My answer was drowned out by the laughter of the other inmates, as they guarded their biscuits from the chubby new porter. Across the hall from them was the nursing station; I saw Hannah with her back toward me, filling the medication cups for the inmates on the yard. I knew she didn't like to be disturbed, and continued down the long grey hallway past the records and X-ray rooms. I opened the last room on the left, which served as my office and exam room.

The exam table was next to the right wall, next to a white cloth screen that I could use to block my door if I needed to do an extensive exam. I was not allowed to close the heavy white metal door to my office when I was with an inmate, because there was no window in it. My large brown desk was on the other side of the room, facing the exam table with a metal chair behind it. It was a fairly small room to use as both an office and an exam room, but I was getting used to it.

I didn't have anything personal in my office except for a few reference books, but I did have a view. Through the security mesh in the window, I could see the educational building on the other side of the fence. When I stood next to the window and looked to my right, I could glimpse two of the grey housing units, which faced the large culinary building. I knew there was an inmate store, chapel, gym, and weight yard on the same side as the culinary, but couldn't make them out from my window.

I sat down at my desk, and was shuffling through the paperwork when Mr. Carter—known as M.C. on the yard—came in grinning and holding a cup of hot tea. He placed it next to me and held up his right hand.

"I know you don't want a biscuit like doughboy down the hall, but you can't say no to a cup of hot tea on a morning like this." He enacted a dramatic shiver, and stepped back so as not to crowd me.

"You're incorrigible, M.C."

"There you go again, Dr. G. Using those big-ass words and trying to

95

teach me something. What does incorrigible actually mean?"

"You need to look it up in a dictionary. I'm sure you'll see your face right next to the definition."

M.C. slapped his clean, pressed light blue jeans with a manicured right hand. "It means I'm your favorite clerk, right?"

I printed "incorrigible" on a yellow sticky note and handed it to him. "Why don't you look it up and see if you are right."

Glancing out the window, I noticed that the inmates were now walking on the yard.

"Looks like count has cleared, M.C. Why don't you go up front and sign them in so I can get started?"

"Sure, Dr. G." He folded the sticky note, put it in his pocket, and walked out the door.

I put my hands around the cup of hot tea and smiled as I felt them warm up. M.C. was incorrigible, but his wit and his buoyant mood were like a lighthouse in a dark storm. He drew inmates and staff alike toward his glow.

My first patient entered, looked at every corner in the room, and sat down in the chair next to my desk with a sigh. He reeked of bad tobacco, and his weathered face was devoid of emotion. His blue shirt was frayed and had stains on it. He gave me the impression that he was severely depressed.

"What can I do for you, Mr. Meller?"

He breathed in and out slowly, and coughed a few times before he began. The tone of his voice was flat; it seemed that he was just reciting a list.

"Well, I've got a few medical problems now and I wanted them checked out. I haven't been to a doctor in years, but I hear that you care about your patients and might know what you're doing, so... I've got this cough that isn't going away and I know you'll tell me to give up smoking, but I'm letting you know right away that isn't going to happen. It's one of the only things that they haven't taken away from me and it gives me some peace. I'm also having

96

problems getting a decent night's sleep, because I have to get up two or three times a night to piss. I'm only forty-eight and I think I'm too young to be having prostate problems. I haven't had blood work since I entered this hellhole thirteen years ago, and I think that should be done as well."

Mr. Meller's thinning grey hair stuck out a bit from the sides of his head, and his sunken cheeks seemed a bit greyish as well. I wonder if that was from the cigarettes or something like hemochromatosis—high iron levels, which could cause serious medical problems. I made a mental note to add an iron panel and ferritin to his basic labs. I looked at him again. He was looking down at his hands resting in his lap. *He's depressed. I'm going to have to address that as well.*

"Hmm. I will do your physical exam and check your labs," I said, "but first let's talk about how you're doing emotionally. You've been here a long time. Is it getting harder for you?" I flipped to the psych section of his chart and didn't see any entries. Instead, there was an intelligence report. His IQ was in the genius range.

I looked up and saw his wrinkles deepen as his shoulders pulled forward. "I was on death row and that was hard. What was worse was the Supreme Court making executing me unconstitutional, and making me spend my entire life penned up in a box with morons."

I didn't pull away from his anger. I leaned a little closer. "That must be very difficult to deal with. How do you manage those feelings? Have you ever tried to talk with the psychologist or psychiatrist?"

He snorted. "Both worthless. If you'd ever talked with either one of them you would know it. They're just treading time till they get their state retirement. They're sick and tired of hearing guys whining all day long."

I didn't see the point in arguing with him. "Is there someone you can talk to, or something you can do that helps you deal with the emotions you're feeling?"

Meller leaned forward, put his elbow on my desk, and balanced his

97

chin on his clenched fist. His grey eyes darkened and his nostrils flared; I noticed what looked like a basal cell cancer on the right side of his nose. "Why do you even care?" he said.

"I care because I know what chronic stress, anger, and depression can do to the body."

His eyes glanced at his chart and he leaned back into his chair. "Yeah, I know I could drop dead from a heart attack. But it wouldn't be a bad way to go."

"I doubt that would happen to you, Mr. Meller. I think you came in today to see if you could feel better. So let me ask you some questions and do your exam."

He answered all my questions, and after examining him, I said, "Mr. Meller, I'd like to do some basic labs on you today, and I also want to get a chest X-ray and an EKG. You also have what looks like a small skin cancer on your nose, and I can make an appointment to remove it for you next week."

He wrinkled his nose and then touched the spot. "That's all I need to improve my looks, is to have a hunk of my nose chopped off."

"Don't worry, it's small now and can be taken care of easily."

"Uh-huh," he said and stood up to leave. He turned when he was in the doorway and added, "Thanks for being thorough."

Later that day, I walked into the X-ray room and asked Rodney to show me the films on Mr. Meller. I appreciated Rodney's skill not only in taking X-rays, but in reading them as well; he was a great asset to the medical department. I knew he only had a year left on his sentence, and wondered who would replace him. I couldn't imagine that another inmate would have his skill level and be certified in X-rays as well as nuclear medicine.

"So Rodney," I asked, "what do you think about his lungs?"

Rodney's blue eyes scanned both films. "Moth's films don't look that bad, considering I've never seen him without a cigarette in his mouth."

My head cocked to the side to make sure Mr. Meller's name was on the films.

"Why do you call him Moth?" I asked.

He shrugged. "Everyone calls him Moth. I don't know why, but you've got to admit he looks like a grey moth."

"What do you know about him? He said he was on death row at one time, so I find it odd that he's on a medium-security yard."

Rodney looked at me like he was scanning an X-ray. His blue scrub top made me feel like I was a medical student again, asking the wrong question. He put his hands in his jean pockets. "If an inmate with a high security level doesn't give them any problems, they eventually put him on a Medium yard. Even if he's a lifer. I guess Moth never gave them problems. He just seems to stick to himself. You'd be surprised how many lifers are on this yard. They mostly stay out of trouble. They're all hoping the pardon board will change their sentence to life with the possibility of a parole."

He paused and then added, "But not in Moth's case."

"Why do you say that?"

Rodney shifted his weight and looked back at the X-ray. "Because they're never going to let someone out who killed a cop."

A week later, Moth came in for his follow-up appointment. After I discussed his labs with him and removed the skin cancer from his nose, he handed me an article that he had ripped out of *Reader's Digest*. It was titled *Doctors and Patients Must Talk*, with the tag line "Communication—and the human spirit—can be as important to healing as medicine."

I flipped through the article, then looked up to find Moth studying me. "What did you take away from that article, Mr. Meller?" I asked him.

He popped his knuckles on both hands. "I was interested in whether you believed that real communication between doctors that care, and patients that want to get better, is as important as medicine?"

"I believe that a patient has the best chance for healing if their body, mind, and spirit are all addressed in a positive way. Is that something you are interested in?"

"I'm considering it, because I'm sick and tired of being sick and tired. The only problem is that I can't stand the shrinks, and I'm an atheist." He laughed and leaned back. "So how did you end up here? You seem to know what you're doing. I get the sense that you actually care about what happens to me."

"I care about all the patients I see. I was placed here by the federal government to do a four-year payback on a scholarship."

He cocked an eyebrow. "So the Feds have thrown you into a battle zone. We have something in common then. The Feds tossed me into a battle zone too, but it was called Vietnam."

"How did that experience affect you?"

"So are we talking for real now, Doc?"

"Yes, I'd like to know."

"Well, it fucked me up." He looked out the window and his body tightened. Then he stood up in one quick movement and walked to the door. Turning back to look at me, he said, "When I write I express myself better. I'll drop off something I wrote a while back about the war. You read it, and when I see you next week to take out my stitches, you can decide whether you really want to communicate with me or not."

Well, Moth seems more animated now, I thought. *He even laughed. I wonder if he's just relieved that his X-ray and labs were normal... but I don't think that's it. Maybe he feels that he can talk to me, and it's given him some hope.*

Late in the afternoon, as I was getting ready to leave for the day, I was surprised to see a large manila envelope on my desk with my name printed across the front. *That was quick*, I thought as I leafed through the eight-page typed manuscript, entitled *Welcome Home Al.*

I read the first paragraph.

Don't read this unless you want to know the same intensity with which I have lived my life, most of my life. It is not the watered-down version of war that I wrote for my college stuff. This is real, it is what gives and sustains the attitudes that allow me to say I can walk down some street and shoot the malignants without batting an eye...and mean it. This is not a story that came easy, it was the first, and although dramatized, it is what killed the cop, put me in prison thirteen years ago as needing to be executed as too dangerous to live, and something you are not involved in except as a therapist in ICWMD.

I closed my eyes and rubbed the bridge of my nose. *Oh, boy. ICWMD? That doesn't sound good. Is that a military term?* I glanced at the clock. *Well, I have enough time to read it before I head home.*

Moth's story was about Al, a Vietnam vet who woke from a nightmare and looked in the mirror and saw his face "ill, sickly, dead: as dead as all those bodies of his friends and comrades he'd left behind." Al wanted the images that tormented him to stop: "he needed something real, something alive to hate. Tick-Tock, Tick-Tock." He eventually shot up a bar, and ended up in jail. In the court room, Al "sat there...listening...not listening. He'd heard it all before. He heard something else too...more ominous, more demanding. It was close now and it called him. It whispered: Tick-Tock, Tick-Tock."

The judge told Al that he would have to submit to medication and treatment, but "Al couldn't stay at all. No more. Nowhere. He was going home and no one would ever stop him again." The story ended with Al disarming the bailiff and shooting him, the judge, the D.A. and the public defender, then pointing the gun at his court-appointed psychiatrist:

"As he swung the gun around to face the doctor's horrified and frozen expression, a strange thing happened inside of Al. A soldier's understanding overcame him. A soldier's tiredness in killing: a soldier's mercy

101

and compassion engulfed him as Doctor Bates stared down the muzzle and into the hole that led to another dimension through death. Tears poured down the soldier's face, and for a long moment both men were brothers again. One of them had to die. Al was closer. The gun turned away from Doc, around toward Al...and in the turning, the clock struck twelve. Tic-Tock, Tick-Tock...BOOM!"

I rubbed the back of my neck with both hands. *This is why I didn't become a psychiatrist. Well, Moth did warn me not to read it unless I wanted to know what made him tick.* But how could I help a patient if I didn't understand them? Obviously, he had issues with what happened in Vietnam. *God, how I hate wars. What WWII did to my mother and her family. What Vietnam did to Coley. Tonight, I have to ask Coley for his take on this guy.*

Coley had been in combat; he'd told me that he had killed people he had nothing against. "Don't think I couldn't kill someone I *did* have something against," he had said. That was one of the reasons he chose not to have a gun in the house.

That night after dinner, I pushed the manuscript toward him.

He picked it up and sniffed. "What's this? It stinks like bad tobacco."

"I know, but I'd like you to read it and tell me what you think. It was written by one of my patients who's a Vietnam vet."

"Okay, but I'm going to sit on the couch and read it while you finish cleaning up."

"It's a deal," I said, knowing that Coley was tired; when he was tired, he got grumpy if I asked him to do too many things at once.

It didn't take long to clean up the kitchen, and a few minutes later I curled up next to Coley. "What do you think?" I asked. "And does ICWMD mean anything to you?"

He put down the manuscript, sighed and looked up at the ceiling. "Nope. Be careful, Karen. He's a bush vet."

"What do you mean by that?"

"A vet who never came home from the war. They can hold it together at times, but something happens and they're right back in the war. War is horrible, but somehow it makes sense to them and they know their place in it. Everywhere else, they don't feel like they belong anymore."

"What about you? Remember that time we were hiking last summer and you tossed me in the bushes because someone left a fishing line on the trail?"

He looked at me, and his brown eyes were hard to discern in the dim light. "That was just a reflex. You know what tripwires could do in Vietnam."

"Well I'm just glad we weren't walking in a field of cactus."

He smiled. "Well, use good judgment with this guy. I know you want to save everyone, but there are some who don't want to be saved, or can't be."

"I saved you, didn't I?"

"Yes, you did," he murmured and gave me a kiss on top of my head.

The following Friday at his appointment, Moth was carrying another manila folder, which he placed on my desk. I removed his stitches, and told him the pathology report showed that the cancer had been totally removed.

Then I tapped the folder. "I read your manuscript. On the cover page, you mention that I'm not involved except as a therapist in ICWMD. I'm a physician and not a therapist, and I don't know what ICWMD means."

Moth shifted in his seat and leaned on the armrest. "I wrote that when I first talked to Joel, the psychologist. ICWMD means 'intercourse with my doctor.' I guess he didn't like the play on words. He's weak and soft. My bet is that everything was handed to him; he's never had to fight for anything. I can't communicate with someone I can't respect. You're different. I bet things weren't handed to you."

This is not going in a good direction, I thought.

Moth went on: "You know, when Joel read it, he asked me why Al saved the doctor and killed himself instead. He got it wrong, but I think you know what would have saved Al."

I flashed back to Coley, and thought about how powerful and healing love could be for someone who was hurting and alone. Instead of meeting Moth's gaze, I opened his chart and said, "I'm not trained as a therapist, Mr. Meller. But I think the question they would ask is whether the patient wants to get better."

"Hmph, well, open the folder and you'll find out."

I opened it, and laughed. Inside were three pieces of paper plastered with cartoons, which he had surrounded with his own comments. The first one was a Far Side cartoon showing a white fence separating a female rhino following a new couple in town. On the other side of the fence was a male rhino wagging his tail. The old woman standing next to him said, "Well, well, King...Looks like the new neighbors have brought a friend for you, too."

I loved the odd humor of Far Side cartoons, and Moth's comments next to them were quite witty, but the theme throughout all of them made me uncomfortable. It was all about the relationship between a male and a female. *What type of relationship does he want with me exactly? And what about IC-WMD? Using the word "intercourse" instead of "talking" or "communicating" is a bit creepy.* In my life, I had met a number of men who didn't understand when I told them I was not interested in their advances. *Is Moth hitting on me?*

I shook off those thoughts and looked up at Moth. His eyes seemed a bit more alive, and his wrinkles were not as pronounced. He didn't appear threatening, and I decided not to launch into a discussion of my concerns.

"This is quite creative and clever, Mr. Meller. I used to copy Far Side cartoons and put them on the handouts for the substance abuse class I'm teaching at the camp. But I stopped, because the guys didn't get the humor."

"That's because those guys are concrete thinkers. They can't think in the abstract, but you can." His eyes darkened again. "Doc, you know what

104

stress and emotional issues can do to a person, and you can see that I'm sitting on a ledge thinking about ending it every day. The psych department says I'm not crazy, so you can't put me in the loony bin. So what are you going to do? Are you going to act as my therapist, and will I be seeing you next Friday?"

Ugh. Should I tell him that wouldn't be a good idea? No, first I should talk to the psychologist. I knew Moth didn't want Joel as his therapist, but I wasn't sure whether I should take on that role. I had worked on psych wards in the past, and had taken courses in psychology, but I wasn't a trained therapist. But I could listen, ask questions, and offer empathy. Sometimes that's all a patient needed, if they trusted you.

"I'll see you next week," I said, "and we'll discuss whether my acting as a therapist is an option."

The muscles in his arms relaxed and he exhaled. "Thank you for caring, Dr. G."

The next day, I tracked down Joel the psychologist and asked him to stop by my office. I had talked to him a few times before, and knew that he had a practice on the outside and only worked in the prison to get state benefits. He seemed knowledgeable, but his heavily lidded eyes and his lack of vitality gave me the impression that he practiced being detached from emotions in general.

"What can I do for you, Dr. G?" Joel asked as he walked into my office. He checked his watch. "I've got about ten minutes before I have to meet someone for lunch."

"Thanks for stopping by. I saw a patient yesterday that you've seen before, and I wanted to ask your advice before I see him again. His name is Mr. Meller. Do you remember him?"

"Oh sure, who could forget that guy? He's intelligent, grandiose, narcissistic, and has a lot of issues. Why do you ask?"

"It's obvious to me that his emotional issues are affecting his health. I also think that he's at great risk for taking his own life or putting himself in a situation where he gets himself killed. He said he saw you, but he didn't feel you understood him or could help him. He's asking me to take on that role. What do you think?"

Joel clasped his hands around his protuberant abdomen. "The more important question is, what do you think?"

Wonderful, I thought. *Now I'm the patient.* "I think I might be able to help him, though I'm worried that he's attracted to me in a way that may be problematic."

He shrugged. "It's something we face all the time with psychotherapy patients. I'm sure you were taught about transference and countertransference in your training. Sometimes the greatest healing can occur when the patient does transfer those issues on you. As long as you act as a professional, I don't see any problem with it."

"Do you remember him giving you a short story about a Vietnam vet who ended up killing everyone in the courtroom except the psychiatrist?" I asked.

"Yeah, he gave me a few of his short stories and poems. I seem to remember that he's in a creative writing class on the yard, or something like that."

"One last thing before you go, Joel. Do you remember what the acronym ICWMD meant to him?"

He stood up and scratched his head. "Yeah, I remember, intercourse with my doctor." I don't know if he was just playing with the word intercourse, or if he wanted to shock me, but I for sure knew I wasn't his type."

I nodded and thanked him for stopping by. I was still not sure whether I should take on the role of therapist. *If I don't, though, who will?* Yes, Moth was grandiose and narcissistic, but he was also angry, depressed, and hopeless. All those emotions put him at risk for taking his own life, and he was intelligent enough to remind me that neither Joel nor I could put him in the psych ward. He was giving me the option of trying to help him.

106

Moth had said he respected me, and had reminded me of the importance of hope. Hope. *What do I hope to accomplish? I hope I can help him.* I hoped that my decision to be his therapist was the right choice.

The following Friday, Moth came in, scanned the room, sat down, and handed me another manila folder. I opened it and saw four typewritten manuscripts—one with an A-plus scrawled across the top, titled *Keep America Beautiful, Please Don't Litter.*

I closed the folder. "I can see that you enjoy writing. In what way do you think it helps you?"

He rubbed the side of his nose where the cancer had been. "So you decided to be my therapist, huh?" He smiled for the first time. "Writing is a way for me to escape this shithole, and I'm good at it. Plus, I know you can only spend so much time with me, and I want you to understand my world."

"In your story about Al, how much of that character do you identify with?"

He looked down at the folder and rocked slightly back and forth. "I know how he felt."

"What was your experience in Vietnam like?"

He pulled on his left ear a few moments before answering. "It was a stupid war, but then that's what all soldiers say about all wars after they're in them. It's the willingness to die that makes it so stupid. I must have been more stupid than most, because when I was twenty I joined the Marine Corps. They give you the best image to follow in exchange for a chance of being the first to fight and the first to die. I was a staff sergeant. I had a career ahead of me showing my platoon what you can do to a human body with a bayonet, machine-gun bullets, and hand grenades." He breathed in and exhaled slowly. "War teaches you to lack fear. Step by step, wearing down all your resistance until you think death is your friend, as if it can protect you against your addiction to life."

"What do you think about death now?" I asked.

A small, twisted smile transformed his lips, but didn't change the rest of his face.

"I survived and a lot of my men didn't, so there's got to be reason. Or maybe it's just dumb luck. I'm not afraid of death."

"What are you afraid of?"

"That there's no end to this torture. The only break I get is when I dream of a different existence and then I wake up. I want to scream, but what good would that do? Everybody here utters a silent scream every time they wake up and find out where they are. Alive, but worthless."

"I can see that you're a good writer," I said. "What message would you like to get across to the people who read your writings?"

"I want to teach. To illustrate, persuade, cajole them to further their knowledge and acceptance of themselves as dreamers, believers, and sons and daughters of God. I want them to understand that the dream is called life and love."

He leaned closer, and I could see the pulse bounding in the carotid artery in his neck. His pupils started to dilate, and their intensity made me draw back. I wasn't quite sure what I should ask next; I saw minefields all around me.

Moth raised his right hand. "I know what you're thinking. You're thinking I want something that you feel you can't give. But is it really *can't*? Or is it *won't*? Where does someone who really wants to be a healer draw the line?"

"What I'm thinking, Mr. Meller, is about something psychologists call transference. You're intelligent. I'm sure you're familiar with the concept of transference, but indulge me in letting me explain what the concept means to me." He nodded, and sat back slightly.

I continued: "Patients come to doctors because they want to be healed. They look at that doctor as someone they trust, someone who cares what happens to them. When a male patient sees a female doctor, he might start looking at her in a certain way. He can feel her empathy, and start transferring his need and desire for emotional and physical intimacy on her, especially if he feels he has no one else."

I took a breath. "You asked me where a healer draws the line. My line is this. I may care about your physical and emotional well-being, but I will not act unprofessionally."

The phone rang suddenly. I welcomed the call, as it gave me an excuse to end my visit with Moth early.

"Sorry, Mr. Meller," I said, covering the receiver with my hand. "I need to take this. Think about what we talked about today."

I watched him stand, and his eyes narrowed when he said, "See you next Friday, Dr. G."

I continued meeting with Moth every Friday for a few weeks. One Friday night, I was mentally replaying the most recent session, when Coley asked me how my day had gone.

"Coley, remember me telling you about the Vietnam vet I was concerned about?"

"Yeah, what about him?"

I was sitting on one end of the couch with my legs stretched out and my feet on Coley's lap. It was the signal that I wanted my feet rubbed, and I hoped he wouldn't stop doing it when he started answering my questions.

"You told me that you thought he never returned from the war. What do you think helped you return from the war?"

"I don't think, I know. It was love and humanity. When I came back, I was twenty-four and I had to raise my twelve-year-old brother. The love and attention he needed helped me get over my issues."

I nudged Coley with my foot so he would start rubbing my feet again, and sighed, "Can you imagine a worse place than a prison to talk about love and humanity?"

109

30 Years Behind Bars

"They make a mistake when they don't address those issues. The real reason you need love and humanity is that they make you actually value life, so you aren't so willing to destroy it." He paused and stopped rubbing my feet again. "You know how you tell me that I don't have a chip on my shoulder about white people, like a lot of the black men in the prison do? I'll tell you why. It's because when I was growing up, I was exposed to white people who loved me. That makes all the difference when you interact with haters and racists. You don't generalize and assume other white people are the same way."

"Well I'm glad you didn't generalize white people, because then you wouldn't have married a blonde like me. And who else would rub my feet?" I said, and nudged him again.

Coley looked at me. "What else is running around in that little gerbil brain of yours?"

"I feel the same way you do, about how love and humanity can heal people. I believe this guy really is searching for it as well. I want to help him and I think I can, but his comments and his writing make me worried."

"In what way?" Coley said, laying his left hand on my leg—the signal that it was my turn to rub his hand.

"He keeps pushing the envelope in regards to intimacy. You should see how he looks at me when he talks about love. He also keeps on slipping in sexual innuendos like he enjoys having 'intercourse' with his doctor. One time he started talking about genetics, and said that if we had children, they could rule the world. It made my skin crawl and I wondered why he threw it into the discussion, because his medical records say he had a vasectomy in the past. He's bright enough to twist everything he says about love and sex into a philosophical conversation, but it still makes me uncomfortable."

"Sounds like you have your work cut out for you. If you think he could be a problem, why don't you stop seeing him, or tell Custody that you're concerned about him?"

110

Karen Gedney, MD

"Do you remember that case I told you about a few months ago, where a psych patient was writing weird letters to me thinking I was his ex-wife?"

Coley shook his head. His eyes were closed, and he was enjoying me rubbing the pressure point between his thumb and index finger.

"When I showed Custody the letter, the captain yanked the guy out of a place he was comfortable in and threw him in Max. When they did, he freaked out and broke the jaw of the forensic officer. Custody overreacts, and I don't want to be responsible for another bad outcome. I talked to one of the psychologists about Mr. Meller, and that didn't help me either. Remember Joel? We met him one time at a Christmas party."

Coley opened his eyes. "Yeah, I remember him. A sorry-ass draft dodger." He snorted. "I can't imagine why a vet couldn't relate to him." He turned toward me. "So what are you going to do?"

"I'll see him next Friday and see how it goes. I just have a bad feeling that if I don't help him, something bad will happen."

"Like what?" Coley asked, and withdrew his hand from mine.

"I'm not sure, but he's been sitting on a very high ledge for a long time. I just think something bad will happen if I do the wrong thing."

"Well, you're the professional. Just use good judgment," Coley said, and stood up.

I thought about Coley's words that week, and considered a variety of options I could take, none of which seemed very appealing to me. *Is it better to try to help, knowing that Moth's attraction to me could be a problem? Or is it better not to try, and see him fall off that ledge?* What was it about him that made me not want to give up trying? Was it because he actually was intelligent, dangerous, and a challenge? Or was it because I wanted to heal something that was really broken, and I didn't see anyone else that I thought had a chance? *So what do I do next?*

I made the decision to keep on seeing Moth, as long as I thought I was

111

helping him. As our sessions went on, he initially seemed less depressed, but as the third month was drawing to a close, his writings became concerning again. Now, they involved me.

I opened the sealed envelope on my desk, idly wondering which of the inmate porters Moth used to drop off his writings every week. I glanced at the four typewritten pages, but paused when I saw my name followed by a disturbing passage:

Karen

Hold me close, gentle all my anger, heal the hurt that dissolves my trust and faith and hope for a good and better world. Be the one that saves me, the only one that could or can or will. Be confident, be all the woman it takes to take me inside and give me life. Take the child I am and wrap your hand around my finger so I don't get lost. Take the warrior man and heal his hurt as a woman that wants me well. For all the world that's taken all my happiness and returned it with hurt and malicious ill will, spare from all your life's events just five minutes for me, to give me back my hope and faith that there's one still left alive that's whole enough and honest enough to love me back.'

Oh brother. Talk about transference. *Didn't he understand where I stood when I discussed transference with him the last time? We discussed that topic more than once.*

What was he thinking, writing something like that to me? *Isn't he worried that I would alert Custody? If I did, what would happen? Nothing good. He'd kill himself—or anyone who got in his way.*

I had to move. I stood up and walked over to my window and looked up at the blue sky. What would it be like to never be able to be free again? To never be able to really be close to another person in the way Moth was fixated on? What was I going to do?

I paced toward my door and back to the window, then leaned my head on the window. *I'll drive myself crazy if I worry about this all week. I'll see him on Friday and try to figure out how I can... can what? I'll figure it out.*

On Friday, Moth sat down slowly, holding the arms of the chair as he lowered himself into it without taking his eyes off my face. His thin grey hair was combed back, and he had a new shirt on.

"What did you think of the folder I dropped off for you on Monday, Doc? I wanted to make sure you had enough time to read it."

"I think if Custody had read it, you would already be sitting in a maximum security cell."

He looked down, and when he looked up a barely perceptible smile was there. "It isn't signed, and you wouldn't have to tell Custody who wrote it. You're the type who protects, and you know it. Do you know why I believe you can help me? You're strong enough to hold your own against any man. It's rare to find an equal with such a quality, where sex isn't the whole object."

Great. It's not the "whole" object—and now he's telling me I'm a protector and strong.

"You know, Doc, I find you attractive most for your warmth and compassion and because you're not intimidated intellectually. Your self-confidence makes me feel that I don't have to impress you. I can tell you what I'm feeling, without you getting upset. You remind me of someone in my favorite book by Heinlein, *Time Enough for Love*. You remind me of Ishtar, Lazarus Long's genetic rejuvenation doctor, the tall, sexy one with the long blonde hair. She was in charge of bringing him back to life from his apathy."

I did like Heinlein's science fiction stories, but of course Moth would pick the one with the sexy doctor.

"Mr. Meller, these sessions are about you, not me. We've talked about transference, and I can understand why you project certain things on me, but I've told you before that what you desire from me—that anything not in the doctor-patient realm is not going to happen. The majority of the writings you have given me involve the topic of sex. Why is that such a central theme in everything you have shared with me?"

113

"Look, sex is the metaphor for life. All psychosocial situations can, between intelligent people, be resolved with a catharsis. For me that catharsis would be five minutes with you behind closed doors."

"Mr. Meller, I've told you on more than one occasion that isn't going to happen, but you persist in bringing it up and it makes me uncomfortable."

His grey eyes looked at me and then out my open door—and then back at me. "You're a healer," he said. "No one has come as far as you have with me. You are an end to me, an end of all the pain, all the suffering, and I can't not ask for your help. Those five minutes with you behind closed doors are more about trust than anything. I trust you with my life, and you don't trust me."

Wow, he's pushing my empathy buttons today. "Mr. Meller, if I didn't trust you I wouldn't be sitting here today and talking with you. I did though find what you said in your last writing concerning. Very concerning. You basically said you would take your own life if I didn't give you what you want."

The idea that he believed I would close the door to my exam room and have sex with him made me shudder. I reached for his last manuscript, and he cringed when I started to read from it:

> *I've given you the power of a woman to play God in my life and to choose life or death for me. I wouldn't ever give that power over me to a doctor, but I would, I did, I have, given it to the woman in you.*

My heart was pounding in my chest when I finished, and my hand shook when I laid the paper back on the table. I looked at him, but he was looking down; I saw the muscles in his jaw clench and unclench. I could hear the porters laughing and talking at the end of the hall.

When he looked up, his grey eyes were cold. "You know me better than myself. I can't commit suicide. If I wanted to go out like that, I would have done it years ago. I had a dream that you were the one, and you crushed it. I have to build a new dream, Doc, or I won't have meant anything to anyone, especially to myself. If I don't, what's the use of having lived at all? It really brings into question a person's essence and existence. No offense, Doc, but

114

you're living off the dreams and pain of others, me included."

"Mr. Meller, remember this session is about you, not me. Now that you accept that I am not in your dream, what do you think you will dream of next?"

"I don't know yet. What happens when I can no longer entertain you with my emotional hurt and anguish, when my emotions flatten out, when my speech becomes monosyllabic and I become a machine again? Maybe we both end up studying each other and expecting nothing in return. I think that's a fair bargain between a doctor and a patient, don't you?"

"Studying each other and expecting nothing in return is not a therapeutic relationship," I said, feeling frustrated and a bit angry by the direction of the conversation.

"Doc, I needed more than I should have asked from you, and I'm not angry at you. I just was in worse shape than either of us thought. You did help me and I'm back on track, in harness, and pulling toward another dream to live. I still want to see you, want to talk, and I want to know you as a friend."

"Mr. Meller, as a doctor I want to help you, but I can not be your friend and feel that I can not help you as a therapist. I think in the future it would be best if you didn't write anything to me. I know writing helps you, but you should pursue it in your creative writing and poetry classes, or write for yourself."

His eyes narrowed and his muscles tightened, but he didn't respond.

I looked at the clock and stood up. "I'm sorry I wasn't able to help you. I hope someone else can."

Moth pushed himself out of the chair, and didn't say anything as he stomped out the door. I let out a sigh of relief and sat down. I went back over what he had said and how he had acted, and wondered what he would do. He had said he wasn't going to commit suicide. So what *was* he going to do?

I hoped I would not see Moth again, but the following Friday he walked into my office with a small brown bag. He sat down. "Dr. G., do you know what day it is today?"

The coldness in his voice made me glance at my open door. I answered, "October, Friday the thirteenth."

He stood up, put his hands on my desk, leaned forward... and his grey eyes glinted when he said, "And that's the day you're going to watch me die."

My body rose in one motion to get around my desk and out of my office. Before I could take the second step, his hands went around my neck and my body went with the rotational force. I flew over my desk and landed upside down on my left wrist.

Moth shoved the heavy desk into me. I tried to get up and the first thing I saw was the knife in his right hand. It was a real buck knife. *Where did he get that?* I froze.

I heard Assistant Warden Ignin yell, "What's going on down there?"

"I've got Dr. G. hostage, and you're going to do what I want," Moth yelled.

There was a pause, then Ignin responded: "What do you want?"

"Give me that jug of water at the end of the counter."

I wondered if I had landed on my head, because what he said made no sense to me.

I heard the steps of the assistant warden come down the hall, and wondered if the officers were behind him. I then saw a plastic jug passed through the door to Moth. He grabbed it, then closed and locked the door.

I felt my jaw drop. *Now what do I do?* The shock of being attacked was over, and all I felt in its place was anger. *How could Moth do this to me? Why didn't the assistant warden do anything?* I knew he had issues with me, but not to do anything... I felt terribly alone. My eyes traveled around the room, searching for options.

Moth took the otoscope off my desk, which I could have used as a weapon. He looked at me and sneered. "Not that I don't trust you, but I don't."

I got up and sat in my chair. The large desk was pinned against it so I couldn't move anywhere else. Moth opened his brown bag and removed a long rope made out torn t-shirts. I felt my heart rate go up. I did not want to be tied up. He looped it around the doorknob and then secured it to the thick electrical conduit bolted to the wall. He kept one eye on me, and touched the buck knife sticking out of his jeans pocket. Then he grabbed the tape and papers on my desk, and covered the windows so no one could see into the office.

Moth then took out the second rope and said, "Put out your hands."

I put out my left hand and pointed to my wrist, which was starting to throb. "I landed on it in the fall, and I think I broke it. There's no need for you to tie me up."

He looked at me to see if I was lying, and then back at my wrist. I could tell he was unsure. "Well... just don't move from that seat."

My heart felt like it was going to beat out of my chest. Moth took the seat opposite me, and pulled out of the brown bag a carton of Camel cigarettes, a box of Junior Mints, and a bottle of Mylanta. *God, he's got this all planned and he's in for the duration.*

He took a single cigarette out and smelled the length of it, lighted it, and took a deep drag. He let it out in a slow exhale, and my disgust for cigarettes reached a new level. I hated the smell and I could already feel the sting of the smoke getting under my contact lenses. Anger welled up in me, and it made me feel strong, focused. *How could he attack me? All those weeks I tried to help him, where the only thing I wanted to do was help...*

He leaned back and smiled. "So what are you going to ask me now, Karen?" He said my first name slowly, drawing out the syllables, and I cringed.

So he wants me to talk. Well, I won't give him the satisfaction. The anger felt safe, and made me feel that I had some control.

117

"You'll talk, Karen, because that's what you do. I know you're angry now, and I'll give you that. But after all is said and done, what will you really have lost? Maybe you miss out on tonight's dinner or some show you were going to see with your husband. You know what I'm going to be missing when all this is done? It's called my life, and you could have saved me if you just had given me those five minutes alone with you. You could have saved me. Remember, you held my life in your hands. By giving in, it would have cost you what? Five minutes, that's all. You could have just let me get inside of you to be healed." He took another drag on the cigarette and blew a smoke ring.

Moth leaned against the exam table and put the buck knife on it. He adjusted his stance, and I heard the crinkle of the paper that covered the table. He hadn't combed his grey hair, and the thin strands couldn't cover his early balding. He was taller than me, but not by much. *Maybe he's five ten.* He outweighed me easily by sixty pounds, and his hands were strong. *I'd never be able to take him on physically.* His grey eyes were the color of the ocean on an overcast day, and they studied me like I was a rat in an experiment.

"Karen, this is really good stuff for a case study. A real-life problem of how far people will go to meet their most urgent needs. I've been forced to do many unlikeable things in my life, just short of murder to get it done." His voice rose at the end of the sentence.

He took another drag and exhaled, letting his shoulders relax. "I've lived twenty-four hours a day for years on end right on the psych ward, as head psych attendant here and at Max. I held them when they cried, I soothed them in their agony and confusion, and I hurt for them all. I care too about the helpless and hopeless, Karen, and don't you ever believe that I don't."

"If I had a patient who asked me to give him a blowjob to save his life," he continued, "I'd consider it very, very carefully if indeed it would save his life. Why is that not abhorrent to me? As far as I know, I have no latent homosexual tendencies, and as a man competing against men in ego and status, that would be the ultimate sacrifice. So why do I see it as insignificant in light of my patient's need?" He took a final drag on the cigarette and dropped the butt

118

into the coffee cup on my desk.

The oddest thought popped into my mind. I remembered a comedy where a guy was bit by a rattlesnake on his penis, and when he asked his friend to suck out the poison, his friend said, "You're my best friend, but you're going to die."

I bit the inside of my cheek and tried not to giggle. Moth took out another cigarette and rolled it between his thumb and index finger.

The phone rang, and I jumped. We both looked at the phone as it rang and rang... Moth picked it up on the tenth ring.

"Yeah, I have Dr. G. hostage," he said. "Yes, she's okay for now." He stared at me. "What I want is for you to kill me at the stroke of midnight.... yes, you heard me right. I put a bull's eye on the door. At midnight, you shoot through the door and kill me." He slammed down the phone.

He's gone off the deep end. That's fourteen hours from now—and how do you bargain with someone who wants to die? I squirmed in my seat and rubbed my hands on my black pants, wincing when I put pressure on my left wrist.

He lit another cigarette. I coughed and rubbed my eyes.

Moth smoked in silence, looking at the door until he finished his cigarette. He stood up and took three steps to the window, lifting the edge of one of the papers to peer outside. When he did so, he flattened himself next to the wall and made sure that his body could not be seen. *Great, not only am I a hostage, but I'm dealing with someone who is trained to kill and feels he has nothing to lose.*

You can take him. No you can't. Yes you can. You've got a pen in your pocket and he won't expect it, but you'll have to incapacitate him with one blow. What, are you crazy? This isn't the movies; he has a knife and is bigger and stronger than you. My eyes bounced back and forth between him and the distance that separated me from him. *Maybe eight feet.* I felt my body starting to get ready to fight. I exhaled and drew my legs under me. *He's looking outside,*

119

now's the time. Are you nuts?

My internal chatter was driving me crazy and I had to do something, but I realized attacking him would only get me hurt. I turned my attention to evaluating my wrist. It didn't feel good, but it took my mind away from thoughts that would not help me.

After some time, the phone rang again and Moth answered it. "No, I don't want to talk to the sheriff... Yeah, I knew him when we were kids... I don't care if he comes around to the window, I'm not going to talk to him." He hung up.

There was a tap on the window.

"Shit." Moth said as he stepped to the window and peered through again. The tapping continued, and he pushed open the slot in the bottom of the window, just enough to talk.

"Paul, what the hell are you doing here?" Moth whispered, shaking his head.

"Kenny, they asked me to negotiate with you because we know each other. What the hell are you doing, Kenny? Is the doctor okay?"

"Yeah, she's fine, and you need to stay out of it."

"Kenny, you know I can't. I care about you and what happens to you. Is there anything I can get you or the doc, like some coffee or food?"

"We were friends when we were kids, Paul, but a lot of blood and water is under that bridge now and you don't know me anymore. Stay out of it."

"I know you don't really want to hurt the doctor. Why don't you let her go, and we can talk. I promise no one will hurt you."

Moth's laugh was brittle. "No one *can* hurt me anymore. You just tell them that I want to be killed at midnight. I put a bull's eye on the door so they can't miss."

"Kenny, think about what you're saying. No one's going to shoot through that door with the doctor in the room. Why don't you let her go, before the situation gets worse?"

"Stay out of it, Paul. And don't come back to this window. I won't talk to you, and you don't want to test me. Go on back to them and tell them you did your duty. That's the last time I'm going to talk to you." He closed the slot in the window with a bang.

Moth looked flushed and he was breathing faster. When he reached for another cigarette, I saw a slight tremor. He inhaled the smoke and held it for a long time before letting it out.

"Criminals and cops. You know, they're just two sides of the same coin." He fixed his gaze on me. "There were five of us back then. We grew up together and we went through everything together." He leaned back his head and snorted. "Three of us became cops, and the other two became criminals. What's the odds on that?"

He sat up and brushed back his thinning hair. "I don't know why you didn't give me what I needed to live. I need to know why you wouldn't give me the one thing that would heal me. Think about how you let rules stop you, when you had the power over life and death. It wasn't just the sex that I wanted, I wanted to be emotionally healed."

He sucked on his cigarette, and I started to feel that salty-water taste in the back of my mouth. I swallowed a few times. *God, the last thing I want to do is puke in front of him.* I had to fight the nausea, and after it passed I felt weak and cold. I pulled my jacket closer around me and curled forward, without taking my eyes off him.

Moth stabbed the cigarette butt on the side of the coffee cup. "I gave you the chance to heal me and you didn't. Just five minutes inside of you is all I wanted, and now I'm going to take it."

I started to squirm backward and heard my voice crack. "Forcing yourself on me is not what you wanted."

He snapped, "Of course it's not what I wanted. Why wouldn't you trust me? I know you're not sexually attracted to me, but I thought you could heal as a doctor and as a woman. Why couldn't the woman in you do that? I know underneath that you're a closet rebel. Why did you let the conventions of society rule you?"

"Forcing yourself on me won't heal you." The pounding in my ears started getting louder, and I started to tremble.

"That's where you're wrong, Karen. The world, and those that live in it, place sexual healing in the category of perverted morality. Sex is a sin to the world, and to the medical community as well. Let me tell you what 'intercourse with my doctor' really meant to me. Let's say I lined up ten people and said I would start shooting them one at a time unless you opened your legs for me. I don't think I'd even get to the first one, if you thought I was serious. That's what the war taught me. Closing the gap between real and illusion sometimes takes extreme measures."

I felt like I was punched in the stomach. All the air escaped. *How did I allow myself to get into this situation? I knew he was dangerous and sitting on that precarious ledge. Why did I think I could make a difference?* The tension in the room was pulling me apart.

Then Moth growled, "Let me show you an extreme example. Stand up and pull down your pants, because I'm going to fuck you dead or alive."

I started to whimper, and he laughed. That cold laugh made every cell in my body angry, and I mean *every* cell.

That's when I made my decision. *He is going to do what he's going to do, but I'll not show or feel any emotion. None. He will get nothing from me. Nothing.* It was like a switch that I turned off.

When he did rape me I did not feel anything, except that I was in control.

He made me stand up, pull down my pants and lean over my desk. I felt the cold desktop beneath me, and knew that he was trying to enter me from behind. It didn't work for him, so he made me lie on the floor.

122

I didn't look at him, but I smelled the cigarettes on his breath. The floor was cold beneath me and I shivered. I bit my lower lip and stared at the beige metal exam table next to me, noticing the dirt and dust that had accumulated where its base met the floor. Moth braced himself above me and my body moved with his thrusts, but all I concentrated on was the side of the exam table and the dirt. I could see what looked like sand particles in the dirt. They were a shade lighter.

When he got off me, I pulled up my pants, feeling stickiness between my legs. I rolled to my side and quickly got up, walked to my chair behind the desk, and sat down.

The tension that had been building up in the room vanished after he had raped me, like the air in a balloon when someone unties the knot. I felt like a weight had been taken off me. I didn't look at Moth, but I heard him fishing around in the bottom of his brown bag. I glanced at the bag and saw him pull out a small joint. He lit it, and I smelled the distinctive smell of marijuana.

Moth sighed and murmured, "I've been saving this for a special occasion." When he finished the joint, he put his hand in the brown paper bag, pulled out his box of Junior Mints, and started eating them.

He looked at me, and I chose to look down at my desk. "You know what's sort of funny, Karen? When I was on death row, I thought about my last meal and all I could come up with was a grilled cheese sandwich. Isn't that pathetic? But who has an appetite when they know they are going to be executed? For four years, I thought about what it would be like to be executed, and then the Supreme Court made it unconstitutional. At that time I didn't know which would be worse—being executed, or spending a lifetime in prison. Now I know."

I stayed silent. After a while, I looked at the clock. Five hours had gone by, and there was no sound on the yard or in the building. I was starting to shiver. *Did they turn off the heat, or is my adrenaline going haywire?*

Nine more hours to midnight. Don't tell me they're going to wait until then, to see what he does? How is this going to end? He wants to die at the stroke of midnight. How is that going to work? They aren't going to shoot through that door while I'm alive in here. Would he kill me to force their hand?

The room seemed to get smaller, and it was harder to breathe. *God, I'm going to asphyxiate from all the smoke in this room. I can't just sit here for hours. I have to do something to keep my mind from racing.* I had paper on my desk, and remembered the pen I had in my pocket. I glanced at Moth; he seemed relaxed after the joint and his box of Junior Mints. I pulled out my pen and started to write.

October, Friday the 13th. Taken hostage at 10:00...

I wrote a full page, and was working on the second when Moth took the first page away from me. He read it silently and handed it back to me. It was a factual account, like a reporter would write, with no emotion. His reading it irritated me, and I switched to writing it in German. My German was pathetic and I improvised the grammar a bit, but when he grabbed the second page and couldn't read it, it gave me satisfaction. I knew he was too narcissistic to tear it up, and even though he appeared annoyed, he didn't stop me from writing.

I wrote odd things, but I didn't write about saying good-bye. I did not allow myself to go down that path. I did not want to think about the possibility of dying.

The phone rang two more times, and whoever was on the end of the line didn't get anywhere with Moth. I watched the hours tick by, and started to wonder what Coley was doing now. *The prison must have notified him. I hope he told the Winstons that we can't make the dinner engagement we had with them tonight.* Then I thought about the news. *God, I hope Mom hasn't heard about me being taken hostage. If she has, she'll worry herself sick and drive Dad crazy.* She was the type that, if you were late for dinner by five minutes, would think you died in a car accident.

Ten hours had passed since I was taken hostage. It was cold and dark now—they must have turned off the power—and the only thing I could think about was that I had to pee. *My bladder will never be the same if I don't pee. I don't care anymore about what Moth thinks.*

I pointed at the plastic urinal that sat on the back corner of the shelf. "I need to use that urinal to pee. Can you please hand it to me."

He looked at it, shrugged, and said, "I'm going to watch."

I didn't care if the whole prison yard watched, I just needed to pee and I didn't want to sit in a pool of urine.

My bladder emptied very slowly while he watched, but it was such a relief that I didn't care. He took the urinal from me and peed in it himself, then put it back in the corner.

Another two hours went by in the dark, and I was so cold that I let my waist-length blonde hair down so it could cover my back and neck for warmth. I was trying to warm my hands by shoving them under my armpits, when suddenly, brilliant lights flooded the room.

I dropped to the floor from my chair in a reflexive action, as the room seemed to explode outward. I saw the door bow out, the ropes pulling taught, and then in slow motion it seemed to fall back into place.

Then I heard pop-pop-pop sounds and saw tracers go through the room.

I'm going to die like this? I didn't even give Coley a baby.

The next instant, a guy in a flak jacket was yelling and screaming at me, and dragging me over Moth's bloody body. He was walking me down the hall and I was shaking so bad it seemed my body had forgotten how to walk. I heard one more shot before I was grabbed and hugged by Kendra Jones, the female warden.

They brought me into a small room at the end of the hall, and some EMT was trying to talk to me and check me out. I didn't want to be examined or touched. I told him to get away from me. I was rattled and not thinking rationally—until I saw Coley. I launched into his arms. He wrapped his strong arms around me and I was safe. He kissed me on the top of my head. We didn't have to say anything.

I didn't want to leave Coley's embrace, but Custody only gave me a minute before I was taken to the warden's office to be "debriefed." I was led out of the prison, but I refused to let go of Coley's hand, and he followed. I looked at where my office stood, and wondered who had put all those brilliant lights outside the windows. I squeezed Coley's hand tightly as they took us across the parking lot to the building where the warden had her office.

When I walked into the building, I saw a line of staff who looked as bad as I felt. I couldn't look them in the eye. *I thought everyone had gone home and left me to die. What are they still doing here?* It was almost midnight.

Kendra stood over six feet tall and had worked her way up from being a custody officer to a warden. I felt comfortable with her.

"Dr. G., I know you've been through a lot, but I need to talk with you before you go home. It's standard procedure that you have to be debriefed. It will just be you, me and Trish, who will transcribe what you tell me." She saw that I had still not let go of Coley's hand. "Would you like your husband to be in the room with you?" I nodded.

I answered direct questions like a machine, with yes and no answers. They didn't ask me whether I had been raped, and I did not volunteer that information. I didn't want to think about it, I didn't want to talk about it, and all I really wanted was to go home. Kendra did not prolong the interview, and when Coley got me out of her office and we walked to his car, I saw the media and their trucks at the edge of the parking lot.

"Coley, I don't want them to see me. I'm going to hide in the backseat, on the floor so they don't see me." He nodded and I climbed in and curled up on the floor.

When we got home that night, Coley fell dead asleep. I couldn't sit still, let alone lie down and try to sleep. I ran a hot bath, sank into it, and didn't start crying until I was warm again.

126

9. Post Moth

I opened my eyes to hear a high-pitched whine. When I turned my head to look around my bedroom, I felt the pain in my neck and it all came back in an instant. His hands around my neck, the room expanding outward. I rubbed my temples and swallowed a few times to see if the tinnitus in my ears would decrease. *No such luck. It must be from the concussion grenade they threw in the room.* I remembered the warden telling me that the assault team had sledgehammered a hole in a kick-out panel in the wall of my office, and then thrown the grenade in.

I sat up, and felt a little dizzy when I looked at the clock on the nightstand next to me. *Eight-thirty. Coley's probably downstairs drinking coffee and waiting for me to get up.* I stood up, stretched, and checked on the range of motion in my left wrist. Sore, but functional. I walked downstairs, smelling fresh brewed coffee.

Coley smiled and patted the kitchen chair next to him. "Take a seat and I'll get you some coffee. How are you feeling? What do you want to do today?"

How did I feel? I didn't know. What did I want to do? I only knew what I *didn't* want to do.

"I don't want to deal with anyone, especially not the media. I also can't just sit in the house, because…"

Coley handed me the cup of coffee, and I put my hands around it. The heat was comforting. I couldn't take a sip, because my throat and chest felt like they were in a vise.

"I tell you what. What do you think about going up into the mountains? We can hike and afterwards I can take you to dinner, get you a glass of wine, and we can dance till you're so tired that nothing will keep you awake," Coley said, and put his hand on my arm.

All the things I loved and associated with escape. I nodded, and got up before I started to tear up. Coley wrapped his arms around me as I buried my head into his muscular shoulder, and he murmured, "You're going to be fine. Everything's going to be okay."

I did dance until I was exhausted, and I did sleep. There were a few moments that weekend when I didn't even think about the events on Friday the 13th, until I saw a newspaper with the headline *Killer takes doctor hostage.*

On Monday, I went back to work. On the car radio I heard a commentator discussing what had happened in the prison. I was about to turn it to another channel, when I heard my name mentioned. "The governor praised the prison director and sheriff for their handling of the hostage incident and also added that the doctor is a heroine. She kept her cool and was courageous, and if she had not been able to deal with the situation calmly it could have gotten out of hand very quickly."

The ringing in my ears started to get louder. *I'm not a heroine of anything. I was stupid. How could I not see that I could get hurt?* I gripped the steering wheel tighter. *What would have happened if I didn't try to help him, or if I had alerted Custody? Could it have been worse? Could more people have been hurt? Would he still be alive?*

I turned onto the road that led to the prison, and saw the squat grey buildings in the distance. I could feel my heart pounding in my chest and hear it in my head. *Breathe, Karen. Slow it down.*

When I walked through the gatehouse, no one said anything to me. I kept my head down so I wouldn't have to look at anyone. The officers that let me in to the infirmary didn't say anything, not a word, and I was relieved. I felt on edge as I walked down the long grey hallway, and noticed that my senses were all heightened. I could even smell the oatmeal, eggs, and banana the inmates had eaten earlier that morning in the back of the infirmary.

The doorway to my office was open, and I started to shake when I turned to enter it. The wall that faced the yard had a large hole in it. I looked down at the grey, linoleum-tiled floor where Moth had been shot, and saw some blood ooze from the cracks in the tiles as I took a step. I closed my eyes and breathed out to steady myself. I looked at my white exam screen, which had some holes in it, and tried to see if any bullets were imbedded in the walls. The heavy desk was back in its spot. I bit my lower lip. *I have to change*

129

how that desk sits so I'm closer to the door than the inmate is.

I sat on the desk, picked up the phone, and punched in a number.

"Warden's office, can I help you?"

"Yes, this is Dr. G. Is the warden in?"

"Sorry, she's in a meeting, can I take a message?"

"Yes, tell her that the doctor has a large hole in the wall of her office from a concussion grenade and she needs it fixed as soon as possible," I replied, and hung up before I said things I would regret.

Hannah tapped on the door. "Will you be seeing patients this morning, Dr. G?"

I wanted to say something like "No, I'm just going to sit here and look at the hole in the wall and watch how many mice come in from the cold," but I didn't.

I nodded instead. "Do we have any patients waiting to be seen? If not, I'll go to the back and check on the infirmary patients."

She pulled her shoulders back and pulled down her immaculate white nursing outfit. "We don't have anyone yet, but when I get them signed in I'll send the clerk back there to tell you."

I watched Hannah walk stiffly out of the office, and wondered whether she was pleased or not to see me back at work. *Not one kind word to spare.*

It felt good to leave my office. The doors leading to the small infirmary were twenty feet from my office. When I walked through them, it dawned on me that there were ten double-occupancy rooms here, full of my patients. They had heard the whole incident go down.

I walked into the first room and Mr. Moore, an overweight diabetic, wheeled over in his wheelchair and grasped my hand. "Dr. G., you're okay. They said you were okay, but I didn't believe nothin' until I seen it with my own eyes." He touched his thick glasses and chuckled. "I don't see so good, but you shoulda seen that young Cubano and what he did when he heard that guy yellin' and sayin' he had you hostage."

The Cuban guy was Mr. Valdez, and he was recuperating from brain surgery. "What did he do?" I asked, hoping he was all right.

"He tore off some metal thing from his bed and was runnin' out there to help you. The guards done grabbed his ass before he got to your office. Boy was he jacked up and cursin' who knows what. Can't understand a damn thing he says even when he speaks English."

"Is he all right?" I asked.

"'Course he is. He's one tough hombre." Mr. Moore patted his thighs. "If the VA hadn't chopped off both my legs, I woulda been right there with 'im."

I felt the tears starting to prick behind my eyes. "I bet you would have, Mr. Moore," I said, and patted him on the shoulder.

I walked to the next room, where Mr. Archio looked up from the book he was reading and coughed.

"How are your lungs doing today?" I asked, and took the stethoscope off my neck.

He closed his book, grabbed his inhaler, and took two puffs before he replied: "I'll live, but how are you doing, Dr. G.?" His hands balled up into two fists and his brown eyes flashed almost black. "How could Moth do that to you? He broke the convict code. You never, and I mean never, use someone else to do what you should do yourself. He was a coward. If he really wanted to end it all he should have killed himself."

Mr. Archio started to wheeze, and had to breathe through pursed lips until he got his wind back. "You know, Vietnam screwed up my lungs when I got shot, and I've always been partial to the other veterans here. But how could he?" He rubbed his knee and looked at the floor. "Moth was a dreamer. I swear he thought he'd get out someday, like he'd be rescued by a UFO or something." He looked up and his face seemed more pinched and aged than it

131

had the prior week. "I'm not a dreamer. The only way I'll ever get out of this hellhole is through an appeal, that's why I'm studying the law every day. You'll see. I killed a cop like Moth, but I'll get out of here someday." His air was running out and the last word trailed off.

"Let me take a listen to your lungs before I go, Mr. Archio."

Afterward, he said, "Dr. G., he should never have used you to get himself killed. God, I'm so angry. How could he do that to us lifers?"

How could he do it to me? I thought.

"Dr. G?" I wasn't expecting anyone behind me, and I jumped.

It was M.C., our medical clerk. "Geez, I'm sorry Dr. G. I didn't want to startle you. Hannah told me to come and get you. They just brought some old guy back from the hospital and he's all worked up about something."

I followed him into the hallway and he turned around to face me. "You're sure you're okay, Dr. G? All of us guys on the yard were praying for you. You're our angel and I knew you'd come back, but… Didn't you want to take some time off and get right again?"

It was the first time I had ever seen a serious look in M.C.'s blue eyes. After a few moments, he was back to his smiling, twinkly-eyed self. He opened his arms wide and said, "But then who would be teaching M.C. big words and making me feel bad about bringing hot tea to my favorite doctor."

"You're hopeless, M.C.," I said, and when I smiled I felt the constriction lessen in my chest.

I walked down the hallway and turned right into the treatment room, where an elderly man was sitting and rocking back and forth, muttering something to himself in Spanish.

Hannah was waiting by the door. Handing me his chart, she said, "He's not one of ours. He's from Max, and the officers tell me they just brought him from the hospital. Seems he was there for a week with a heart attack or something, and we didn't get a call or a discharge note or anything. I don't know what he's talking about. See if you can find out what's bothering him, and I'll try to get some information from the hospital."

Before I could say anything, Hannah was leaving the room. I opened the patient's chart and saw that the last entry was a telephone order from Dr. Marla, sending the patient out for a suspected myocardial infarction. There wasn't much in the chart, except that he was being treated for hypertension.

"Mr. Lopez, my name is Dr. G. You seem upset. Are you in pain? Is there something I can help you with?"

He didn't look up at me, and was twisting his hands together over and over again.

"Do you speak English?"

He nodded, and I thought I heard him say, "I should have known. I should have known."

"You should have known what, Mr. Lopez?"

He looked up, and I could see the pupils dilate in his brown eyes. He stammered, "I n-n-knew he was going to do it on that day."

I felt a chill, and the small hairs on the back of my neck rose. I had to swallow before I could say, "Who are you talking about, Mr. Lopez?"

He whimpered. "Moth. I'm so sorry."

I was confused. How could an inmate at another prison know what Moth was going to do? Moth didn't seem the type to share his plans with anybody.

"Mr. Lopez, I'm not sure I understand. Are you upset about what happened to Moth, or are you upset about the medical problems you had in the hospital?"

"The hospital said I had a bad heart, and I thought I was going to die. I made my peace with God and told him I wasn't going to do bad anymore, and the next day I see on TV what Moth did and that he's dead." He put his hands up to cover his eyes and rocked back and forth. "I should have known, he wanted to be killed on the fourteenth. Fourteen calendar years, the planet in the fourteenth position, you see?"

I could feel the wrinkles forming on my forehead and rubbed them with my right hand. *Do I even want to know what that means?* I didn't see any report of mental illness or delusions in Mr. Lopez' chart.

"How well did you know Moth? Why do you think you knew what he was going to do on Friday the 13th?"

He stopped rocking, and started poking his finger through the holes in his worn-out jeans. "You see, I always hid the fact that I'm a gypsy. When I was put in Max, Moth heard me playing the guitar and came over to me and called me a gypsy."

He dug his finger deeper in the hole, pulling hard enough to tear the cloth. He looked at me and patted the tear as if to heal it. "I told him I wasn't a gypsy, but he said he knew I was, and he wanted me to read the cards and tell him the future. I don't know how he knew, but when I was growing up in Spain, my grandmother taught me. She told me I had the gift. I had stopped doing it because it's against my belief, and the gift started to scare me."

Mr. Lopez looked up, but his eyes looked past me. "Moth wouldn't take no for an answer, and no one said no to him. So I read the cards for him. King of Hearts, Queen of Spades and King of Spades. I told him the King of Hearts was a man who fell in love with a woman, but she betrayed him and married his best friend. He asked me her name, and I said Sharon. Then he started jumping up and down and told me that he knew I could read the cards. I told him it was a coincidence, but he believed I had the gift. He told me that he had got out of death row, and he would someday get out of prison. He taught me how to figure out when the full moon comes up at any month or year, and I remember how he was shouting about that date, Friday the 13th, and how he had to be ready in 1989. He told me that in 1984. I knew he talked about getting out that day at the stroke of midnight, when it turned to the fourteenth... I should have known he would do something."

134

Fourteen! *God, that was my fourteenth visit with him.* Had he set me up from that first visit? Fourteen... *Oh it can't be, there are fourteen letters in my full name.*

Stop it. Stop it. You'll start to see fourteens everywhere. Get a grip.

I looked at the large hole Mr. Lopez now had in his pants from tugging on the rip. I put my hand over his hand. "Mr. Lopez, that's quite a story. You can't change what happened in the past, and we should concentrate on what's best for you now. After I examine you, I'm going to put you back in the infirmary to monitor you. When I think you're stable, I'll send you back to Max. Is that all right with you?"

He hung his head. "Do you think I could talk to the priest here? I don't want to die before I talk to him. I have a lot of things to confess."

"I'll let him know, Mr. Lopez. Why don't you take off your shirt, so I can listen to your heart and lungs?"

When Mr. Lopez finally shuffled out of the room, my thoughts went back to the number fourteen. *Okay Karen, don't drive yourself crazy. It's just a lot of odd coincidences.* Another voice in my head was saying, *Yes, but remember how he loved numbers.*

A voice behind me made me jump, for the second time that day.

"Sorry to bother you again, Dr. G. Hannah wants to know if you can see Lefty, he has some weird skin thing going on."

M.C.'s blue grey eyes studied me. "You sure you don't want some hot tea? I hear it can help calm nerves and stuff."

"Just send him down with his chart, and don't worry about me."

"Can't help it, all of us inmates that count are worried about you."

Mr. Rodin, known as Lefty on the yard, walked in and placed his chart on my desk. Then opened up his shirt, took something out, and handed it to me. "I wanted to be the first to give you a card."

I motioned for him to sit and took the handmade card. Drawn in great detail on the front was a horse with a cowboy falling off it. On the inside were the words: *When you fall off a horse you have to get right back on, buckaroo.* Inside it, he had written, "I knew you would — Lefty."

"My mother would agree with you, Lefty. Thank you for the card. What can I do for you today?"

"First I have to tell you that we were all rooting for you. What Moth did was not what a con would do. We know that you actually care about us guys, and for him to take you hostage and..." His left hand balled up in a fist. He punched it into his right palm. "Shit, what was he thinking? If he got out alive we would have killed him."

I hadn't thought about that, and didn't want to think about it.

He went on: "When I drew the card over the weekend, I decided I had to come in and see you. I knew you'd be the type to just get right back on the horse. I needed to tell you that us cons appreciate what you do for us. Don't let 'em change you."

My throat tightened, and I could start to feel my eyes sting.

The afternoon passed without incident, and when the maintenance guys came in the late afternoon to fix the hole in the wall, I decided it was time for me to leave. When I walked out of the infirmary and through Operations where the officers sat, I kept my head down. I didn't want to see Assistant Warden Ignin, whom I felt could have done something different in the hostage situation.

I flashed back to the time my mother and I ran into the Ignins in a store. My mother did not know them at all, but after they said hello to me and walked away, she said, "Who are those people? They hate you." Mom was a survivor of WWII and Russian POW camps; she said what her gut felt, without a filter. My sister and I found it amusing and enlightening... most of the time.

Coley was waiting for me at home, and I could smell the comfortable fragrance of black bean soup when I walked into the kitchen.

136

I hugged him and he asked, "How did the day go?"

I lifted off the lid of the crockpot and inhaled deeply. "Biscuits will go great with this. I'm going to make some."

"So, I see you're going for the comfort food, are you?" he asked, and put the box of biscuit mix on the counter. "You want me to make them while you get out of your work clothes?"

I nodded, and went upstairs to change into my soft bathrobe and warm slippers. When I came down, Coley was taking the hot biscuits off the tray and putting them on our plates. I opened the refrigerator to get some butter, and saw a solitary beer on the top shelf. An ice-cold beer sounded good, but I was glad it was one of Coley's non-alcoholic beers. Alcohol intensified moods for me, and I didn't want to start crying over bean soup.

The hot biscuit with butter and the hot bean soup started to make me feel warm and relaxed.

"Anything good happen today?" Coley asked.

"Well, Maintenance showed up, and hopefully when I go in tomorrow the wall in my office will be fixed and I won't be freezing."

He smiled and grabbed his third biscuit. "How about the rest of your day?"

I breathed in and rolled my head around to get out the stiffness in my neck. "Weird. I seemed to jump at every odd sound or movement and..." I rubbed my neck and closed my eyes. "You know, Custody didn't say anything to me. Part of me was glad, and part of me wonders if they don't care or even wanted to see something bad happen to me."

Coley swallowed his last mouthful of soup and put his spoon down. "Maybe they just didn't know what to say and didn't want to bother you."

I studied my empty bowl of soup. "What struck me is that almost every inmate I saw today wanted to tell me how they felt about what happened, and that they wanted me to be okay. You should see some of the cards they gave me. One of the guys brought me in a card signed by a bunch of the guys on the yard. You've got to see it."

I retrieved the card from my bag and handed it to Coley. On the front was a beautiful yellow rose with a dewdrop on one of its petals. Beneath it was an hourglass with the sand half gone and the stem of the rose running behind it, and the profile of a woman's face with a tear hanging from her lower lid.

Coley studied it, and opened it up to see what was written: "Thank you for being here." He closed it and handed it back to me. "Great artist," he said. "Who are all the guys who signed it?"

I opened it and looked at the names again. Each name had a number by it, and from the numbers, I knew that these men had already been in prison for twenty or more years. Then it dawned on me. "Coley, these are the lifers on the yard. These guys will never leave prison."

I started to tear up. *How odd that the guys who society put away forever showed me more compassion than the people who run the place.*

Coley put his hand on my shoulder. "You want me to give you a back rub tonight? I see your neck is bothering you. Do you think you need to see anybody?"

I shifted in my seat so his hand fell off my shoulder. "I know how to take care of my stiff neck."

It took me a while to fall asleep that night. In the middle of the night, I heard a sound and woke up with a start. *Where is that sound coming from? Don't tell me it's from under the bed.* Coley was sound asleep next to me, snoring slightly. *There it is again, it's like a scratching.*

Fear came over me and I didn't want to move. But it didn't go away. I had to look. I peered over the side of the bed… and a hand came up and locked on my right arm.

I tried to scream, but nothing came out. I tried to fight, but I couldn't move. I was being pulled off the bed. Moth's voice said, "I'm Hades and you're Persephone and I'm going to drag you down into the underworld with me."

I gurgled out a "Noooo…" and then Coley was shaking me. "Wake up! Wake up, it's just a dream." He wrapped me in his arms and held me tight. "You're okay. It was just a bad dream."

When I stopped shaking and whimpering, I laid down again and pressed my cold body into Coley's warm one. He was asleep in a minute. I felt safer. *Don't you ever have a nightmare like that again*, I told myself. Every few minutes, I would look at the clock. I gave up trying to fall asleep at 4 a.m., the time I would usually push myself out of bed to go to the gym so I could work out before I started my day.

When I arrived at the gym, I got on the elliptical and started pedaling. I was about to start reading the book I had brought with me when another early-morning gym regular hopped on the machine next to me.

"Hey," she said. "I just wanted to tell you that I heard what happened at the prison over the weekend. I'm so glad you're okay and nothing happened to you."

"No," I said tightly. "Nothing happened to me, except that I was taken hostage by force, raped, exposed to a concussion grenade, and saw someone blown away."

Her mouth dropped open and she stopped pedaling. "Um… you need help," she said, got off the machine, and walked to one further down the row.

Where did that come from? Don't tell me I'm becoming like my mother and saying whatever pops into my head. Maybe I do need to talk to someone… I haven't even told Coley that I was raped.

A few weeks later, I jumped when a man behind me in the prison parking lot touched my arm. "Oh, I didn't want to startle you," said a good-looking man with friendly brown eyes. "I just wanted to say how sorry I am for what happened to you." He extended his hand. "My name's Sean, and I'm one of the college professors. I teach creative writing here, and Mr. Meller was one of my

139

students. I somehow feel that I should have known."

My views of Mr. Meller were still changing even after his death. When I first met him, I thought he was called Moth because he had an aspect of greyness to his skin, hair and eyes. After the hostage event, I thought of him more as a moth drawn to a light and getting snuffed out. I wondered what this man thought he knew.

"You see," he went on, "two days before his death, Mr. Meller read a poem he wrote for the class. It was called 'The Last Poem.'" He shifted his weight. "I have a copy of an article I wrote for the paper, where I included his poem. I hear from the guys on the yard that you are one of the most humane and dedicated medical professionals to work here in a long time. They say you treat them as patients, not prisoners. I wanted to give you my condolences for what happened to you, but I also wanted to know if you wanted a copy of the article I wrote."

"Yes, I'd like to see it."

He opened his briefcase and pulled out a copy. I was glad my hand didn't shake when I took it.

"I don't want to hold you up, Doctor. I just needed to let you know how sorry I am for you and your family. I hope what happened to you won't interfere with you being a doctor."

I nodded. "Thanks for taking the time to talk to me, Sean." I felt the tears start as I turned away from him and walked to my car. He was the first staff member in the prison to let me know that he cared- and he worked for the college, not the prison.

I sat in the car and opened the glove box to grab a tissue so I could blow my nose. I took a few deep breaths, until the tightness in my chest left. *God, who am I crying for? Me, Moth, or Sean for caring? It was the compassion in Sean's eyes, that's what did it.*

I looked at the newspaper article and couldn't help reading the poem first.

The Last Poem

I know death no more from fear,

I know life and love will never disappear,

I know wishes, hopes, and longing needs to fly,

I know too to evaporate and join the sky…

Poems that rhyme I leave to those

That sit for hours then compose

From hints and wisps and pieces of heart

Then write them all down and soar in the art…

The whole art of healing and promises kept

To send to those, those that dreamt and leapt

To worlds above and some below

To worlds like mine the Gods bestow

On dreamers dead and happier still

The quiet comes and know peace until

Born of flesh just once is all

To life again and another call

To bounce among the stars and weep

For the joy to dream and sleep

I started crying again, and now I didn't know whether it was the anger or sadness that had me bent over the steering wheel.

When I got home, I read Sean's article. I could tell that his compassion also encompassed the inmates, including Moth. I agreed with his points, and especially with his assessment of the system.

Incarceration is not conducive to living things, Sean's article said. *Prison is a system designed to fail. People simply mark time, learn little, and return to*

141

society with almost no hope of a future. If the recidivism rate is too high, let us begin by examining the system that creates it. He ended his article: *In all societies throughout history, violence begets violence. We must find a better way.*

I took a deep breath. How much of my anger was due to what Moth did to me? How much was directed at the system for allowing it to happen, and then basically ignoring me? How much was I directing at myself, for being the catalyst that tipped him over the edge? I took another deep breath. Regardless of what caused the anger, I had to let it go.

A week later, an article in the local paper caught my attention. It had been written by one of the inmates—one of the lifers who had signed my card.

It was titled *Moth Man, you risked a life and damaged the other cons.* Halfway through the well-written article, I was introduced to the convict code.

Moth's wish to die was his own business as far as the con goes, but solid cons don't sell out at the expense of their friends. Far worse, he gave some naive jittery cop the job of accomplishing something he couldn't do himself.

Moth chose to make a damn fool out of himself at the expense of the lifers on this yard who take pride in their responsibility toward their own particular society. He placed in danger the life of a respected professional who in all reality has provided this particular institution with a whole lot more than we used to have, folks. There is not a lifer out here who will condone that nut act.

Moth was a model prisoner. That's why he was here. His suicide was his own business. Some men prefer death, but none has the right to in front of another con. The con code gives a man the right to do anything you need to do to get out, but never at the expense of another con. Moth did not have the right to force his need to die on his friends.

Lifers keep this joint going. They're responsible, highly motivated men who provide the nuts and bolts of the prison. They're plumbers, welders, electricians, clerks, cooks, kitchen help, and medical assistance workers.

142

Those lifers who have worked their way to Medium are the cream of the crap, as we are so often jokingly referred to.

I wish you all the luck in the world Moth wherever the transition from life to death takes us. I love the hell out of ya, ole thing, but damn boy you sure could have gone out with more respect and a hell of a lot more class.

I hadn't really thought about the impact on the other lifers. I only remembered how much I appreciated their get-well card.

10. To Execute or Not To Execute

Karen Gedney, MD

I brushed the sweat off my face and leaned forward to answer the phone. I was hoping it would be head of maintenance telling me when the new air conditioning unit would be put in, but it was a voice I didn't recognize.

"Dr. Gedney, this is John Rand from Central. I was asked to call you about the execution next week. We need you to write the medications for the lethal injection."

I felt my eyes widen. "I, ah..."

"All we need is a prescription for sodium pentothal, curare and potassium chloride," he said in a clipped tone.

"I was hired to give medical care to the inmates," I said. "When I became a doctor I took an oath that I would first do no harm." I sat up straighter in my chair and added: "And I'm not going to do it."

"Look, you're the doctor and the prescriptions have to be written by a doctor. Who else is going to write them? This has never been a problem in the past, and the doctor usually shows up to make sure things go right."

My hand tightened on the receiver. "You can't make me write a prescription for drugs that will be used to kill someone."

"Well then, we're going to have to pay some doctor on the outside to do it, and it's your job." He let out a loud sigh. "If you won't do it, do you know a doctor who will?"

I did know a doctor who valued money more than people, and his name popped out of my mouth.

I was relieved when Rand hung up without asking me any further questions. I had heard the officers talk about the execution coming up, and I knew it was going to be done at Max, but it never occurred to me that I would be asked to participate in such a thing. I couldn't imagine how someone would want to be part of the process; it sickened me to hear some of the officers talking about people who wanted to watch it.

Two weeks later, I saw the article about the execution in the local

145

newspaper. Coley had left it on the coffee table in the living room for me to read: *Murderer receives lethal injection.* The inmate was a fifty-two-year-old white male who was convicted of three murders and did not file to stop the execution.

I wondered why and how many individuals on death row would actually choose to be executed. *What would I do if I was on death row?* I shuddered and my insides went cold. What about people who were innocent and were executed anyway? I had read stories about that happening.

I glanced at the rest of the article and learned that he had spent his life since the age of twelve locked up, in reform schools and then prisons. *What caused him to end up in reform schools, and what would have happened if his early life had been different?* The end of the article highlighted his choice of food for his last meal: two double cheese and bacon burgers, fries and a Coke. *How could a person eat such a large meal while they were contemplating their last few hours of life?* I remembered Moth saying that all he could come up with was a grilled cheese sandwich when he contemplated his own last meal.

What a life. Reform schools, prisons, and then a last meal from McDonald's before being executed. I knew staff that believed in the concept of an eye for an eye, but it wouldn't bring back the people this man had murdered, and I had a hard time believing it helped heal the families that were left behind.

I remembered the saying "if you want revenge, you should dig two graves." What *would* help those families? The world of psychology would say forgiveness was the solution. What if someone I loved was murdered? I don't think I'd ever be the same, but I couldn't see how revenge and retribution would help. *As long as those dark emotions were present, it would be a weight I would have to carry. If I was strong and wise enough to drop the weight and forgive, I could start to get on with my life again.*

I put down the newspaper and leaned back into the soft sofa, closing my eyes. It had been two years since I had been taken hostage. I had forgiven Moth. Had I forgiven myself for allowing myself to be put in that situation? Not exactly. Part of me felt that I had to keep it, like a pebble in my shoe, a reminder so I would never make that mistake again.

I had struggled to forgive Assistant Warden Ignin, who had started the investigation on me and always seemed to want to get rid of me. When I was taken hostage, he could have done something, but he did nothing. I was still unsure why, but after the hostage event, he was sent to another institution. As long as I did not have to interact with him again, I could drop that weight as well.

A few days after the execution, I found a large envelope on my desk, sent from the chaplain at Max. I opened it, and was surprised to find six pages of lined yellow paper covered with handwriting I didn't recognize. There was a white sticky note on the first page. It read *He wanted you to have this.*

I leafed through the pages, and was shocked to see it had been signed by the inmate who had been recently executed. He had written the date below his name: three days before his execution.

Why did the inmate want me to have this? I never met him. How would he even know me? I sighed. *Of course... through the prison grapevine. It's faster than the mail.* I slipped the envelope into my black bag. *I'll read this at home, when I have time and won't be bothered.*

That night, Coley was at a meeting. I heated myself up some chicken soup, sat at the kitchen table, and opened the manila envelope. The man's handwriting was legible, and all the letters leaned to the right. I sat for a moment studying his penmanship, and wondered what I would write if I was going to die in three days. *What would I say?* Would I say goodbye to the people I loved? Would I want to try to explain what I did with my life? I was only in my thirties, could I rail against the injustice of dying young? Would I want to leave some message for the world?

Okay, this is not about me. This is what he wanted to say, and for some reason he sent it to me. I took a few spoonfuls, enjoying the heat and saltiness of the soup, then turned my attention to the contents of the yellow pages.

In his first paragraph, the inmate gave his name, prison number, and

147

death row status. In his second paragraph, he explained his reason for writing. He was sending a message to young kids, urging them to stay out of crime and stay out of prison.

> I would like to talk to you about "fun and games" and prison. I have spent most of my 52 years in prisons or jails, and I have seen a lot of things happen in my day. Please believe me.

The next two pages involved him talking about gangs. He explained how new prisoners were considered "fresh meat," and what the gangs really wanted was for you to be their "old ladies."

> If you think you're tough, well check it out, can you fight or beat 3 or 4 old pro-cons at once? If you do not make the right choice of gangs they will rape you and take what they want from you along with your TV, radio, stamps, money, but most of all your manhood and your pride...

> It's always "fun" when you have your first visit with your parents or friends or loved ones or girlfriend. Because the first thing they see is the hurt and tears in young eyes, and they see your shaved eyebrows and believe me you won't have to say a word to them...

> Now after your unhappy visit, you have to go back to the prison yard and all your new friends will ask you if you snitched to your parents on them...

> Believe me there are some that can survive in prison, I did, but what did it get me. Three life sentences for murder and plus the death sentence... Do you realize what I had to give up? Nothing but my freedom, life and all my youth and most of all my family, children all that loved me once!

Then, the inmate started dispensing his advice to the "kids." He explained that trouble always starts small—*with the first pill or smoke or booze and the first time you decide to skip school*—but once you start, it grows. He advised talking to parents, teachers, and pastors.

> Now what I'm going to tell you will come as a very big shock to you. Go talk to the cop on the beat, they do other things other than arrest you.

148

They work with kids and different groups, you see they see all of this every day and they are parents also. Most of all they love you and care for you also.

And believe me, I can't see where you will be doing wrong by trying to live by your society's rules. Remember when you get older, you will be making some of these rules of your society, think about that. The youth of today will be our government of tomorrow and making rules for other young people to live by.

So if you love your parents look for a way to keep from making these awful mistakes like I have made and others like me make!

I really wish I could undo all my wrongs and mistakes that I have made, so through my small story I pray to Jesus Christ my savior that you will read this story and that it touches your small and young heart and life in some way.'

You see I will die 2:00AM Monday June 19. But this will be a relief for me for I have made my peace with Jesus Christ.

I'll say this before I close, I love you kids and all the young kids out there no matter where you are and my love and prayers will always live in this letter to you.

So please open your young hearts and eyes and you will see the love awaiting you!

Wow. That was not what I had expected, but what did I know about the last words of people who are about to be executed?

I put down the yellow papers, and stared at the bottom of the bowl where my chicken soup had been. There was one small noodle left, and when I went to spoon it up it broke. *So fragile, just like life. One wrong decision and it could be over.*

A few minutes later, I heard the garage door open and smiled. Coley was home. He walked into the kitchen with a white box, which I knew held

149

something from his dinner meeting.

"Did you bring me something tasty?" I asked.

"Why don't you see?" He opened the lid and placed it on the table.

Inside was a slice of cheesecake surrounded by fresh strawberries and blueberries.

"Can we have it now?" I asked, feeling my saliva kick in. I loved berries, and Coley loved cheesecake.

"That's why I brought it," he said, and sat down at the table. He pointed at the yellow papers. "What are you reading? Anything interesting?"

I handed him a fork and gave him a kiss. "Remember that guy I told you about, the one they executed?"

"Yeah," he said, and stuck the fork into the cheesecake.

"Well, it's something he wrote, and it made me think of Moth again."

His fork stopped halfway to his mouth. "In what way?"

I stabbed a strawberry and studied it before I put it in my mouth. It had that tart, sweet taste I enjoyed. "I suppose it had to do with him talking about choices in life and where those choices take you, and who you hurt on the way. I started thinking about Moth's choices, my choices, and even your choices."

"What do you mean, my choices?" he asked, and a crease appeared between his full, dark eyebrows.

"I mean the choices you made after your first wife left you, when they told her you wouldn't survive your injuries from Vietnam. You told me it took years for you to realize that you suffered from PTSD." I paused, feeling confused. *Where am I going with all this?* "I guess what I'm trying to ask is: What made you realize, after all those years, that you had PTSD?"

Coley sat back in his chair and rubbed the lower part of his face, where the dark stubble was starting to show. "Are we talking about my PTSD or your

PTSD now?"

"Let's talk about yours first. I mean, you went through war, saw a lot of comrades killed, you were shot, you almost died, and your first wife left. How could you not realize you had PTSD?"

He finished off the cheesecake, and pushed the berries toward me. "I don't think you realize the depth and impact of PTSD until you are willing to ask yourself one question."

My mind went blank. *What would that question be?* It felt like I was staring down at the edge of a deep dark well and couldn't see anything.

"What question?"

He leaned forward, put his chin in the palm of his hand and looked at the empty plate between us. *Oh, come on now*, I thought, suddenly irritated. *You're not just going to let me hang out to dry.*

Coley pressed his lips together, sat up, and said, "You don't realize that you have PTSD until you're willing to question how the event, and your own actions following the event, affected the people around you. Especially the ones who love you."

My mind skipped and blanked. *What did he say?* I had to replay it in my mind; I thought I may have not heard right. My mind had been poised to think of my issues, not others'. My emotional self was not ready to conceive that I could have caused pain to others.

I pushed down those feelings. "So let me get this straight. It took you years to realize that you had PTSD, but it happened when you asked that question. So... what caused you to ask it?"

He leaned back in the chair, and put his right hand on the table. I watched his face and heard the light tap of his fingers. He had shared stories with me about his past, and I knew that he had issues with abandonment, but he had never talked to me specifically about his PTSD.

"There was this woman I really cared for. You know, I thought I had made it. I had the house, the car, and I came home to tell her that I just got a promotion at the bank that I had been busting my balls for... and she told me that she couldn't do it anymore and left me."

Coley swallowed. "That night I had a dream about Vietnam. We were out on patrol and took fire. When I checked on my men, two were dead and Scramblin had a hole in his side as big as a football." His voice started to crack. "His head was on my lap and I held him while he died." I could see his eyes tearing up. "I was really rough on him that day. Just military stuff, but he wasn't a guy cut out for the military. He was the type of guy who would have been a great professor teaching in a university. A helicopter known as a jungle penetrator came. It had these things that looked like prongs on it, to pick up the dead bodies. I tied Scramblin and the other guys to it, and was stabilizing the bodies when the penetrator hoisted them in the air. It was dark and I thought it had started to rain." He looked down and put his hand over his face. "It wasn't rain, it was their blood and then..."

He sniffed. "Then the dream changed. I was sleeping in bed with my baby next to me, and I woke up to find I had rolled over on it in the night and suffocated it. When I woke, it was like all the air had been kicked out of me."

Coley didn't have a child, but the metaphor was powerful. Dreams, and why and how the mind weaves things together. The trauma of his comrades dying, and then his subconscious wondering why the woman he cared for left when everything was going well for him. His mind answered: *Because of you.*

Now I was starting to get it, and it made me feel uncomfortable. *Have I asked myself that question? No.* I spent my time not allowing myself to feel too much. I had learned to suppress emotions from my parents. My mother learned it as a young German girl surviving WWII, and my father learned it when his parents abandoned him.

I didn't want to ask, or think, that my actions after the hostage incident affected Coley. I mean, I knew he was affected by the incident, but... *He's basically telling me that my actions are affecting him.* I understood, but I didn't like it.

Coley was waiting for me to say something. "So…" I stammered, "I know why you are telling me this. Why didn't you say something to me before?"

He closed his eyes and rubbed them. "Look, when you see someone you love who has survived a traumatic event, you don't start bringing up your issues about the event or how that person is acting toward you. They have enough on their plate."

How did my actions after the event affect Coley? Others?

He was right. I didn't think that much about how the incident, or my actions afterward, affected other people. I had put a hard shell around myself and acted like I was in control.

Maybe that's why the officers and medical staff didn't say anything to me. They still didn't handle it right, though. I remembered the sheriff telling me that the SWAT team was going through debriefing and counseling after the hostage incident, and they needed me to decipher what I had written during the event. Seems no one could read bad German. The sheriff was really surprised to hear that while the SWAT team was getting counseling, I had had none, and had gone right back to work.

Coley was looking at me. I felt butterflies in my gut and asked, "So how did it affect you?"

"You know, that's the first time you asked me. You have no idea how much you changed, and how it affected me."

Great, now I feel guilty. "So how did you think it changed me?"

"You're more emotionally disconnected."

Emotions. I could empathize and feel deeply for others from a distance, but not if I put myself at risk for loss of control or heartbreak. I could feel deeply for my patients, but when they started the process of dying, I disconnected from them. I could care for someone I was involved with romantically, but I didn't let myself get to the point where it would break my heart if

153

they left me. People and events could anger me, but I would never allow myself to lose control.

When I didn't say anything, Coley said, "I'm never going to abandon you, I love you and you don't know how wonderful you are."

My throat constricted. *How did the conversation end up here?*

I thought of Moth, who had been on death row for killing a cop, and how his experience in combat in Vietnam had led to that action as well as what he did to me. How PTSD affects people different ways. I had met many vets and patients who dealt with trauma by turning to drugs, alcohol, or any activity that could numb their feelings. Drugs and alcohol did not interest me, because I associated them with loss of control. But was I any better by just disconnecting myself from my emotions? *No, it's just a coping mechanism I learned from my parents, just like other people learned from their parents to use drugs, alcohol, or violence.*

I wasn't in the mood to talk anymore. I stood up and joked, "Well, your wonderful wife is going to wash the dishes now."

Coley didn't say anything as he left the kitchen. I concentrated on washing the dishes, and tried to analyze my feelings. *Do I feel I still suffer from that incident?*

At first, I had been angry at Moth, but I had read enough articles on anger to understand it was an emotion that arose when you felt threatened. He was dead, and no longer a threat to me in that way. If I held onto my anger, it would just hurt me, and that made no sense to me at all. Therefore, it made sense to me to forgive him. In fact, I felt sorry for him. He was damaged, angry, and in emotional pain, and I made the mistake of believing I could help. Letting go of my anger regarding Moth made me feel better.

How about other people, though? Was I asking how my actions after the incident were affecting the people around me? *Not really.* According to Coley's definition, that meant I was still suffering from PTSD.

I had never asked what Coley thought when I just went back to work

154

in the prison. Maybe he wanted me to ask him. But then again, he hadn't asked me whether I was going to keep working in the prison after my four-year payback was up either, and it had ended months ago.

What do I want to do next? If I stay a few more months, I'll be vested with the state as a state worker. I'll qualify for retirement and benefits. Dr. Marla at Max was in the same position, and she said she was going to stick it out while she was looking for a new job.

Should I stay? If I left, what would I do, and would we have to move again? That would be a problem. Open a private office? No, that would be a disaster. I wasn't oriented toward business enterprises or making money from patients.

I could try to get a job in the VA hospital in the next city, but I had tried that as a resident; I enjoyed taking care of the inmates more. *Plus, who would provide medical care to the inmates and protect them if I left?* I knew the National Health Corps wouldn't assign a new doctor, and I knew they preferred that I stay in the prison.

What about the danger? I was less naive now. I also knew that what had happened to me was a rare event. Medicine as a profession carries risks. I knew that when I started out in the field, and it's one of the things that made it interesting.

By the end of that night, I knew I was going to stay as a prison doctor and make it my career.

11. Poems, Prose, and Other Living Things

The stream of patients in the clinic the following day kept me interested and occupied. When I got home, I found a note from Coley, telling me he'd be back late due to another business meeting.

I wasn't hungry, so I curled up on the couch and opened my briefcase. *Well, I guess I can amuse myself with some reading.* I rummaged through the bag and pulled out a small dark blue paperback entitled *Razor Wire*. Sean, the friendly creative writing teacher in the prison, had given it to me last week. I flipped through its pages and found it to be a journal of poetry, prose, and art from the inmates who took his class.

The touching foreword the teacher had written resonated with me.

How this artistic creation continues, that is, the fluorescence of the human spirit behind bars—remains an enigma, understood only by those who must create where there is little light.

I knew what he was talking about. I'd seen some of the art from the inmates, and they were talented. I started to read their poems, paying special attention to the ones that had something to do with the prison. I wanted to see how they emotionally dealt with being in prison.

A prayer for the Insane, by I.S.

The gate shrieks open

the sound of dying mice

as the crazy one drifts

out for his day in the sun

he keeps his thoughts in a Bugler can

entangled with tobacco strands

rolled tight afraid perhaps

his thoughts might dissipate

he shuffles in circles

as psych technicians measure his dampened dance

a circus performance for the slow sighted

a mourning for the mentally marooned

with a thick cigarette-burned finger

he draws a circle on the palm of his hand

a symbol of completion of being whole

then lightly blows it away like a kiss to the air

as he whispers fly my little butterfly

and the strength of his kiss

devours the world

he sits in a corner of the fenced in grass

and begins rocking to some inaudible chant

a mantra perhaps for dying

as dying the one redemptive way

a dying perhaps the only way

and for an hour he cradles himself

slowly gaining momentum

until his back-tilt face opens wide like a flower to the sun

as he remembers perhaps some human heart

lost for years in flood-lit antiseptic hallways

158

torrential bright lights screaming down

drowning the obscurity of genius minds

of child minds of butterflies

he screams at the massive blue sky an invocation of genetic defiance

goes into some frenzied primal dance

flat on his back

arms and legs snapping out like whips

growling like some mangled lion

the distress signal of ancient shamans

pleading for the compassion of a lonely sun

and the wisdom of blind frogs

but the only blind wisdom

comes from psych technicians

who drag away the violent man

his head whipping out

at the intrusion of his holy dance

his tongue lasing out

in a wild attempt to taste freedom

as he pleads with the voice of an innocent child

The insane. A hundred and fifty years ago, it was believed that mentally ill people were possessed by the devil. We would lock them up in asylums and try all sorts of barbaric therapies, including removing parts of their

159

brains.

I thought back to my days on the psychiatric ward as a medical student, and remembered the first time I saw someone treated with electroconvulsive therapy. It was gruesome. She was an elderly woman, and her eyes rolled back in her head, her back arched, and I thought I could hear her bones breaking. Then came the drugs: Thorazine, Haldol, Prolixin... They didn't make those poor people sane; they turned them into the walking dead. I knew that the drugs helped some of them, but there were still patients that no drug seemed to help, and those ones seemed to end up in prison. The ones who would just scream and throw feces and urine at you, no matter what you did or tried.

Yes, they were a challenge.

Time Served? by D.O.

The years crush on, saturating mind, body, being:

>*twisting at the thoughts, ambitions, hopes as*

Slowly changing rhythms align the person

>*with the circumstance of existence.*

Time seeps, pools up like wax beneath a candle

>*coagulating into a formless mass of frustration.*

Cooling, shaping to contours of a lower plane

>*something less, cast off, the apportioned waste.*

Dregs, shamed dejected pieces of society

>*scraped or chipped from the surface*

Longing to be a lamp, filled countless times

>*burning perpetually, useful acceptable.*

But the years crush on, the candle dwindles,

>*the flame mutes, life's residue, hardened*

160

formless mass, thoughts, ambitions, dreams.

Years and years behind bars. I had seen men who seemed to accept it, if they had hope or something to live for. Moth was not one of them, and he had put himself in a situation where he knew he would get killed. If the SWAT team had not killed him, he knew the inmates would. In fact, I remembered Coley telling me that an inmate had told him the same thing. Moth wrote his own death sentence.

Our Recidivist, by J.L.

Is handcuffed and howling

on the six o'clock news

just a year after leaving us and

swearing never to return. So of course

we cluster in our smug concrete cells

to sneer and jeer the latest prodigal

son about to rejoin

our convicted little circle of hell.

watching the cop shepherd him safely

into the patrol car.

a firm hand pressing down

on his deranged tangle of hair,

an almost tender gesture

as the car door seals like a tomb,

concealing the half-smile

of a man

who has not been touched

in a year.

161

Recidivism. I don't think I ever thought about the word until I worked in the prison and saw how many inmates came back. Every Tuesday morning when the medical department would have to process the new "fish," I would recognize half of them. They would give me their reasons, but rarely take responsibility. They tended to blame their probation officer, the employers for not hiring them, their family or "old lady," their addictions, and so on.

It was clear to me that as long as these men viewed themselves as victims, they had little chance of doing well on the outside. I had to help them perceive themselves not as victims, but as people who had what it took to be responsible for the choices they made in life.

Metamorphosis, by J.L.

It's extremely late for me to be awake

but tonight I feel the need to undress

my soul of this hate.

Here in the pen, I'm around everybody,

Alone, this place is not more than afterlife, yes, death.

I don't know mercy, I don't know love.

This is a pernicious place where religion

is no more than a tool.

I remember knowing a friendly young adult within,

poor him going through the pain of metamorphosis.

Dear place, let me be myself—the one

162

I've ignored.

Let me show the world I am

a man with a tender soul.

Metamorphosis. The caterpillar turning into a butterfly, or... a Moth.

I remembered moths being drawn to the light on the patio at night when I was a child. *Was I that light for Moth?* I cringed, remembering the bright electric device on my uncle's patio that had zapped and fried the moths and insects drawn to it. *Was I responsible for his death?* I curled myself up into a tighter ball on the couch, and hugged my knees. *Or did I just live into some fantasy where he wanted to get himself killed?*

I forgive Moth, but can I completely forgive myself? I pulled my knees closer. It was easier for me to forgive someone else.

After a while, I uncurled and went into the kitchen to make myself some hot tea. It was apple cinnamon, and it smelled sweet. My hands started to warm around the cup, and all the poems started to swirl around in my head. *Such a waste of human potential and talent.* Some of the men had been thrown away as children, some had been thrown away by society, and some had thrown themselves away. Abandonment, whether it was physical or emotional. That was the crucial piece. From it came fear, anger, and all the coping skills—like drugs and alcohol—that put the people at highest risk into prison.

There had to be a better way. *We are addressing the problem at the tail end by locking them up in a cage and punishing them.* The paradigm was one of not asking the right questions, and not being open to different solutions. It had to be changed.

What if society was willing to ask *why* punishment and prisons do not deter crime? What if we asked what changed human behavior the most— positive or negative reinforcement? What if we were willing to try different programs and see what was the most cost-effective? What if we asked ourselves who truly benefitted in the prison-industrial model? *What if society valued understanding and healing over loathing and punishment?*

I took a sip of tea, and held it in my mouth before I swallowed it. I smiled. *Well, I've always been inquisitive, empathetic, and open to new ideas. My career as a prison doctor should be an interesting one. I'm not going to abandon the inmates, and Coley isn't going to abandon me, so maybe some healing will take place for all of us.*

PART

TWO

12. Houdini

Almost a year had passed since I had decided to stay on as the permanent prison doctor. I now had my desk on the other side of my office, so I sat closer to the door than my visitors did. Maintenance had put in a new kick-out panel in the wall below the windows, where the hole had been. The shade of it was a little lighter than the rest of the wall. I still had that annoying ringing in my ears, and I still jumped right out of my skin at loud, unexpected sounds.

I cracked my neck to relieve some stiffness in it, pushed back my chair, and spied a long column of ants that had marched out from a crack near where the wall had been repaired. I was deciding the best way to commit mass murder on an insect population, when the phone rang.

"Doc, this is Warden Binman. We have a high profile inmate coming in tomorrow, and I want you to come over to my office and read his I-file before you process him."

"Why, is there something I should know?"

"I-file" is short for "inmate file," and it includes information such as an inmate's arrest record, gang associations, enemies, prior disciplinary actions in prison, family contacts, etc. Custody used it to help them decide where to house an inmate. It was not a file I ever looked at (in fact, this was the first and last time I ever did look at an I-file).

"Look, I'm late for an important meeting downtown and it's a long story. Read it and you'll understand. Call my secretary and tell her when you're coming over. I've gotta go." His voice had an edge to it and I let him go without further questioning.

What was that all about? I've processed new inmates every week for five years, and no one has ever asked me to look at their I-file. If an inmate was considered unstable or dangerous, one or two officers would remain in the exam room while he was assessed medically or psychiatrically. I replaced the phone and decided to schedule my trip to the warden's office that day during my lunch break.

The warden's office was outside the prison fence line, and when I walked through the parking lot I smelled oncoming rain. I lengthened my stride and ducked into the grey, squat building before the drops started to fall. To my right was the area where an officer sat behind security glass and controlled visitors coming into the institution. There was a long covered walkway, surrounded by a wired fence, which connected his area to the visiting room on the prison yard. To my left was the office of the warden's secretary, which I had to go through in order to see the warden.

Laurie the secretary was yawning and rubbing her eyes when I knocked on the doorframe. "Oh, Dr. G. I didn't see you there." She handed me the thick, cream-colored folder, and told me to sit in the conference room next to her office "I'll be back in twenty minutes," she said.

I sat down in a soft, comfy chair behind a long, beautiful mahogany conference table, and opened the file. It was easily four inches thick. The first page had a black-and-white mug shot of an average-looking thirty-one-year-old white male, with his arrest record recorded below. I flipped over the next few pages, and started to see dozens of magazine clippings and colored pictures. The headlines included phrases like:

Martial Arts Champion

Tibetan Wonder

Undefeated on the West Coast

Master opens Elite School

Why is this stuff in here? I thought, and stared at a glossy picture of a young man with chiseled muscles in a martial arts stance. I looked at the face, and turned back to the mug shot. *Is that the same guy?* I had to look at each once more to convince myself that it was the same man. Then I re-read his arrest record. Four counts of lewdness with a minor, two counts of sexual assault with a minor. No prior felony convictions.

I turned over a few more pages and realized that the information I was looking at was not from our system, but from another state. The letter sent to our prison director captured my attention.

Thank you for accepting T.J. on inter-state compact to be housed in your new maximum-security prison. As you know he has become an embarrassment to our system. He has escaped multiple times and we are at a loss to confine him. Chains, secured keyed doors, or electronic ones don't hold him long. I am including copies of his pertinent records and wish you luck.

I skimmed over a few more pages, and came to one of his psychiatric evaluations.

T.J. is of below average intelligence. He is compliant and answers questions in a childlike manner. Born into a dysfunctional family in West Virginia and removed at age two when his mother was committed to a mental asylum for killing her husband with a hatchet. Fostered and raised by the state until two and a half, when he was adopted by a couple who immigrated to Tibet three months later. Spent childhood in Tibetan monastery with his father until age eighteen and returned to United States at age nineteen. Fought in numerous martial arts competitions and never beaten. Full contact Martial Artist Champion at age twenty-one. Opened Karate school at age twenty-eight. Complaints of sexual impropriety filed one year later. Convicted on six counts, including lewdness and sexual assault.

This is interesting, I thought, and turned to the section where Custody had filed multiple reports. The first report stated:

Inmate T.J. placed in secure cell at 0730. At 0815 found said inmate on tier walking down the hall. Called for backup. Inmate ordered to stop, place hands on wall and spread-eagle legs. T.J. strip-searched for contraband. Returned to cell with no resistance.

Another officer's report:

Inmate T.J. placed in belly chains, arms chained behind him and leg irons. Placed said inmate in holding cell waiting for transfers. Said inmate on opening door was found sitting next to wall with chains next to him in a neat pile.

How cute, a real Houdini, I thought. I leafed through a variety of officers' reports, and came upon an entry from a transportation officer.

T.J. placed on van at 0930 in belly chains with eight other inmates. Three officers in attendance. At 1015 said inmate started to sway slowly from right to left. T.J. ordered to stop and comply. Van began to sway back and forth and I could not control it. Stopped at nearest rest stop. Officers ordered T.J. to stop making the van sway. Attempted to continue, but the erratic movement of the van became dangerous. Called lieutenant at 1030.

I chuckled, wondering what was going through that lieutenant's mind—and the look on his face—when he received that call.

I skimmed over multiple reports, and each one was more outrageous than the one before it. There were accounts of him pulling his toilet out of the cement floor, pole-vaulting over fences, and moving objects without touching them. Then I saw a report from another psychiatrist and slowed down to read it. His last two written sentences were:

Patient T.J. after his interview stood up and said, "Watch this Doc." The patient then levitated six inches off the ground for a few seconds, came down, and walked out of my office.

"You've got to be kidding," I said out loud, and started laughing. I had met some odd psychiatrists in my time, but this was too much.

Laurie coughed and leaned on the doorjamb. "You have to leave now, because I'm locking up and I have to get this file over to Central Transportation. The Warden said he would call you after 3 p.m. when he gets back from his meeting." She started tapping her foot and looking at her watch for emphasis.

On the walk back to the infirmary, I thought about all the reports I had read and also what was conspicuously lacking: I had not seen any reference to altercations or violence. Odd, for someone who was a champion in the martial arts and arrested for child molestation. Someone in prison would have tested him. Then I had an odd paranoid thought, and started to wonder if someone was playing a practical joke on me. *No*, I told myself, *the warden is not the joking type.*

The warden called at 4 o'clock and got right to the point: "What do you think about the case?"

I wasn't sure what I thought, but I replied. "It seems the incidents became more unbelievable as his reputation grew in their system."

"Exactly, but I'm taking no chances. The van bringing him in is supposed to arrive at 8 a.m. We're going to shut down the infirmary and clear out all the staff but you. You will have to do the medical assessment and blood work while he is in full restraints. There will be four officers with him at all times. Then they will bring him over to Unit 5 to get his ID picture, and the psychologist can do the assessment there. At ten a.m. his ass needs to be back in the van to Supermax. I don't want him on my yard a second longer than necessary. Is that clear?" He hadn't taken a breath between sentences and sounded a bit winded. I felt the acid start to churn in my stomach, and wondered whether it was related to his agitation or me skipping lunch.

The next day, I informed Hannah that she and the rest of the medical staff had to leave the clinic by eight o'clock. Her thin red lips tightened, and her stiff, white curly hair bristled.

"Hmph. I still don't see why all the staff has to leave." Her eyes narrowed as she looked at me. "We've never done anything like this before, and this is going to put us behind schedule."

Nonetheless, at 8 a.m. I was waiting alone in my office, which also served as my exam room. A few minutes later, I heard the voices of officers and the clink of chains coming down the hallway.

Two burly officers in green uniforms entered my office. "Where do you want him, Doc?" I motioned to the chair in front of my desk and two other officers, one on each side of the inmate, brought him in and placed him in the

171

chair.

This does not look like the man I saw displayed on the covers of magazines. I found myself disappointed. He was pale, had dark hair that he kept under a hairnet of all things, with lackluster brown eyes and an average physique.

His demeanor was calm and reserved, contrasting greatly with the demeanor of the officers. They were all standing with muscles tensed, and I could almost hear their hearts pounding. Their tension pervaded the room and started to affect me. I felt my heart rate go up, and more than anything, I had a perverse desire to ask the inmate to levitate from his chair or move something on my desk with his mind.

With effort, I repeatedly pushed down the questions I really wanted to ask him, and concentrated on a milk toast standard history and physical exam. I started to wish that Custody was not in the room, so I could ask T.J. about his experience in Tibet. What he learned and was able to do with his body. How he had escaped his cell and gotten out of chains at the other prison system. I also wanted to hear his version of what had happened in the martial arts schools he had started, and how he was charged.

As I neared the end of my questioning, I started to have very intrusive thoughts. *This is your last chance to ask him to do something extraordinary. I know the officers look like they're going to jump out of their skin any minute, but you can chance it. ...What are you saying? If T.J. levitates out of his chair, they will freak. Who knows what they would do, and it could be dangerous for them as well as for him. ...Don't fool yourself; this isn't professional curiosity. You just want to see something you might never have the chance again to see. ...Why am I talking to myself? Stop it. You won't be able to convince yourself to ask him to levitate, so just stop it. You're going to be mad at yourself for being a chicken. I know, I know...*

With effort, I tried to shake the chatter in my head as I continued asking T.J. my standard questions. His answers were all delivered in a soft voice, and his eyes never left my face, which I found unsettling. His gaze reminded

172

me of a child who just wanted to please an adult. Open, no guile, no defenses.

Somehow he knew what I was thinking. Our eyes locked, and I shook my head *no*. He looked at the officers, then back at me, and I could tell he was disappointed. It was the look a child gives when they want to show you their favorite toy, and you have to tell them "not now."

The rest of the exam was anti-climactic, and ended with me looking at the broad shoulders of the officers as they led T.J. away. I was already starting to regret my decision to not ask him to levitate for me. *It's a good thing you didn't take the chance*, a small voice in my head whispered. *Remember the last time you took a chance? You were taken hostage.*

The next day, the new psychologist Mabel walked into my office and sat down. Her brown eyes twinkled behind her glasses. She leaned forward and asked, "What did you think of our high-profile inmate?"

"He wasn't at all what I expected. In fact, he seemed like a child to me. What did you think of him psychologically?"

She laughed and straightened the neck of her wool sweater. "He wanted to please me. He really wanted to show me what he could do. I told him no, because I wanted to complete the psych testing, and I was worried how the officers would react. When I walked out of the room he whispered my name and I looked back." She shook her head a few times and I noticed the grey in her curly brown hair.

"I don't know how he did it," Mabel went on. "He lifted off the floor a few inches, hung there, and came down."

By this time, I had known Mabel for six months. I had only seen compassion and rationality in her interactions with others. "How do you think he did it?" I asked, feeling the small hairs on my forearm go erect.

She shrugged, and twisted a brown curl that lay behind her ear. "I don't know how he did it, but I can tell you he was quite pleased with himself."

I nodded. *I would be too, if I could levitate.*

The next day, I ran into one of the officers I knew who had escorted T.J. into my office. "What were your impressions about him?" I asked. I didn't have to elaborate; the officer knew who I was talking about.

"I wouldn't have believed it if I hadn't seen it with my own eyes," he said. "I chained him up myself. We even had the black box over the locking mechanism of the belly chains." He paused and looked at his hands. "When he stepped into the van, he turned and handed me the belly chains, black box and everything."

"How do you think he did it?" I asked.

"Hell if I know. I heard he grew up in Tibet. Who knows what he was trained to do there."

When I drove home that night, I started to speculate about what could have transpired in T.J.'s life to give him that unusual set of skills. The psych reports did say he had below-average intelligence, and I started to remember stories I had read about savants: individuals with extraordinary skills in one area, though profoundly lacking in others. Maybe he was a savant in the area of kinesthetics, and the training in Tibet amplified it.

T.J. also wasn't like the child molesters I had met before. He just seemed like a child to me, and I wondered what would happen to him in the new Supermax up north. *He might be a martial artist, but how is he going to protect himself up there?* Some of the inmates housed in that prison were lethal. If Custody let it be known that he was some sort of famous martial artist who also was a child molester... he'd be attacked and maybe killed. It would not be the first time that I had seen Custody let information be known that would make an inmate's life more miserable than it was to begin with.

I thought back to one horrendous case, where an inmate was supposed to be placed in protective custody for giving delicate information to the Attorney General's office. Instead, he was placed on my yard. Supposedly, the officers let the information be known, and the inmate was attacked with a sort of homemade napalm bomb. It was a balloon filled with glue and gasoline, set

174

on fire and thrown at him. That inmate was still in the university burn center a year later.

Could T.J. really do the impossible, or had he learned how to make himself larger-than-life in order to keep the officers' respect and keep himself out of danger? Prison was a hostile place, and everyone here had their own individual way of gaining power—and holding on to it.

Abuse of power: it occurred on both sides of the fence line. What was that saying again? *Power tends to corrupt, and absolute power corrupts absolutely.* T.J.'s fate could be decided in the blink of an eye, by someone who hardly knew him. Or he could keep his power by keeping his legend alive. I hoped he would be successful.

As for me, if I had any power, I had to use it to protect the powerless and stand up against the corrupt.

13. Regional Medical Facility

Karen Gedney, MD

The officer opened the iron gate to let me into the clinic, nodding toward the hallway that led to the infirmary. "Lucy needs to talk to you about that new guy we have in the back."

I dropped my briefcase off in my office, and walked to the back of the infirmary to find Lucy. She was coming out of Mr. Nobein's room, and motioned for me to follow her. "Let's talk in your office," she said.

I noticed that she had her hair cut in a new style. When we sat down in my office, I teased, "Is the new haircut responsible for making you look cuter and younger, or is it because Hannah's gone?"

She laughed and patted the side of her red head. "Probably a bit of both."

Did I miss Hannah's disapproving looks and thin, unsmiling red lips? Not at all. I did find it odd, though: one day she was there, and the next she was gone.

I nodded. "Before we talk about Mr. Nobein, I'm curious. Any new gossip about why Hannah quit?"

"Gordy told me that she wasn't interested in working in the new Regional Medical Facility, and that she was tired of being a nurse."

"Hmph. She probably found out that if she stayed charge nurse at the new facility, her responsibilities would expand dramatically. Could you see Hannah running a place that size? It makes this place look like a matchbox."

When I first saw the plans, all I could think was *how could we possibly run a building that size with just a few nurses?* The new medical facility was going to have sixty medical beds, sixty psych beds, eight or nine treatment rooms, and a ton of offices. It was huge.

"Hannah would have never been able to control it," I went on. "She only felt safe dispensing meds. I understand they have multiple areas in that building to dispense meds, it would have made Hannah nuts."

Lucy smoothed her pink scrub top and chuckled. "Who would have

Karen Gedney, MD

thought they'd need to build a place that size to get rid of her? I for one am glad she's gone. Maybe now we can do some real nursing around here without getting in trouble. So speaking of doing real nursing, what are we going to do with Mr. Nobein?"

Mr. Nobein was an unfortunate thirty-five-year-old white male who was sentenced to prison for growing marijuana on his property. He had been placed in the infirmary two days ago, after Custody took his two prosthetic claw arms and his specialized wheelchair, which was customized for someone missing his right leg above the knee and his left leg below the hip.

Nobein's traumatic injuries were the result of high-tension electric wires that fell on him and blew off his arms and legs. At home, his live-in girl-friend acted as his nurse. After his arrest, the judge had deemed it was better to put him in a prison than to fine him or put him on house arrest.

I rubbed my neck and sighed. "I tried to convince Custody that his prosthetic arms were medically necessary, but they wouldn't budge. They made it very clear that they considered those prosthetic claw arms weapons, and they wouldn't give weapons to an inmate. I pointed out that he couldn't do much with them because of the damage in his upper arms and the fact that he had no legs, but they said it was a threat to Custody and the medical staff just needs to take care of him."

Lucy leaned back and shook her head. "Well he's going to be a real problem. You know we can't use the inmate porters anymore to feed an in-mate. He accused me today of making him eat off his plate like a dog. We try to feed him when his food comes, but you know how it is in the clinic. We have to take care of the serious medical problems first. He's threatening to sue all of us. Can you go back there and talk to him this morning?"

"Sure. I'll go now, before it gets too busy." I pushed myself up and walked back to his room. *Too bad I can't assign an inmate clerk or porter to feed him.* I could've done so in the past, but six months ago, the attorney gen-eral's office informed the prison that inmates no longer could give any medi-cal care to another inmate. I wasn't sure if they had lost a case, or another

Karen Gedney, MD

state had lost a case. All I knew was that it created a problem for the medical department, because we did not have enough staff to take care of patients appropriately.

Rodney could no longer take X-rays, and the prison had taken a while to hire a replacement. His name was Sammy, and I wondered if he would be as good as Rodney was. Lucy, Gordy, and I were stretched a little thinner now, unable to ask the inmates for help with some of the small tasks especially after Hannah's departure. And now I was saddled with trying to figure out how we could best take care of a man with no arms and legs. I did not see how feeding someone qualified as medical care in the first place, but Custody wouldn't allow it.

I tapped on Mr. Nobein's door and entered his small grey room. His bed was pushed so the head of the bed was in a corner of the room. He had wiggled his body into a partial sitting position in the corner. His grey blanket had fallen onto the food-stained floor.

I picked up his blanket and shook it out, and some pancake pieces dropped from it. "I'll have the inmate porter come in and clean up the room, Mr. Nobein. Can I help you get into a more comfortable position?" He squirmed, and I could see him eyeing the small pink plastic jug on his bed stand. "Would you like a drink of water?"

His dark eyes matched his dark hair. "It's warm. Can I get some ice in it?"

"How about you take a sip now, and I'll have the porters bring you some water with ice in it when I leave."

He nodded. I helped him get into a better position, and placed the straw in his mouth. He drank almost half of the water in the jug. I knew that if he had tried to lean over on his own and get the straw into his mouth, he would have fallen out of his bed.

He leaned his head against the wall and snorted. "I know about all your excuses, but if Custody doesn't give me my arms and no one is going to

179

feed me when the food is actually edible, I'm going to sue this place. I told the judge a prison couldn't take care of someone like me, but he assured me they could."

His dark eyes were penetrating, and made me feel like this situation was my fault.

"You know," he went on, "some of your nurses aren't strong enough to get me onto the commode, and the officers won't help them. I'm not going to shit in a bed and lie on it for hours."

"Would it help if I gave them an order to put you on the commode at a specific time every day?"

His eyes narrowed. "You could, but you'd need to also give an order to get me off it ten minutes later. I don't want them forgetting about me."

"Mr. Nobein, I know this infirmary was not set up for someone like you. But the new regional medical facility on this yard has hospital beds and an intercom system, and I understand we will be moving our infirmary patients there next week."

"I'll believe it when I see it, but if they don't give me my arms I won't be even able to scratch an itch."

"Is there anything else I can do for you, before I go?"

He rubbed his back on the concrete wall behind him. "How about another pillow?"

I left his room in search of another pillow, walking past X-ray as I went. *I miss Rodney.* Times were changing. I wondered what it was going to be like in the new medical facility.

The rumors on the yard were numerous. The gossip inferred that I was somehow responsible for the new medical facility being built. One of the rumors the inmates especially liked was that I had told the state they had to build a real medical facility, or I was going to sue them for letting me be taken hostage.

180

I smiled. *I wish.* I had nothing to do with building the facility. The plans for it had been in the works for years: the correctional system wanted the sickest inmates in one place to centralize their care.

I just hoped they gave us time to acquire good staff and train them, before they dumped all the problem children in one spot.

When I walked into my office later, I saw a plaque on my desk. *What's this?* I traced the embossed leaves and acorns on the leather, and marveled at the artistry. Tears sprung to my eyes as I recognized my certificate from the National Health Service Corps, in recognition of completing my four-year service obligation to the prison.

My porter M.C. did this. I smiled, remembering him telling me that it needed to be in a special frame. How long ago was that now, two years? I had never taken the time, so he had. Six years in this matchbox of a clinic, and finally I was moving on to a new medical facility—but my commitment to the prison and its inmates was just as strong.

At the top of the frame, in between the leaves, were the engraved letters *Dr. G.* I turned it over. It had a beautiful, deep red leather backing, with a leather clasp to hang it from a wall. There was no note or card, but I knew the inmates had made it.

A tap on the door made me jump, and I looked up to see M.C. himself with a mug of tea in his hands. He put it on my desk.

I smiled. "M.C., I don't think bringing me tea is in your job description as a porter."

His light grey-blue eyes twinkled as an impish grin spread across his face. He didn't look at the plaque on my desk, but instead pointed at the scraggly philodendron in the corner. It now sported a few shiny green leaves. "I know, Doc, and that's why I cleaned up your dusty plant."

"It doesn't look the same without all the dust," I said, and turned back to face him. "What did you use on it?"

His head tipped back and he laughed. "The mayonnaise in the refrigerator that had some mold on it. The nurses told me to throw it out, so I put it to some good use first." He rolled up the sleeve of his pressed blue shirt and pointed at his cafe-au-lait skin. "I even considered putting some of it on this weird rash, which is starting to spread all over me."

"Let me see that." I put down my tea and examined the scaly, red patches, which ranged from the size of a dime to a half-dollar.

"Doc, do you know what this creeping crud is? I'll freak out if it gets on my face."

"Do you have it on the rest of your body?" I asked, and walked around the large desk to get a better look.

He slipped down his clean, ironed, light blue jeans to show me the spots on his legs. The sight of his black silk boxer shorts made me chuckle. "Hey M.C., when did the prison start issuing silk boxer shorts?"

He pulled up his pants and flashed me a grin. "I can't give up all my stylin', can I Doc?" The intricate pattern of his gold ring sparkled in the light as he smoothed back his closely clipped kinky hair, which had blonde highlights. "Now Doc, tell me you know how to get rid of it. I don't want to look like some goddamn leper."

The urge to tease him disappeared when I saw how worried he looked. "Have you taken any new medications, or used anything new on your skin?" I asked.

He waved his manicured hand dismissively. "I've done nothing different."

"Any new food?"

He rolled his eyes. "Boy, I wish I could get some new food in here. How about some lobster?"

I couldn't help but smile. "And how about stress?"

"What's to be stressed about? I wasn't stressed till I broke out in these

182

spots." He leaned forward. "Please tell me you know what it is and how to get rid of it."

"It looks like a type of psoriasis to me. Don't worry, I'll order a medicated ointment for you, which should get rid of it."

"Doc, you're the best. Is there anything else I can do for you, before I go back to work?"

"I thought you were at work, M.C."

He grinned and shook his head. "It's not really work if you're having a good time."

A good time. Somehow he always seemed to be having a good time, and it was infectious. I had even seen him make Hannah smile once.

I saw the morning patients, and at 11:30 the officers closed the yard and did their count. It was now time for me to walk over to the new medical facility and check it out. Lucy should already be there, checking on the medical supplies; I had told her I would join her.

The officer opened the white door that led to the yard, and I walked to a steel gate and waited for it to be buzzed open. I had only been on the yard a few times in the last six years, and had never been in the northwest corner where the new facility stood. The yard was empty; all the inmates were locked down. I headed down the path past the educational building, noticing the smell of hot dogs coming from the culinary.

The next grey building was Visiting; I had seen a graduation take place there last year. Proud family members, teachers, and a few prison staff were sitting in the audience as the inmates filed in with their hats and gowns to receive their high school diplomas and AA degrees. It was very emotional. I had heard one young, tall, blonde inmate tell his parents that he knew they were proud of his brother graduating from Penn State, "and I hope you can also be proud of your youngest son for graduating from the state pen."

Then came the canteen and the store. I smiled, thinking about all my

183

efforts to get the inmates not to live on Ramen soup. *Well, it kept me alive as a poor medical student.* The last building was the large gym, where the men played basketball; next to it was a weight yard, with rusty free weights and chin-up bars. On my left, a long fence separated the baseball and soccer fields from the rest of the yard. Tucked in the back was the sweat lodge for the Native Americans, the only green thing in a large expanse of brown.

Then the path took a right-angle turn, and I could see the new, two-story, grey medical facility in the distance. It was the largest building on the yard, behind its own fence, and it had windows outlined with a pleasant green color.

At the end of the path, I entered through an open gate, walked to the main entrance of the building, and looked in through the door. An officer saw me and buzzed me into an anteroom. He pointed to the right-hand door, and buzzed that one open as well.

I was now in my new waiting room. It was a concrete box, about fifteen by twenty feet, with two long, light-green metal benches bolted into opposing walls. It had a large security window facing the center of the clinic. Through the window, I could see the large nursing station. The waiting room had two other doors: one opened into a treatment room, and the other led into the clinic. Both had to be opened by an officer with a key.

The officer opened the door to the clinic for me. "It's impressive, isn't it?" he asked.

I looked at the three long hallways that led away from the central clinic and asked, "Have you seen my nurse, Lucy? This is my first time in the building, and I don't want to get lost."

"Yeah, she's in the stockroom down that hallway, and you can't get around this place without her keys anyway. She'll have to show you around, because I can't leave my post."

Lucy heard me walking down the hallway, and stepped out of the storeroom to see who was coming.

"How's it going?" I said, looking at all the empty brown boxes on the floor and the stocked shelves.

Lucy put her hand on her lower back, and arched backward. "This room is about done. Do you want me to give you a little tour? I could use a break."

"That would be great. Lead the way."

I followed her down the hall, and she showed me the large treatment room, the X- ray room, and a large room with three dental chairs. I marveled at how everything looked so modern and clean.

Next, I looked into a large room with rows of grey countertops and cabinets above them.

"What's this room for?" I asked.

"I'm told it's the dental lab. They're going to teach the inmates how to make dentures."

"Really? That would be great. I've never seen so many guys with rotten teeth or no teeth at all."

We started walking back, and I pointed at another large empty room. "What are they going to put in there?"

"They told me it's going to be used to process the new inmates when they come in. Like a classroom or something."

I peered inside. "I wonder if Custody would let me teach a class in here for the inmates like I do out in the camp."

"I didn't know you taught out there. What do you teach? Do they even have a classroom out there?"

"No, they don't, but they let me teach a life skills class as a volunteer. It's in the culinary on Wednesday nights. You remember Harold Green, the nice officer who used to bring the inmates from camp to our clinic?" Lucy nodded. "Well, he got several classes started out there, including a GED class, and asked me to teach a substance abuse class that eventually evolved into a life skills course. I call it Health Related Recovery."

"Well, that may have worked at the camp. But who knows what they'll allow you to do in this place?"

"I know, it's a long shot. The room does sit right next to the officer's station, though. And it would be nice to have a real classroom."

As we entered the central clinic area, I gazed up at the skylights and smiled. "This place feels less oppressive. And I like the colors they picked."

"So do I. It was Warden Jones' idea to use teal and eggplant for the accents. We're lucky it wasn't a male warden who picked the colors, otherwise everything would be grey," she said, and opened the teal-painted door leading to one of the exam rooms.

I walked inside and turned on the faucet above the sink. "Look at this, Lucy. Not only do we have running water in a exam room now, but there's even a soap dispenser." I opened one of the cabinets. "It's a good thing they let me see the blueprints before they built this, because they weren't going to put any cabinets in the exam rooms. Can you imagine that?"

Lucy laughed. "Sure I can, if it was a guy who drew up the plans. Every woman knows you can never have enough storage space or closets."

I laughed too. "Not to mention bathrooms." I had specifically pointed out to the architect that if you were going to keep dozens of sick men waiting to be seen by a doctor, the holding room needed more than one toilet.

"Let me show you the other side of the building, so you can pick out which office you want before the other people put in their dibs."

We walked down another long hallway that held four offices for the psych department, and then passed through a locked door to the administrative side of the medical building. After looking at the offices, I picked the one closest to the clinic. Looking out its window, I could see the prison yard with its housing units, and the mountains in the distance.

I stared at my new, clean white walls. *This is the first time I am going to have a real office, not just a room that doubles as an exam room.* I also wouldn't be sorry to say goodbye to the bullet holes in the wall of my old office, a daily reminder of my hostage incident.

Lucy leaned on the wall outside my new office. "They're still working on the back, but Central told me that in two weeks they're going to move the infirmary patients over. When they're settled in, they will open the clinic. There are eighteen patients, so that will leave us forty-two open beds in Medical, and there will be sixty Psych beds upstairs. I heard the rest of the state is going to dump their worst patients on us. If they do, there's no way we'll have enough nurses to cover it. Dr. G., we have to get Central to hire more nurses or block the rest of the state from sending us patients."

"I know what you mean, and I'll see what I can do. There's no way I can handle it either if the whole state dumps on us, without getting another doctor for this place."

Three weeks later, I was sitting in a new, comfortable chair at my new desk, looking out the window, when I saw an open truck bed filled with an assortment of odd equipment approaching. The truckload included Mr. Nobein, who was strapped into a wheelchair held steady by two inmates. He had still not received his prosthetic arms (nor would he in the future, despite all my best efforts). A third inmate was holding on to the philodendron plant that had been in my old office. Fortunately, they all looked like they were enjoying the ride.

Am I going to enjoy the ride in this brand new medical facility? I loved the fact that it smelled clean, and the warden had agreed that the facility would be non-smoking. But I also wondered who would be the director of nursing in this facility. I had heard that Central was going to interview candidates next Monday; I needed to see if I could be on the committee that chose the candidate. I didn't want to deal with another Hannah, or another Ignin.

14. Mitad

I dodged large puddles and fought the wind for control of my umbrella on my half-mile walk to the new Regional Medical Facility. The two-story, grey structure was on the furthest side of the prison from the entrance. Finally, glad to have reached the building where there was some shelter, I punched in my four-digit security code. The door popped open into a small vestibule, where I typed the code again to get through the second door.

I was soaked, and squished down the hallway in soggy sneakers to see my first patient. Mr. Mitad was already sitting on the exam table waiting for me. Sad, doe-like brown eyes blinked at me, framed by shoulder-length chest-nut hair. A timid smile accentuated his fine features with perfect white teeth.

"Hi Doc, you look a little wet."

"I won't melt. What can I do for you today?" I asked, and opened up his medical chart.

"My asthma is acting up. I think I need a stronger inhaler."

"Why don't you slip off your shirt so I can listen to your lungs and ex-amine you."

He stiffened. His eyes darted toward the large window in the exam room, through which the officer in the clinic could easily see us from his sta-tion. The door in the exam room also had a window through which an officer could look inside. Gone were the days that I was in an exam room down a dark hallway, where there was privacy for a patient and no one could see what was going on.

"Is something wrong, Mr. Mitad?"

"There's no need to examine me, I.... My lungs will be okay. I just need another inhaler."

I closed the blinds so the officer's immediate view was obscured. "Is there a reason you don't feel comfortable taking off your shirt?"

He shrugged, looked down and started rubbing the knees of his damp, faded blue jeans.

189

"Everything is going to be all right," I said, and put my hand on his shoulder. "Why don't you slip off your shirt?"

Keeping his head down, he slowly unbuttoned his long-sleeved blue shirt. When he removed it, I saw multiple bruises on his arms. His hairless chest was marred with abrasions and long scrapes.

My mouth felt dry. "When did you get those injuries?"

"Three days ago," he whispered.

"Can you tell me what happened?"

He shook his head, and his long hair covered his eyes. His respiratory rate went up and he started to wheeze.

"It's going to be okay. Just slow down your breathing. Do you have your inhaler with you?"

He nodded, took it out of his pocket, and took two long breaths. I waited until he got control of himself and said, "See, you're breathing better now. Is it okay if I examine your legs as well? Can you remove your pants?"

His hands shook as he stood up and he gingerly slid down his pants. Both knees had crusty abrasions, and there were dark bruises on the backs of his thighs.

"Did anyone force you to do something that you didn't want to do?" I asked.

He wrapped his arms around his abdomen and murmured, "They were only playing, Doc. Nothing happened." He glanced up quickly, but couldn't hold my gaze. "You're not going to tell Custody, are you?"

"What would you like me to do about what happened to you?"

He didn't respond.

"Would you like to talk to someone, like a psychologist, or a caseworker that could put you in protective custody?"

An inmate could request to be placed in protective custody if they

190

were concerned about their safety. Many of those housed in protective custody were child molesters or inmates who were victimized for other reasons.

He remained silent, so I went on. "Mr. Mitad, I know you say they were playing, but I'm concerned about your safety. First I need to see how many injuries you have, and whether I need to do something for you medically. Please slip down your underwear and let me examine you down there."

His body sagged, and with a small nod he complied. He had no obvious trauma in the genital or rectal area. When I was done, he dressed with care and brushed back his hair.

"Mr. Mitad, I think you came in today because you wanted my help for more than just your asthma. Is that right?"

His right hand trembled. He reached up and started tugging and twisting his hair. "You can't tell anyone, Doc. I'll be okay. It just got out of hand."

I touched his hand. "If you change your mind and need my help, will you promise me that you'll come back right away?"

He gulped and stood up quickly. "I promise, Doc. I just need another inhaler. Don't worry about me. I'll be all right."

Not worrying about him is not an option. I watched his graceful body exit the room, wondering what I should do. I thought back to my conversation with Sumtin, the first prison director I had worked with. He'd said I was only obligated to disclose information about an inmate if they told me they were going to escape or kill someone. *No one told me what to do when the inmate is the victim and doesn't want Custody involved.*

I decided to do what Mr. Mitad wished: nothing. Six months passed, and I had almost forgotten about the incident. Then one late Friday afternoon, my new nurse Suzy brought him into the triage room.

Suzy handed me Mr. Mitad's chart. "God, he's gone crazy. He must have got into something. His blood pressure is 260 over 140, and his pulse is crazy. He's freezing and I can't even get an oxygen reading on him."

191

We entered the triage room together. Mitad's clothes were dirty and smelled of vomit, and his hair was in tangles. His brown eyes searched the room with the panic of a cornered rat.

"Suzy, get some oxygen on him, do an EKG, and I'll put in an IV. Mr. Mitad, do you remember who I am?" His glassy dilated pupils briefly held mine, but there was no recognition.

"Mr. Mitad, we're going to take care of you. I need to know what drugs you took. Did you take anyone's medications or any drugs on the yard?"

He was shaking so hard that I couldn't read the EKG. I knew he had overdosed on some stimulant. I didn't have the resources to take care of him adequately in the clinic. I turned to the custody officer. "Tell the lieutenant to call 911. Tell him Mr. Mitad has to go to the emergency room."

When the paramedics wheeled him away, Suzy asked, "What do you think he got into? He looked psycho."

"Probably something like meth. The stimulants tend to make their pupils dilate, it's the opiates like heroin that make them pinpoint. Do you remember that young guy they brought over from camp, the one that was saying all those crazy things about the lieutenant?"

Suzy laughed as she opened her desk drawer and rummaged around for the candy she kept in there. "How could I forget that one? He accused the lieutenant of having sex with cows, and all sorts of other bizarre stuff." She found the silver-wrapped chocolate kiss, unwrapped it, popped it in her mouth, and sighed. "Boy did I need that."

"That young guy became psychotic after taking a bunch of meth, and I think Mr. Mitad did the same thing. I'm just not sure why his blood pressure was so high, and why we couldn't get a reading on his oxygen level. Who knows what he took? The hospital will be able to sort it all out, though. They have resources we don't."

Suzy pointed at the watch on her freckled wrist. "Well, it's quitting time for me, and I'm getting out of here before anything else happens. See you

Monday, Doc. I hope you have a nice weekend."

On Monday morning, Suzy quickened her step to match mine on the long walk across the yard to the clinic. "Hey Dr. G., what happened to the guy we sent to the ER Friday?"

"Seems he overdosed on his asthma medications. The hospital found that he had taken an entire bottle of his Theodur. He admitted to sucking down all the inhalers he had, and then he topped it off with meth."

A few strands of faded blonde hair blew across Suzy's face and she brushed them away. "Has Custody found out how the meth is coming in?"

"Not that I know of, though one of the officers told me they last found meth in a bunch of tennis balls that were shipped in. Seems an officer became suspicious when the balls didn't bounce and didn't feel quite right."

"Well, if there's a will there's a way. I remember a case down south where a woman brought in a bag of meth through Visiting and the inmate stuck it up his rectum, and later that day they found him dead in his cell. The bag broke and that was that."

"I think we could trade stories all day long about how drugs get into the prison, but as long as people want to use and don't care about the consequences, someone will bring it in if the price is right. Including the custody officers."

"Yeah, you're right. So when do you think the hospital will send Mr. Mitad back to us?"

"Probably today, but he'll go upstairs to Psych because the hospital thinks he's suicidal."

My morning passed without incident, and I went to the lunchroom to warm up my mug of tea. The nurses had lined up their meals on the counter, waiting for the microwave. As I waited for my turn, Suzy spotted me and slid over. "Dr. G., they just brought that guy back from the hospital and took him upstairs. Do you need to see him right now? You know, you have a lot of afternoon patients out there waiting."

I smiled, deducing she didn't want a long day. "Don't worry, Suzy. I'll take care of my afternoon appointments before I go upstairs."

When I finally climbed the stairs to the mental health unit that afternoon, I stopped at the first landing to look through the wire-meshed glass at the ten-by-ten concrete exercise yard below me. *Look at that, you don't see that every day.* Sure enough, there was a bird's nest in the outdoor metal urinal, surrounded on all four sides by two stories of cinderblock, with three small white eggs in it. I chuckled to myself. *It's amazing what can survive in a concrete world.*

I continued my climb and entered the psych ward. Once inside, I walked to the front rooms, which were closest to the nursing station and under camera observation. I found Mr. Mitad in one of the suicide watch rooms, face down, tied to the bed with leather restraints around both his legs and arms. He was covered in an old grey blanket, and I could see his body heaving with the effort of breathing.

"Who put an asthmatic with a wool allergy in restraints face down?" I asked, looking into the face of a nurse I didn't recognize.

She stuttered, "I... they... we thought it would be better to restrain him until the psychiatrist evaluated him."

"Better for whom?"

She looked at the officer and the other nurse, but didn't get any help. Tim, the forensic officer, played with the keys in his pocket and studied the tiles on the floor. His job was opening security doors and helping the nurses with basic medical care in the mental health unit.

"Tim, open the door for me. I need to examine the patient."

Tim opened the heavy green door and shifted from one foot to the other while I kneeled next to Mr. Mitad. I brushed back his matted hair and saw his puffy, tear-stained face. He was wheezing and whimpering, but his bloodshot eyes recognized me.

I turned to Tim, who had his hands crossed over his large chest. "Tim, I need you to help me take the restraints off Mr. Mitad so we can sit him up and give him a breathing treatment. And please tell the nurse I also need her to get some vitals on the patient, and then she needs to bring me a cotton blanket."

When Mr. Mitad was sitting up and breathing better, I asked, "Do you feel well enough to tell me what happened and what I can do to help you?"

He shook his head and rubbed his puffy red eyes, then pulled the cotton blanket around his naked body, which was covered in a faint pink rash from the wool.

"You don't have to talk about it now if you're not ready, but I'd like to know if you're feeling so bad now that you want to hurt yourself or end your life."

He started to sob and choked out, "I didn't want to kill myself, I just had to get out of there." He looked at me through long wet lashes "Don't let them tie me up again. I'm not going to hurt myself. I can't breathe like that."

"I'm not going to let them tie you up or hurt you. Can you promise me that you won't hurt yourself?"

He nodded and curled up in a fetal position, hugging his blanket.

"Mr. Mitad, I'm told the psychiatrist will be in later. All I want you to do now is rest and take it easy, and I'll see you tomorrow. Is that all right with you?" I touched his shoulder. "Is there anything that you need before I go?"

He murmured, "Could you tell them to give me back my clothes? I'm freezing in here."

The next day, I went back to the mental health unit and found that the psychiatrist had cleared him to be discharged. When I entered Mitad's cell, I found him sitting on the bed hunched over with the blanket wrapped around him.

"Can I come in and talk to you, Mr. Mitad?" He looked up, then moved

195

over on his bed so I could sit next to him. The low-lying, metal bed was bolted to the floor and had a thin, grey mattress on it.

"How did your talk with the psychiatrist go today? Are you feeling better?"

He scratched the rash on his neck. "I couldn't understand anything he said, Dr. G. Anyway I don't need psych drugs or to be up here in this nut unit, I'm not crazy."

"According to your chart, the psychiatrist has discharged you from this unit. Did they tell you where you would be going?"

His eyes widened. "I can't go back to the same unit, don't let them take me back there." He started to tremble and breathe faster.

"I'm not going to let them take you back to that unit. Now slow down your breathing. That's right, nice and easy." I waited for a minute. "See Mr. Mitad, you know how to calm yourself down." I patted the blanket over his thigh. "You're safe now. I want to help you. Why don't you tell me why you took all those drugs to get off the yard?"

He wrapped his arms around himself and started to rock back and forth. He didn't say anything for a while, and didn't look at me. I stayed quiet.

Then in a soft monotone, he started. "They were always after me. I thought I could handle it because Hank protected me. He really cared about me and kept the others off of me, but those fuckers were jealous of what Hank and I had. They set him up. They ratted to Custody that he was the one bringing in the shit. Those fuckers brought the meth in and they planted some in his area."

He clenched his fists and put them on his forehead. "When Hank was gone, I had no protection at all and... and... six of them jumped me and they shoved a rag down my throat." He tried to pull in some air, and started to wheeze.

"You're safe now, just let your air out slow through pursed lips. That's right, you're going to be fine." I placed my hand on his back and waited until he regained control.

He swallowed a few times and coughed. "They hurt me so bad. I thought I was going to die because I couldn't get any air. I took everything I had and nothing helped. I wasn't thinking right, I don't know why I took all my Theodur and that meth. I just wanted to be out of there." He turned his blotchy face towards me. "You've got to believe me, Dr. G. I didn't want to kill myself. I just didn't want them to do that to me again."

"Would you like to come downstairs and stay in the medical unit for a while until we can decide what would be best for you? I can ask one of the psychologists to see you down there, as well. How does that sound?"

He glanced up. "You'll still see me, won't you?"

"Of course," I said, and smiled.

Mr. Mitad spent a week in the medical infirmary, getting his asthma under control and talking to Jake, the portly psychologist. I stopped in to check on him at the end of the week.

"Mr. Mitad, you're looking better every day. I see that you're still holding on to your blanket, though." He was clutching the same cotton blanket he had been given upstairs.

He looked at it as if surprised to see it in his hands. "It's just... you know, it's always cold in here."

His room was actually warm. "Do you remember keeping a blanket or a stuffed animal for security, when you were a child?" I asked.

"Hmph. What security? My mother was crazy and my stepfather beat on all of us."

"How far back do you remember?"

"I can still smell the stink of stale beer sometimes. When he smelled like that, I tried to hide my little brother Johnnie. Sometimes I was lucky and he only beat me." He started to twist the end of the blanket. "Mom got the

197

worst of it and sometimes she wouldn't come out of her room for days."

"Who took care of you, if your mother wasn't able to? Did you have any other relatives?"

"If I did, I never met any. My real dad left when I was six. And then it only got worse."

"In what way?"

He studied the holes in his blanket before he answered. "Mom would be nice one day, and the next day she wanted both of us to die. She wouldn't feed us for days, and then she would make a cake and sing. I never knew if I needed to hide Johnnie or not."

"What happened to Johnnie?"

He wiped a tear from his cheek. "He ran away and I never saw him again. It was all my fault, I couldn't protect him."

I felt drained. *Why did I bring up the blanket issue in the first place? I'll have to tell Jake about this conversation and let him take over.*

"I know the psychologist has been seeing you and talking with Custody on your behalf, and it sounds like they feel you would do better in protective custody. Is that something you want?"

He shrugged, put his hand over his mouth, and looked down at the floor. I had to strain to hear him say, "I just can't go back to the yard."

When I walked out of Mitad's room, I saw Jake coming out of another cell with an officer. I lengthened my stride to catch them at the security door that led to the other side of the infirmary. I found the size of the infirmary almost overwhelming, compared to the old ten-room facility where I could walk from one side to the other in less than twenty seconds. The medical infirmary in this building was easily ten times the size of the older one, and it had two separate areas so the inmates who needed to be in isolation were kept apart from the general infirmary population.

The officer opened the door, and we all left the isolation side. "Jake," I said to the psychologist, "I just saw Mr. Mitad. How do you think he's doing?"

He stroked his short grey beard. "He'll be affected by the gang rape for a long time, but I think his childhood traumatized him more."

"I think you're right. I don't know what he told you, but it sounded like his father was an abusive alcoholic and his mother was mentally ill," I said. We stopped, and I looked into Jake's kind brown eyes to see what he thought.

"I think his mother was a bipolar schizoaffective. Did he tell you about how she would leave him and his brother on a curb somewhere and tell them she never wanted to see them again, and then pick them up hours later?"

"No, I missed that one. I don't want to imagine what that would have been like if it happened to me and my little sister."

"She did it more than once. In my experience, abandonment issues seem to be at the bottom of all the self-worth, addictive behavior, and acting-out problems I tend to see."

"What's going to happen to him?" I asked, and thought about my sister. She was one year younger than I. What would have happened if I felt I wasn't able to protect her?

He shrugged. "He'll be sent to another prison and put in protective custody. There's no rush, is there?"

"No, I'll keep him as long as he's benefiting from your help."

"Sounds like a plan to me."

I walked through two security doors to get back to my office. Nothing was on my desk for me to take care of, and the nurses in the clinic had already gone home for the day. I sat down on my large, sturdy desk, and stretched out my legs. I glanced at the stark white walls and decided I had to put something on them. *Even the inmates hang things on the walls of their cells to make it more bearable. I should too.*

I thought back to Mr. Mitad. *What will become of him? How many other inmates experience a rape in prison and just never let anyone know?* I had been

199

here over six years, and he was the first case of rape that I had actually taken care of.

I thought back to the letter the executed inmate had sent me, and how he went into great detail discussing how gangs pressured new inmates to be "fresh meat" and "old ladies." Gangs sold themselves by offering an inmate protection from another gang, but according to that inmate, it was really about sexual exploitation. He had written that it would be almost impossible to stand alone in a prison as an inmate and not get victimized.

Over the years, I had heard there were other groups that watched inmate's backs without victimizing them. One of them was the Incarcerated Vietnam Veterans chapter. They looked after their own, and unlike many groups, their ranks were not formed based on race or religion.

Mitad had spent his life as a victim. He even let himself be victimized, in order to protect his brother. Protective custody inside a prison might be the first place he could experience a little protection and get the psychological help he needed.

15. Life Sentence

I picked up the light green medical chart and took a second look at the number on the front. *That can't be right,* I thought as I flipped through the thin chart. This inmate's number was only four digits long, which meant he had been in the system for decades—and there was hardly anything in his chart. *Maybe he has other volumes, and the medical records people forgot to put the volume number on the chart.*

I opened the door to the exam room, and the inmate stood up quickly. "Thank you for seeing me, I hope I'm not bothering you." He had a grey crew cut, bright blue-grey eyes, and a physique that was trim and athletic for an inmate in his sixties.

"Why don't you sit down and tell me what I can do for you today, Mr. Olsen." I laid his chart on the exam table and sat down on the little rolling stool. "I see you've been here a number of years. Do you have any other medical charts besides this one?"

He shook his head, and looked out the window of the exam room, into the clinic. My eyes followed his, but all I saw was a typical day in the clinic. The nurses were sitting at the nurse's station, and two custody officers at the entrance were patting down inmates coming into the clinic.

He picked at a seam on his faded blue jeans and didn't look at me. I started to wonder why someone who never came to Medical was sitting in front of me deciding whether to talk or not.

"Is there something you'd like to discuss with me?" I asked.

"I..." He swallowed with difficulty. "I... uh, I just wanted to tell someone..."

I waited, watching him pull a stray thread out of the seam on his jeans. His eyes were still looking at the thread as he said, "Today is the anniversary of my fortieth year in prison."

Wow. He's been in prison longer than I have been alive. I was thirty-eight, and this was my eighth year in prison. I heard my voice catch as I asked, "Is there something that you want me to do for you today?"

After a long pause, he shook his head and murmured, "I don't know." He looked up and searched my face.

"Do you have anyone to talk to?"

He closed his eyes, exhaled and tilted his head back before he replied. "Not anymore. They're all gone."

"Do you feel comfortable talking to any of the other inmates, or the psych staff?"

He snorted. "I try to avoid the other inmates. They're just into playing their stupid games."

"What do you mean by that?"

"You know, it's all about the hustle for them. To get cigarettes, drugs, sex, extra food, favors, whatever." He waved his hand dismissively. "They're institutionalized. They've lost sight of the outside world and what really matters."

I rubbed my chin and looked at the clock. I didn't know where this was going, but I could give him fifteen minutes.

"What is it that really matters to you?"

The blue in his eyes intensified. "To get out of this place. Even if it's just a few feet on the other side of the fence."

"You've been in prison a long time. What would you do on the outside?"

His voice strengthened. "I'd *live*. I want to do something worthwhile in my life. I want to make my own decisions. I'm so tired of being told what to do all the time." His mouth tightened and he leaned a little closer. "I was twenty-four when they put me on death row. I'd never even been in a jail. What was I going to do? Kill myself?" He took a deep breath and let it out. "I rejected the

203

thought as soon as it came into my mind. I decided the system was never going to break me for something I didn't do. I'll never give up hoping that I can get out of here someday."

"Since I'm not seeing you in chains and with an officer in attendance, I'm assuming you are no longer on death row. Was your sentence changed to a life without a chance for parole back in the seventies?"

"Yeah, how do you know about that?"

"I know the Supreme Court declared that the death penalty was unconstitutional in 1972 or so. When that happened, the men on death row had their sentences changed to life with no possibility of parole. If I'm remembering the dates right, I think a few years later the death penalty was reinstated, correct? I don't know the particulars, but I did take care of another inmate who had been on death row and came off it when the Supreme Court made their initial decision." *That was Moth. Don't tell me this guy is going to be another Moth.*

"Mr. Olsen," I continued, "I know some men in your situation who have done decades in prison try to get before the pardons board. Have you ever gone?"

"Yes. Twice."

I had been to the pardons board myself a few times as a medical expert, and found the whole process unsettling. The last pardons board that I went to had helped me understand the rationale for having it. The attorney general had presented a woman who was given five consecutive seven-year sentences for writing bad checks. Thirty-five years in prison, for bad checks that totaled less than two thousand dollars, had shocked me. But what really shocked me was the reason the judge had given her that sentence. It appeared that her husband had emptied out their joint checking account without telling her, and then asked the judge, who was his best friend, to sentence her. The poor woman had spent eight years in prison before the attorney general presented the case. I remembered that none of the Supreme Court justices had looked at the woman as they cast their vote to pardon her.

I looked at Mr. Olsen closely. "Who helped you get to the pardons board?"

"The prison director."

"What happened when you went to the board the last time?"

His body tightened and his hand clenched into a fist on his thigh. "They wanted to hear that I was sorry. They wanted to see remorse." His voice quavered slightly. "I'm not going to say I'm sorry for something I didn't do."

I had heard many men rationalize, minimize, and blame others for their actions, but I rarely heard them tell me they were innocent. I'm sure they did in court, and with people who could judge them or make their lives worse. But I couldn't remember any of my lifers telling me they were innocent, and I knew many of them by that time.

I checked the clock. I knew he had come in to talk, and we had some time. "Why don't you tell me what's on your mind?"

He looked off in the distance, and I could feel him turning back the clock. "I had just finished a construction job down south and was hitchhiking back to my wife and little girl." His lip quivered. "She was only two."

He sighed. "A Mexican in an old beat-up station wagon picked me up, and we hadn't gone ten miles before he told me he had to piss and we pulled into this motel parking lot. It was the longest goddamn piss in history. After a while, I got tired of waiting and decided to get out of the car and find him." He started to tremble, and put both hands on his knees to brace himself.

"These two cop cars tore into the lot, and they came out with guns yelling at me to get on the ground and show my hands." He looked at me and took a few breaths. "I was scared. I didn't know what was going on... but later I found out there had been a murder up the road where a woman and her daughter were found stabbed to death. That was their station wagon."

He shook his head and ran his hand through his crew cut. "I was the

205

first death row case the state brought to trial on circumstantial evidence." His teeth clenched and his voice rose. "The whole trial was a joke. It was a small town, and the prosecutor wanted to make a name for himself. And he did… he later became the governor."

I was contemplating what to say, when Mr. Olsen stood up. "I'm sorry, Doc," he mumbled. "I've taken up too much of your time."

I stood up and put my hand lightly on his arm. "You needed to talk today. Mr. Olsen, you haven't seen a doctor in decades, and it's time we checked some labs. When you come back to see me after your labs are done, I'll do your physical and then we'll see how you are doing. How does that sound?"

"I've gotta go," he replied, as he opened the door to leave.

I stood next to the nurse's station and watched him walk toward the officer, who handed him his ID as he stepped out of the clinic door. Then I turned around and handed his chart to Suzy.

She brushed back her faded blonde bangs and pushed a thick chart toward me across the counter. "Look at the size of Mr. Mandel's chart. He's only been here a year, and he's on his third volume. I swear that whiner puts in kites to be seen every week, and he's driving me nuts. Can't you do something about him?"

A kite was a special green sheet of paper on which an inmate wrote his name, number, and the problem he wanted to see Medical for.

I lifted the heavy chart, and thought about Mr. Olsen's chart with only a few pieces of paper in it after forty years in prison. *What a difference.* "Suzy, I know it's aggravating, but if they feel they need to be seen, I have to see them. Even whiners and hypochondriacs can get legitimately sick."

Suzy adjusted her dark blue scrub top with a huff. "Well, you should have the director of nursing talk to him, because he's driving all of the nurses nuts. I bet the director could get Custody to ship that whiner to another prison."

Karen Gedney, MD

"They don't all whine," I said, thinking about Mr. Olsen.

"Oh yes they do," Suzy replied.

I opened the door to the exam room, and saw Mr. Mandel sitting on the edge of his chair.

"Mr. Mandel, why don't you sit on the exam table and tell me why you're here today?"

He easily hopped up on the table and said, "A couple of days ago my back was killing me. I wanted to see if you could write me an order for an extra mattress."

"It appears to me that your back is doing better now. And double mattresses don't necessarily help people with back issues."

He leaned forward. "Well, one of the guys in my unit got one for his back, and I don't see why I can't get one for myself. You should see the thin mattress I've got on that metal bed. It's ridiculous."

"I can understand that the bed may not be comfortable for you, but I do not consider that a medical problem. Is there something else I can do for you?"

"Yeah there is. They just moved this guy into my cell who smokes like a train, and I swear I can't breathe in there half the time. Can't you give me some note I can take to my caseworker to get him the hell out of my room?"

I flipped open his chart and looked at his classification. He was not classified to a non-smoking room. I asked, "If you have problems dealing with cigarette smoke, why haven't you complained before now? You've been in the system now for a year."

He coughed. "I ain't sayin' I can't handle some, but this guy never stops. I swear he's even fallen asleep with one in his mouth. It's a wonder he hasn't caught on fire yet."

Mandel reeked of stale smoke. I couldn't imagine a non-smoker living in a cell constantly filled with smoke. When the medical facility was built, I

207

had been able to convince the warden to make it a non-smoking building. Unfortunately, I was not successful in having cigarettes banned throughout the prison. The system was making too much money from selling cigarettes, and they didn't care about the long-term health consequences.

"Mr. Mandel, I don't know if your being exposed to cigarette smoking is the real reason you want me to give you a note, but I want you to know that they may move you out of the cell instead of your cellie."

"Well that ain't right, I was there first. Shit, just forget about it. I don't want to move my stuff."

A-ha. *If the smoke was really bothering him, he would move. He must just want a different cellie.*

"Mr. Mandel, we need to talk about the number of kites you put in every week. The nurses get hundreds of these kites every day from inmates, and they have to decide who needs to be seen first. If they get multiple kites from one inmate and start to believe that person is a whiner, that person in the future may not be scheduled to be seen when they need to be. Do you understand why I'm explaining this to you?"

He turned and glared at Suzy through the window. "That fat-ass lazy nurse over there has never liked me," he hissed. "She doesn't want to do her job. I'm not a whiner, I've got real problems."

"Let me ask you something, Mr. Mandel. When you were on the outside, how many times did you make an appointment to see a doctor?"

His head jerked up and his jaw dropped. "That... that's not the point."

"My guess, Mr. Mandel, is that you probably never went to see a doctor on the outside. And now I understand from my nursing staff that you put in five to six requests a week. I'm not saying you don't have medical issues, I'm just advising you that you should put in a request only when it is something serious. Many mild aches, pains, or colds go away on their own. Remember, if you put in multiple kites a week, the nurses will never know what should be taken seriously. Am I making myself clear?"

208

He jumped off the exam table. "Yeah, and I can see you don't want to do your job either," he said, and stomped out of the room.

I watched him go, rubbing the back of my neck. *That guy puts in more requests to see a doctor in one week than Mr. Olsen did in forty years.*

I saw Mr. Olsen the following month and diagnosed hypertension and non-insulin-dependent diabetes. Every four to six months thereafter, I would schedule an appointment with him again. At each visit, he would always do two things: he would ask my opinion on some current event he had read about, and he would tell me a joke.

Five years after our initial visit, he came in and I noticed that his blue eyes were brighter than usual.

"Mr. Olsen, you seem to be in a good mood today. What's up?" I asked as I looked at his current lab work.

"Did you ever hear about the old farmer and his cow?"

"No, I don't think so," I replied with a smile.

He rubbed his calloused hands together and grinned. "Well, there was this old farming couple who were curled up in bed together, cause it was freezin' outside. The old guy looked at his toothless wife and squeezed her breast and whispered, 'You know, if these still gave milk we could get rid of the cow.' His wife looked at his wrinkled old face and wanted to get back at him. So she squeezed him between his legs and whispered, 'You know, if this still got hard we could get rid of the field hand.'"

I chuckled and shook my head. "That one was a bit more risqué than usual. Mr. Olsen, why do you tell me a joke every time you see me?"

His blue eyes softened and he said, "I love to see you laugh, and it's the one thing I can do for you."

I studied his face and realized that he hadn't aged in five years; he was going to be seventy when I saw him next. "How's life going for you now?" I asked.

He sat up straighter, scratched behind his right ear and said, "I quit my job in the inmate store, because I got tired of dealing with all the petty little crap. Besides, the pardons board is coming up next month, and I'm on it." He sighed and then looked at me. "It's my third time back, and I don't need any more hassles in my life right now."

I thought back to that first conversation I had with him. "Are you going to give them what they want this time?"

He put his left hand to his mouth and bit his thumbnail. "You know, the board basically told me that they would consider pardoning me if I confessed. They said they wanted to hear me say I was sorry." He shook his head and his voice lost its strength. "Even though I didn't do it, I don't know if the principle of the thing is worth it anymore." His eyes caught mine. "Do you think I should give them what they want?"

I couldn't answer. Maybe I should have mimicked the standard response that psychologists use and asked him "What do you think?" but I couldn't do it.

A month later, Mr. Olsen sat before the pardons board and was not pardoned. Another five years passed before he sat in front of them again, and this time, he got his pardon. I heard it from the officer who had taken him to the hearing, before I saw Mr. Olsen for what would be our final visit.

When he entered my exam room for the last time, his blue eyes were sparkling and the grin on his face gave him the appearance of a young man.

I almost hugged him, but instead shook his hand. "I heard the news. When are they going to let you out?"

He bounced up and down on his toes. "Can you believe it? In two days I'll be walking out of here and those gates will close behind me for the last time."

"What are you going to do out there in the real world?"

He looked around my exam room, out the window at the clinic nurses, and then back to me. "The assistant warden helped me get a place to stay and a job. I'll be working for the Salvation Army. I will finally get to do something worthwhile in my life."

I tried to imagine what it would be like to re-enter a world that you had not seen or been a part of for fifty years. "Are you afraid? The world's really changed since you've been in here."

He shifted his weight and the lines in his face softened. "I know, that's why I always attached myself to one of the free staff. It was my connection to the outside. For the last decade, it's been you. I've seen it through your eyes."

I almost started to cry and couldn't swallow. I had to wait for the wave of emotion to pass before I could say, "Mr. Olsen, it was a pleasure to know you and I hope you do well on the outside. Good luck."

I shook his hand, and he cupped his other hand over our two hands and smiled. When he let go, he strode out with a gait of a man who had a purpose.

Fifty years in prison. How does one survive that so well? How did he manage to walk out with that confidence, into a world that would be so different from the one he knew? And if he was telling the truth, and truly was innocent... I didn't want to think that was a possibility, but I had read about cases where innocent men and women spent years in prison before they were exonerated.

I had seen Mr. Olsen a number of times in the last ten years and found that he never whined or asked for anything. So many men became institutionalized over the years: so accustomed to prison that they could not function in the outside world. Olsen was not one of them.

16. Terminal

I could hear one of the inmates screaming and kicking his door before I even entered the psych unit. The noise seeped through the large security door, which had to be buzzed open by a custody officer.

Fay, one of the psych nurses, waved me over to the nurses' station. I turned my head toward the cell where the screaming was coming from.

"Don't worry, that's not the guy you have to see," Fay said, and pushed over a thin chart with her wrinkled hand. "It's this guy. He just arrived this morning from Max, and the medical staff there think he's faking not being able to walk so he doesn't get executed in four months. I hear he's run out of all his appeals, and there's no way the governor is going to delay execution on this one. He's a real sicko. Do you know what he did? This guy is famous."

I opened the chart and looked at the last few notes. It appeared that three days ago, Mr. Malchen told the officers he couldn't move his legs. Since then, he didn't get out of his bed to eat or go to the bathroom. I didn't see much of an exam from the provider.

"Fay, has anyone seen him move his legs or urinate since he's been here?"

"No. The officer's got a camera on him and says he's real good at playing possum."

"Have any of the nurses assessed him yet?"

"No. You know how hard it is for us to get three officers up here to let us into a room with these high-security guys. So we decided to wait till you came up."

"Are the officers up here, so we can get the door open and take a look at him now?"

Her light blue eyes sparkled. "They're down the A wing right now. I'll tell them we're ready."

There wasn't much else in Malchen's chart, except that he had been complaining of low back pain for the past year. Not unusual for a guy in his fifties stuck on death row and lying on a hard metal bed covered by a thin mattress.

The three custody officers opened the door of his cell, and went in to put him in restraints. He didn't move and looked calm. I told Custody not to restrain his legs, because I needed to examine them.

"Mr. Malchen, I'm Dr. G. I'm going to ask you a few questions and examine you. Is that okay with you?"

His dark, dull eyes looked at the ceiling and he gave a small, resigned nod. The first thing I noticed was his abdomen, which seemed too large for his thin frame.

"I'm going to take off your pants and open your shirt. When was the last time you urinated?" No response. "When's the last time you peed?"

He shrugged and said in a soft voice, "A couple of days ago." I felt his abdomen, and his distended bladder was hard to miss. "Fay, I need you to get a Foley catheter and a 18-gauge needle for me."

He had no feeling in his legs, and was numb up to his belly button. The Foley drained a liter of yellow urine before I told Fay to clamp it. "Leave it clamped for fifteen minutes, and then let another liter out every fifteen minutes until there is no more urine in the bladder," I told her.

Clearly Malchen wasn't faking, but the officers were still unconvinced until I finally set a needle on the table with its point facing upward and dropped his leg onto it—and he didn't flinch.

"Fay, the X-ray tech is here today, and since we have the officers, let's bring him downstairs and get the X-rays I need. We can also do his blood work at the same time."

We put the inmate on a backboard, loaded him onto the gurney, and wheeled him down to X-ray. When my X-ray tech brought out the films and put them up on the viewing box, he was shaking his head and looking at me over his glasses.

"Wow." I said and rested my chin in my right hand. "You can't miss that." Malchen's t10 and t11 vertebrae were basically gone. He had a huge mass that obscured half his right lung.

I looked at my tech. "His chart says he's been a smoker for forty years, and has been complaining of back pain for over a year. It's got to be a lung cancer that metastasized to bone."

"What are you going to do?"

What *was* I going to do? He was terminal.

Will he demand we give him treatment? If he does, do we have to do a biopsy, chemo, radiation and so on? I took care of the cancer patients myself, along with Lucy as chemo nurse, but... I winced thinking of oncologists who would recommend a biopsy and try chemo on terminal patients, even though they would never follow that course of treatment if they were in the same position.

I looked at my tech. "Well. When I get back his labs and the official reports on the X-rays, I'll talk to him and see what he wants me to do."

That day at lunch, I decided to run it past my new colleague, Dr. Alie Tiernan, who had recently been hired to serve the increased patient load in the new facility.

Alie took a sip of her tea and put it down with care. "That guy deserves to suffer. Do you know what his crime was? He would kidnap young women, bring them up into the mountains, and rape and kill them."

I cringed. I couldn't comprehend his type of behavior and didn't want to imagine what those victims experienced. But I somehow lacked the capacity to want to see anyone suffer, even someone capable of something so terrible. I was more interested in understanding what caused a person to engage in that type of behavior.

As a child, I wasn't indoctrinated into the mindset that some people were "evil" or "possessed by the devil." *Behavior* could be evil, but what about

215

the *person*? A hundred years ago or more, we looked at mentally ill people differently than we do now. We no longer believe they may be possessed by the devil when they commit pathological acts. In the future when we know more about the brain and how it malfunctions, I wonder what we'll think about a person who did what he did.

I looked at my lunch, and it didn't seem so appetizing.

I transferred Mr. Malchen downstairs to live in the medical infirmary. The next day, when I had his labs and the official X-ray reports, I went in to see him with my accompanying security officers.

"Mr. Malchen, I need to talk to you about your medical condition." His gaze was fixed on the ceiling and he didn't say anything. "The tests show that you have a large cancer in your lung. The cancer has gone to your spine and destroyed it in a way that has made you unable to walk or urinate on your own. I'm sorry, but no matter what treatment we give you, you will not get better. Do you understand what I'm saying?"

A slight nod. His expression didn't change, and he didn't take his eyes off the ceiling. I looked up, and could see the stains on the ceiling from past water damage.

"You basically have two options," I went on. "We can treat you as a hospice patient and keep you comfortable, or you can go through procedures and treatment that would cause you pain and discomfort, but would not change your condition. Sometimes getting treatment could give you a little more time, or it could hasten your death. I'd like to know what you would like me to do for you."

A few seconds went by before he turned his head toward me and looked at me with black eyes that reminded me of the eyes I had seen on a dead shark. I could feel the small hairs on my neck go up.

He muttered, "Just keep me comfortable," and turned his head to stare at the ceiling again. I glanced at the officers, who had heard the exchange and would be my witnesses.

A week later, I received an unexpected phone call during my morning clinic. "Dr. Gedney, my name is Jim Tyler and I am an attorney representing Mr. Malchen. You may not know this, but all the inmates on death row are appointed a lawyer, and this is a high-profile case. He is scheduled for execution in four months, but we are still working on an extension. I hear he has cancer and is now housed in your facility. I hear he hasn't even received any treatment in your facility. You may not know this, but medical treatment can't be withheld from an inmate, even if they are on death row facing execution."

The muscles in my jaw tightened. "Mr. Tyler, I'm aware that inmates have a constitutional right to healthcare. As his physician, I discussed his terminal cancer with him and presented him with his options. He has chosen hospice care instead of going through painful procedures and treatment that would not benefit him. I also have three witnesses that will corroborate that."

"Dr. Gedney, I'm not trying to give you a hard time. I just wanted to know that Administration hasn't pressured you into withholding medically necessary treatment. I hear that's happened in the past, and I needed to make sure it didn't happen with my client. In that case, how long do you think he has? Will he make it to the execution date?"

"I don't know, though cancer patients that give up, like Mr. Malchen appears to be doing, often die sooner than you would think."

Mr. Malchen died a month later, without complaining, and without wanting to talk to the medical staff, Psych, or the chaplain. One of my nurses who saw him last said he was waving away bad spirits and staring at the ceiling.

I still had lingering questions about executions. I pulled aside one of the custody officers, Jose, who was training to be part of the team for executions.

"Jose, do you get assigned to that job or do you volunteer for it?" I asked. Jose was one of the calmest and most professional officers that I had met, and I had a hard time believing he would want to be part of executing anyone.

His brown eyes softened. "I take pride in being an officer and making sure things are done right." His shoulders straightened and he tapped the stripes on his shoulder. "I'm an immigrant, Dr. G. I'm proud to be an American and to be given the responsibility of being an officer. To do this job is an honor because the responsibility of doing an execution is very great. It has to be done right. There can be no mistakes. You understand?"

A scene from a movie where a sadistic officer botched an electrocution on purpose popped into my mind. I nodded. "So I take it that you agreed to be part of the execution. How do they actually do it? Does someone volunteer to push the lethal injection?"

He shrugged. "Well, they do ask for volunteers to push the injection, but no one knows if they are giving the lethal one. There are three lines that are running into the IV, so no one knows if they are the one who caused the heart to stop."

"So tell me, Jose, what type of training did you get?"

He leaned back against the wall. "There were three of us, and I played the role of the inmate. We have to make sure that we practice. They cuffed me, but when you go into the death chamber you have to make sure you lay them down right and that all the restraints work. You have to be ready if they resist you. You have to be ready for anything. There can be a lot of people watching, like the victim's family, reporters, politicians, even the inmate's family."

Jose tilted his head to the side. "Some people are mad at you, Dr. G., because you didn't keep Mr. Malchen alive long enough so he could be executed."

I brushed my hair back. "He's dead. Isn't that enough?"

He shook his head. "There are a lot of families of victims that want revenge. They were waiting to see him executed. Haven't you ever wanted revenge?"

I took a deep breath in and let it out. "Revenge has never made sense to me. It doesn't change the past, and if you're consumed by emotion, I can't see how that is going to improve your future."

Jose laughed. "You think too much with your head and not your heart, Dr. G.," he said, and walked away.

I considered his comment, but no matter how I thought about it, the only thing that made sense to me was trying to gain an understanding of why someone commits a crime, and what could be done to prevent or stop the behavior. I had read studies showing that executions do not affect crime, and I knew the United States was one of the few industrialized countries that still did it. *So yes, I suppose I feel more comfortable not being ruled by my emotions, especially ones like revenge.*

As time went on, I continued to choose not to have any part in executions, but I also remained curious about how people reacted to it. One day, I had a chance to talk to the chaplain; he was intimately involved in the whole process and might be able to enlighten me.

"Chaplain," I said, "you've been here a long time. When did you first start working in the prison?"

The chaplain had white hair, kind blue eyes and a manner of speaking that made people feel safe. "Oh, I've been here since 1977. Did you know I was the first chaplain the prison system ever hired in this state?"

"Really? How did you decide to become a prison chaplain?"

"Well, I wasn't making any money at all in the little church I was placed in. I needed reliable work. So when I saw an advertisement in the paper for a prison chaplain, I applied." He smiled and put his hand in the pocket of his pants.

"What denomination are you? And what do you do with the inmates who practice a different religion?"

"I'm a Presbyterian. Back when I started, I knew the Native Americans wanted to practice their spiritual beliefs instead of mine. So I convinced one of their elders to come in and start a program for them. That's why there's a sweat lodge out there by the gym now."

"How about the other religions, like Judaism and Islam?"

He looked up and then back at me. "Well, I brought in a rabbi who had been a survivor of Auschwitz, and I also found a very nice professor from the University who taught about Islam."

I chuckled. "That's probably why the Muslim guys I've met so far are so mellow."

He cocked his head. "Mm. The only beliefs I didn't invite representatives in for were the Satanists and devil-worshippers."

"Chaplain, I know you have to get back to the other prison, but before you go I wanted to ask you about how you feel about being involved with executions."

The chaplain leaned against the wall in the empty corridor, and sighed. "I always found it the hardest part of my job. But I'll tell you about one of the guys I had a lot of respect for. Did you ever hear of Jesse Beson?"

I shook my head.

"Well, he was one of the original Weathermen. He was their hit man. He had no remorse for what he had done serving that organization. But at one point he was involved in a situation where two innocent people were killed. They had just married. Beson was charged with murder. He felt bad about that incident, and had no problem being executed for it. I remember him telling me, 'This ain't nothin' brother,' as they led him to the gas chamber. When he sat down in the chair, he told the officers 'This is a good day to die.'"

The chaplain looked at me thoughtfully and added: "Jesse Beson died like a man."

My mouth was a little dry just thinking about this, but I had to ask: "They use lethal injection now, was there a reason they changed to that method?"

He nodded. "The gas chamber leaked. The system felt it could be dangerous to spectators."

I drew back a little. "Who wants to watch someone suffocate and foam from the mouth?"

"Well, the families of the victim and the inmate are normally there, and sometimes politicians and prison staff show up. I'm supposed to be there to offer support for all of them. In fact, the officer who went in after the inmate died had to be in a special suit with a respirator. He had to pierce the guy's chest to let the gas come out. More than one officer had a real hard time with that and never came back."

My hand went up to my throat, which felt a bit tight. "I heard the last execution was a twenty-six-year-old who waived all his appeals. Did you know what was going on with his case?"

"Yeah, that one was a hard one for the family. Before he was executed, he talked to the press and lambasted his family about all the sexual abuse they did to him."

"Wow, he must have been very angry to get back at them that way," I said.

"You know what really disturbed me about it, Doc? One of the pastors I knew asked me why we were even executing him, when he only killed two homosexuals."

My brows raised, and I decided I had heard enough about executions for one day.

17. Panda

Karen Gedney, MD

Jagged, snow-capped mountains stood out in the early morning light, lifting my trepidation as I walked to the prison gatehouse. I hugged the large stuffed panda bear to my chest, and wondered what the officer would think when he buzzed open the door. Everyone entering the gatehouse had to show identification, have their bags checked, sign in, and walk through a metal detector. Bringing in a stuffed panda was not exactly routine, even for me. I could just imagine the look on the officer's face when I showed him the memo signed by the warden, allowing me to bring it in as an occupational therapy aid.

The panda was a promotional gift I had received from Macy's, and his fate had been decided a few days earlier when I noticed how much Mr. Walters, one of my senile patients, enjoyed touching and stroking soft material.

Walters had been sent to the Regional Medical Facility from another prison at the age of fifty-three, with a diagnosis of advanced dementia. His work-up did not show why he had lost his cognitive skills and ability to speak, and the only behavior I noticed was that he grunted in excitement when his food arrived. Other inmates would have taken advantage of him, if it wasn't for his protector: Mr. Archio.

Archio was a lifer and had been a heavyweight on the prison yard, but multiple medical problems relegated him to being a permanent fixture in the infirmary. He had bad lungs, severe allergies, and a right leg amputated below the knee. His explosive temper reminded me of a wolverine, and I found it oddly charming that he demonstrated tremendous patience with Walters and had chosen to protect him. In fact, it was Archio who had bought a pair of soft sweatpants for Walters, which caused me to notice how much he loved touching soft things.

I ran my hand over the panda's soft fur while the officer read the paperwork, eyeing the panda with suspicion. He shook his head and muttered, "Now I've seen it all."

When he eventually buzzed me through, I smiled to myself and wondered if one of the guards in the towers would be calling the gatehouse and asking why the doctor was bringing in a large stuffed animal. As a child, I had great attachment to my stuffed animals; I still remembered how comforting they were when I was lonely or sick. Why couldn't it be the same for Mr. Walters, who seemed to derive comfort from soft things? *He's going to love you and you're going to help him*, I thought as I walked into the medical facility.

It was early, and I decided to head toward the back of the building where the infirmary patients were housed. The infirmary held sixty medical patients, and was divided into two different sections. One section was for the general population, and the other was for high-security patients, or inmates that had to be in isolation for any reason.

Entering the front section, I first visited Archio in the treatment room where he was getting a breathing treatment.

"How are you doing, Mr. Archio? And where's the nurse?"

Archio took the nebulizer tube out of his mouth. "The officer took Nurse June to see some guy on the isolation side, and the other officer is in the bathroom. Guess he knows I'm not going anywhere fast." He raised his stump in the air. Then he pointed at the panda. "Who's your friend, Dr. G.?"

I placed the panda in his lap and said, "Do you think Mr. Walters will like it?"

His obsidian eyes lit up and his pinched features softened as he broke into a smile. He lightly caressed the panda's back and murmured, "God, he's so soft."

Then Archio re-adjusted the oxygen cannula under his black mustache, and handed me the nebulizer. "I don't need it anymore, Dr. G. Can I go and give the panda to him now?"

"Let me take a listen to your lungs first, and I think we have to wait till the officer gets out of the bathroom before I whisk you away."

Mr. Archio snickered "That's Gerund in the bathroom. Can you imagine the look on his face if I wasn't sitting here when he got out?"

"I can imagine, and I don't want to get on his bad side."

Officer Gerund was a stickler for rules. I found it odd that he had left an inmate unattended in the treatment room, even though Archio didn't have the respiratory capacity or the musculature to hop on one leg anywhere. *He must have really had to go to the bathroom... or else he's only strict about rules when they apply to other people.*

I looked down the hallway. "What did they do with your wheelchair?"

"He put it down the other hallway."

I retrieved Archio's black wheelchair, and helped him get into it from the exam table. When I handed him the panda, he placed it between his atrophied thighs and looked up at me. "How did you get approval to bring it in, Dr. G.?"

"I was lucky. Chalk it up to having a more open-minded warden, who understands that therapy isn't just giving out pills. Plus, it being almost Christmas didn't hurt either. As a true therapy device, it cannot leave the infirmary. So he's here to stay."

Archio picked it up and looked at it between the legs. "How do you know it's a he?"

I rolled my eyes. "Mr. Archio, you know I couldn't have brought a female panda in here."

We were both laughing when Officer Gerund walked into the treatment room. He ran his right hand over his black crew cut, and glared at the panda. "What's that doing here?" he said through clenched teeth.

I handed him a copy of the warden's memo. "The warden has approved the panda as an occupational aid that will stay in the infirmary."

He stared at the memo and sighed loudly. "I'll need a copy of this for my report."

I smiled. "That's yours, officer. I have the original."

225

Archio was enjoying the exchange, but his strong hands were on the worn tires of the wheelchair: I could tell he wanted to leave the room and show the panda to Walters.

I turned my back to the officer and pushed the wheelchair out of the exam room and down the hall to Walters' room, which was directly opposite the nursing station. Pulling the heavy set of security keys out of my pants pocket, I peeked through the security window and made out Mr. Walters curled on his side facing the wall, under his frayed grey blanket. The reflection from the multi-colored Christmas lights from the fake tree at the nurses' station played over the Plexiglas, creating a surreal effect.

"You ready, Mr. Archio?" I asked, and gave him a tiny wink.

"We're both ready," he said, and pulled the panda closer to him.

As I opened the door, Archio rolled past me into the room. "Hey buddy, rise and shine. Wake up and see what Dr. G. and I brought you."

Walters stretched, kicked the wool blanket off, and sat up on the side of his bed. His brown eyes darted back and forth and he started to wring his hands. He rocked back and forth, eyes bouncing between Archio and the panda.

Archio rolled his chair closer. "Come on and touch him. You're going to love him, he's so soft."

Walters continued to rock back and forth, but he started to make his sound of pleasure: "Heh, heh. Heh, heh."

Archio placed the panda on Walters' lap, and he stopped wringing his hands and gingerly touched the panda's belly. Then he picked it up and rubbed the panda's back across the grey stubble on his cheek. "Heh, heh. Heh, heh, heh," he said with his eyes closed. His rocking stopped.

Archio grinned, gave me a quick nod, and murmured, "Thanks, Dr. G." He lowered his eyes so I couldn't see his tears.

I left them both in the room, and went back to the nurses' station.

226

Nurse June looked up from her charting. "How'd it go?"

"Better than I hoped for. He even stopped rocking back and forth."

June tilted her head and pushed her glasses back. "I wonder what the other inmates back here are going to think about it."

"The panda is an occupational therapy device. It will be assigned to Mr. Walters alone. The other inmates aren't going to mess with it, especially with Mr. Archio around as Mr. Walters' protector."

June took a sip of her coffee, then reached over and handed me Walters' chart. "You better write it as an order, so the officers don't take it away."

I wrote the order and handed it back to her. "You know, Officer Gerund has already put it in the officers' log. I'm not as worried about them as I am about Kate."

June smirked and rubbed her nose. "Yeah, I'd love to see her face when she sees the panda. She'll probably write you up for bringing in contraband. I don't know what her story is, but she thinks the inmates shouldn't get anything. She's also been bitchin' at me about my little Christmas tree. We've always decorated the infirmary at Christmas, and it's the one time of the year I get to change the look of this grey cinderblock. Plus, all of the rest of us like it."

"I know, I like it too. We don't often have an excuse like Christmas to encourage goodwill toward men. Have you heard that the warden is allowing a small group of inmates to come over and sing Christmas carols for the guys back here?"

June shook her head and smiled. "That'll send Kate over the edge. She's always saying how the warden is too soft. Maybe she would be better off on a Max yard."

"I've seen a few wardens before this one. I like him. I don't think he's soft, I just think he understands human behavior better than the wardens before him. All the studies show that human behavior is more affected by reward than punishment. You can only take so much away from a person before they have nothing else to lose. I don't find those types of individuals safer to deal with, I just find them more dangerous." I looked at the clock on the wall. "Well June, I'll get off my soapbox. I have to get back to the clinic to see my morning patients."

Over the next few months, I saw improvement in Walters' anxious behavior. No one took it away from him, and I felt the panda experiment was a success.

I hardly thought about Walters after a while, until four months later when June pulled up a chair in the lunchroom and sat down next to me.

"How's the rabbit food?" June asked as I picked through the chopped red peppers, broccoli, and snow peas nestled on top of my Romaine salad.

I speared a snow pea with my plastic fork. "Never better. What's up?"

She squeezed my arm. "You'll never guess what happened."

I finished munching and took a sip of water. "They let all the inmates go home for the weekend?"

She punched me in the arm. "Mr. Walters said hello to me today."

I put down my fork and looked at her to see if she was joking. "Our Mr. Walters, who hasn't said a word since he got here seven years ago?"

She was bouncing in her seat. "Mr. Archio told us that he had said hello to him yesterday, and we thought he was pulling our leg. But now he's said hello to all of us, even Kate. It's just like that movie *Awakenings*. Do you think he'll really start talking now? And why didn't he say anything to us for all those years?"

"Good question. Has he said anything to you except hello?"

June's blue eyes sparkled. "Not yet, but wouldn't it be wild if he did?"

"It would be something all right, but you know Mr. Walters has more problems than just not talking. He's impaired on all sorts of levels."

"Oh, don't be such a spoil sport." June pushed back her chair and eased herself up. She looked down at me and gave me a crooked grin. "You just wait till he says hello to you."

I didn't make my way to the infirmary until the end of the day. When I sat down at the nurses' station to look at the list of patients, June tapped me on my shoulder.

"I wish you were here earlier to see what Mr. Walters gave Mr. Archio," she said.

I turned around and saw with surprise that June had tears in her eyes. *What could Walters possibly give?* I thought. He didn't seem to have the capacity to give something to anyone. He would accept cookies from Archio like an old dog getting his favorite biscuit, but you never would expect the old dog to give a present to his guardian.

"What did he give Mr. Archio?" I asked, and leaned back in my chair.

The tears in her eyes almost started to brim over. "Mr. Walters went to his room, brought out that panda bear, and gave it to Mr. Archio. Mr. Archio tried to give it back, but Mr. Walters wouldn't have it." Her voice cracked. "You should have seen the look on Mr. Archio's face."

I could see the scene, and felt the tears start to prick behind my eyes as well.

Over the next two years, Walters' speech and his ability to do basic activities slowly improved, to the point where he was able to live on the prison yard and hold down a simple job. Archio, still in the infirmary, missed his friend—but one afternoon I found out how he still kept track of him.

"Mr. Archio, I hear that you go over every week to Visiting now to see your wife. When did she move out here?"

Archio adjusted his oxygen and took a puff on his inhaler. "She came out here about two months ago. And guess who pushes me over to Visiting every week?" He smiled, wrinkles fanning out from the corners of his eyes.

"I'm guessing it's not the officer or the forensic."

Archio chuckled and slapped his thin thigh. "You should see my buddy now. He won't let anyone push my wheelchair but him."

"How is Mr. Walters coping on the yard? The last time I saw him, he was talking in basic sentences and could get his point across, but I am really surprised that he is able to function out there without getting in trouble."

Mr. Archio rubbed his dark mustache. "I've got friends out there keeping an eye on him. Nobody is going to bother him. Plus, he doesn't have anything they want."

"I have to ask you, Mr. Archio. There have been a lot of inmates who have come through this infirmary with all sorts of problems, but for some reason you decided to take care of and protect Mr. Walters. I'm curious: why him?"

He tilted his head up and looked at me searchingly. "You know, Dr. G., I never thought about it like that." He shrugged. "I guess because he was... a clean slate."

"What do you mean, a clean slate?"

"He was sort of like a baby. Helpless, not tainted in any way. No past. I didn't know anything about him, and I didn't want to know what he did to be sent to prison either." He looked down and sighed. "I had a son once. The last time I saw him, he was four. Who knows, maybe... hell, I don't know. He was helpless."

"Can he actually carry on a real conversation with you now?"

He rubbed his stump. "Sure, we talk, but nothing fancy. He doesn't understand complicated issues." He laughed. "Or even not-so-complicated ones. Do you think it was the medicine the shrink gave him that got him talking again?"

I thought back to the sequence of events. "I'm sure it played a part. We were just lucky it worked. I remember that medication had only been on the market for about a year, and the psychiatrist just wanted to try it. You know,

230

when he was shipped up to us, his records indicated he had dementia. We just were supposed to do nursing care. Looking back on it, he probably had a mental illness in addition to his low baseline of function. Who knows, but I'm glad you protected him all those years."

Mr. Archio leaned back and said, "Well, I liked the guy, Doc."

18. The Drain of Pain

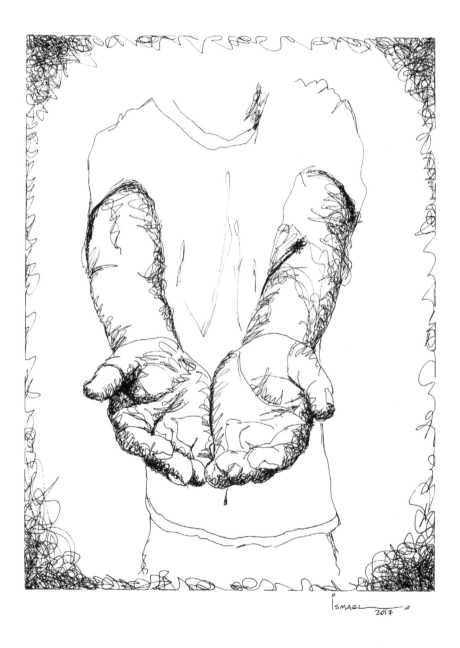

Hail bombarded the roof, causing me to cringe. I looked up at the skylight in the center of the clinic. White hailstones were exploding against it.

"What a racket," Suzy said, putting her hands over her ears. She arched a thinly plucked eyebrow and pointed at the furthest exam room. "You've gotta see that drug seeker, because I've had it with him today."

I walked to the room, took the chart from its plastic holder on the door, and entered the room with a resigned sigh. A flushed face, dripping with sweat, glared at me. He was clutching his left side and panting.

"Doc, I can't take this pain any longer. It's killing me. You have to give me something to stop it. You hear me?" His voice was getting louder and shriller over the sound of hail still clattering on the roof. "I said do you hear me?"

Mr. Dolen had a prior history of kidney stones. Those could cause excruciating pain for someone who was trying to pass them. But in the last year, he had undergone multiple diagnostic studies that did not find a kidney stone or any other cause for his complaints. The urologists and nurses felt he was just an addict manipulating the system. I was inclined to believe them, but I wasn't sure why he had blood in his urine when we collected samples from him.

"Mr. Dolen, when did your pain start?" I asked, and opened his chart.

"I've been suffering since I woke up this morning. Those nurses of yours are worthless. They told me to make an appointment, but I'm in pain now. I can't wait." He slammed his fist against the exam table and his red face darkened. "Doc, you're the only one here who cares about us. I know you'll help me with this pain." He started to tremble, and wiped the sweat off his face with the back of his hand.

"Where is your pain now?"

"It's on the left side of my back and it's going down into my testicle. It hurts so bad I want to rip it off."

233

His physical exam was only remarkable for his complaints of pain when I tapped over the area of his kidney. Not exactly informative, in a patient who has had kidney stones before and knows that he should complain when a doctor taps on that area.

After the exam, I handed him the obligatory specimen cup to check his urine. He grabbed the container, jumped off the table with more speed than he had displayed laboring to get up on it, and left the room. I watched as he told Suzy what I wanted; she looked back at me and rolled her eyes.

Shortly after, Suzy opened my door and handed me the specimen.

"I don't know how he does it. I even made him put on gloves this time, so he couldn't introduce blood into it from a cut on his finger. I watched his every move, and I collected it midstream." She put the specimen cup down on the counter. "Look at all the blood in this one. How do you think he pulled that one off?"

"You know, Suzy, it's possible he could have a real problem this time."

"In a pig's eye, Dr. G. You're being had by this one. What do you want me to tell him? I can tell him to get lost." Her brown eyes lit up.

"He'll just be back again tonight if you do, and I'm on call. Send him in."

Dolen opened the door and pointed at the specimen cup. "I told you I was passing another one. Look at all the blood. It's ripping me apart." He sat down, hunched over, and grabbed his knees. When I didn't make a comment and he realized he couldn't see the expression on my face from his vantage point, he stood up again.

"You can't let me suffer like this. I know the tests keep coming up negative, but something's wrong. I can't be in this much pain without something being terribly wrong. Just give me a shot to take the edge off this unbearable pain."

"Why don't you sit, Mr. Dolen? We need to talk."

His mouth tightened and his dark eyes narrowed. "What do you mean we need to talk? Give me a shot, and then we can talk. And don't give me crap like Toradol; you know how sick it makes me. Morphine is the only thing that helps." Toradol could help with the pain from a kidney stone, but not if a patient was looking to get high.

"Mr. Dolen, I know you feel you're in pain, but I'm concerned you've become dependent on narcotics."

Before I could continue, he jumped up again (with no discomfort, I noted) and yelled, "Don't tell me you're listening to your fat nurses. You're the doctor, don't let them tell you what to do."

"The nurses have nothing to do with what I'm trying to talk to you about."

His nose crinkled and he growled, "Do you want to torture me? Are you going to become like all the rest of them? Just picking up a paycheck and not doing anything. You know as well as I do that the staff here couldn't get a job in the real world. We only get the losers. Don't tell me you're going to let me suffer like they would."

I saw nothing but anger in his face. I moved closer to the door. "I do want to help you, but I need you to sit down so we can talk."

Hatred filled his eyes. "This is horse shit," he hissed. "You've been brainwashed. You think we're all addicts. Well I'm telling you, I'm in pain. If I can't talk sense into you, we'll see if the courts can. Doctors get sued for not helping their patients. Do you want that to happen to you?" He stomped out of the room, sneering at Suzy as he left.

She walked over to me and dimples appeared in her round cheeks as she gave me a big, winsome smile.

"Well, Dr. G., I can see that went well."

I leaned on the counter. "Suzy, this is only the beginning."

"Cheer up. He was your last patient today. And who cares? They're all scamming for drugs." She patted me on my shoulder. "The sooner you realize

235

it, the better off you'll be."

I looked at her skeptically. "Sometimes even the scammers get sick. Remember Mr. Mendelson last week?"

I knew she had conveniently forgotten the case. He was a notorious drug addict who complained of chest pain over the weekend. When Suzy called the doctor on call, he told her the inmate had nothing coming. On Monday, Mr. Mendelson stopped me as I was walking into the prison and begged me to see him before the morning clinic started. He didn't look good to me, so I brought him over and diagnosed a pneumonia with a 103° temperature.

She shrugged. "Yeah, well, that was a rare case and he deserved to wait. That guy has made me jump through hoops for years."

After Sylvia Ignin had left as Director of Nursing, a few different people had tried to survive in that position, but none of them stuck until we finally got Lisa. Lisa was a gruff person, but she was a professional, and I had to admit her position was a stressful, challenging one. A week after Mr. Dolen left my exam room in a huff, Lisa walked into my office and dropped his thick chart in front of me.

"This idiot called four man-downs this weekend. We've all had it with him. Custody is asking you to do something. We don't have the officers or nurses to keep responding to him crying wolf all the time."

Man-down was the term for a medical emergency on the prison yard. When man-down was called, a nurse and an officer had to respond immediately. Calling four man-downs when there was no life-threatening emergency would be like a person in the outside world calling an ambulance four times in a weekend for no good reason.

"Did he have an emergency?" I asked, and opened the chart.

"You know it's always the same thing. He just wants a narcotic. You need to handle him. I told the nurses to put him on your schedule at seven-thirty this morning, before the clinic opens."

236

It was currently 7:25. I watched her leave and my guts twisted. *Five minutes to showdown.* I walked to the clinic.

Shortly after, Dolen slammed down his ID card on the officer's desk. As the officer patted him down he muttered, "Somebody better help me with this pain or I'm going to file a grievance."

He didn't acknowledge my presence, but stomped directly into the exam room. I reached for the handle of the door and took a deep breath. Before the door had closed behind me, he was snarling, "It's about time I got to see someone. That goddamn doctor on call didn't give me anything all weekend long. You better give me something right now, or I'm gonna go off."

My mouth was a bit dry. "I know how frustrated you are over not being evaluated quickly," I said. "Mr. Dolen, because of the frequency and severity of your complaints, I think it's best that I admit you into the infirmary."

His brown eyes widened. "Now wait a goddamn minute. I've got a good job on the yard. I'm making money. I can't lose it."

"I understand, and I'll talk to your supervisor, but in the meantime you will be placed in the infirmary."

Dolen jumped up, and I edged toward the door. His finger shook as he pointed it at me. "You can't admit me, because I refuse. You think I'm stupid, but I see what you're doing. You're gonna lock me up in there so nobody will have to deal with me. You're punishing me because you're too stupid to figure out what's wrong with me."

He put his hands over his face. "If you want me to continue suffering, I'll leave and find some relief on the yard."

I opened the door and stepped into the doorway. "Mr. Dolen, you can't refuse to come into the infirmary. I'm going to advise the officer I am admitting you." I closed the door before he could reply.

I wrote the orders, and decided to see Dolen in the afternoon when I would have the results of his labs and X-rays. When I walked into the infirma-

237

ry later that day, Officer Gerund motioned me over. "Hey, I've got to talk to you about that nutcase Dolen. He's been screaming and kicking his door for the past few hours. You know, when I was passing a kidney stone I didn't want to move, and that guy hasn't stopped." He picked up his cooler. "Make sure you don't go into his room without an officer. When I'm done with lunch, I'll go with you."

I nodded and walked to the nursing station to look at the list of patients to be seen. *Let's see, why don't I start with someone who isn't angry with me?*

I walked down the hall and opened Mr. Brock's door. A tall, thin young man stood and smiled, displaying one missing front tooth. He was recuperating from back surgery, and could finally stand straight after walking for months hunched over from severe spinal stenosis.

"You look great, Mr. Brock. It's nice to see how tall you really are. Let me examine the incision to see if it's healing well."

As I examined him, I could hear distant screams and banging sounds. Brock turned around and snickered. "Don't worry Doc, that's just Dolen. They dragged that idiot in here kicking and screaming. He's a real asshole. I bet the guys he owes money to on the yard are pissed."

Brock had grown up in prison. He knew almost everyone on the yard, and what they were up to.

"What does he owe money for?" I asked.

"Drugs, of course. The guy is a real sicko. You should have seen what he was doing in the unit. He got one of those catheters and a big syringe from a guy in a wheelchair, and used it to inject his urine back into his bladder after he put blood into it."

I was speechless.

Brock shuddered and wrinkled his nose. "I know a lot of guys try to scam drugs out of you, but Dolen goes the distance." He laughed and leaned against the wall. "I wonder how he's going to do it in here with none of his property." He watched my face, eyes twinkling.

"Well, time will tell. Won't it, Mr. Brock?"

He gave me a radiant smile. "Go get 'im, Doc".

A few days later, I went through Dolen's chart and smiled ruefully. The urine samples collected without giving him any advance notice were clear of blood, in contrast to the bloody urine the nurses collected when they told him they would be back in an hour. *But he has nothing in his cell, so how does he do it?*

I almost jumped out of my seat when June slapped me on the shoulder. "Guess what I found?" she asked.

I looked up at her brown eyes and could tell she was quite pleased with herself. "I hope it's the answer to how Mr. Dolen gets blood into his urine."

She nodded.

"Really?"

"It's your lucky day, Doc. Look what I found in his Bible." She held up a straightened paper clip, filed to an exquisitely sharp point.

I took it and held it up to the light, then gave her a sidelong glance. "What did he say he used it for?"

"He told me he used it to pick his teeth. Can you imagine the balls on that guy? He even said it with a straight face," she said, and started to laugh.

"Have you written a report on it yet?"

"I wanted to show it to you first, before I hand it over to Custody. Are you going to see him now and confront him? I'll get the officer," she said, and started bouncing up and down on her toes.

"I don't think I'm as excited about this as you are, June."

"Oh come on, Doc. This'll be fun." She raced down the hall to get rein-

239

forcements, leaving me with the paper clip.

I gingerly touched the sharp tip with my index finger—and quickly drew it back to make sure I hadn't drawn blood. *Boy that was stupid. The last thing I need is to put a hole in my finger, considering he was probably scratching the inside of his urethra with it.*

I shuddered, and thought about the lengths people would go to get their drug of choice. I remembered one of my first cases in the prison, where an addict was pressuring weaker inmates to get their teeth pulled so he could get their medication. *At least Dolen is only hurting himself, but he has wasted a lot of other people's time and resources.*

Within a few minutes, June returned with the officer and we walked down to Dolen's cell. The officer opened the outer door, then yelled at Dolen to sit on his bed as he pulled out the large key and pulled open the second door.

Dolen glared at me and bellowed, "Come to torture me more, Doc? Aren't you happy enough that you've ruined my life?"

I breathed in and let it out slowly. "I've evaluated your urine tests while you've been here," I replied, "and it's clear you're manipulating the tests." I held up the sharpened paper clip. "It appears this is the device you used."

His eyes darted to June and he sneered. "I told her, it's my toothpick. You people will use anything to frame me." His eyes narrowed. "I'm going to make your life miserable, Doc. I'll get you one way or another."

I'd had enough, and turned to leave. The officer closed the door behind us, and Mr. Dolen started kicking the door again. "If you're not going to do anything, let me the hell out of here!" he screamed.

I felt a bit nauseous as I wrote the discharge order. I did not enjoy hostile confrontations like some of my staff, who seemed to enjoy the adrenaline rush.

A week later, June stopped me and asked, "Hey Doc, how did you get Mr. Dolen shipped off the yard? "

I shook my head. "It wasn't me. It seems he complained to the warden. He was stupid enough to put in writing all his graphic threats toward me. Custody was already fed up with him. So he was sent to that new Supermax prison up north."

June slapped her right thigh, and her head of brown curls shook with her laughter. I just sighed. *Some people just want to wear you down until you break. Good luck in your new home, Mr. Dolen.*

19. Mighty Mouse

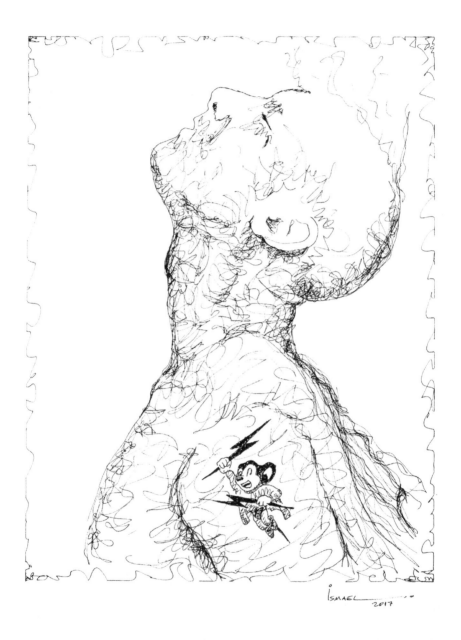

"Hi, Dr. G. I'm sorry I'm back." A thirtyish, well-muscled white male stood up as I entered the exam room.

"How many times has it been, Mr. Harris?"

He hung his head. "This is my fourth time back."

"What for?"

"Stupidity," he said, and sat down. "I know you've heard this a million times, but this is the last time I'm coming back to this place. I thought if I was working and keeping out of trouble, I didn't have to jump through all their hoops to stay on parole. My parole officer didn't see it that way."

"What hoops do you have to jump through?"

He counted them off on his fingers. "Well, first, no drugs or booze. Second, you have to have a job. Third, you have to have a place to live. Fourth, you have to see your parole officer every month and pay him. Fifth, you can't hook up with any ex-felons."

"So, which hoop didn't you jump through?"

"The last one. I needed a job and one of the guys I knew gave me some work selling cleaning agents. He was a guy I knew from the joint."

"Is that the only reason they said you violated parole?"

"Well, he was selling some weed on the side, but I'm telling you I didn't know that."

"A-ha. If I remember correctly, you told me last time that you weren't coming back to this place. Why will this time be any different?"

"I'm a father now, to a beautiful little girl. It's got me thinking differently. I feel like I have a purpose now, and becoming an old man in prison isn't what I had in mind for myself."

"What do you have in mind for yourself now?"

"I have to take control of my own life. In the past, I always blamed others for my troubles, but now I realize that I'm the one responsible for all my

243

problems."

I looked up and studied him. "It does sound like you're thinking differently since the last time I saw you. It's the first step, but what counts are your actions."

"Watch me, Dr. G. I'm not going to be a peckerwood anymore." A peckerwood, in prison slang, was someone white, strong, thickheaded, and usually involved with drugs and gambling.

Two years passed before I heard Mr. Harris's name again.

June handed me the clinic list and brushed a stray brown curl behind her ear. "Did you have a nice weekend? It looks like you got toasted."

I touched my red nose. "Skiing gives me the Rudolph look, no matter how much sunblock I put on. How about you?"

She giggled. "You wouldn't believe it. I went to my first prison Toast-masters meeting."

"What was that all about?"

"It's a club where the inmates learn public speaking. One of them asked me to go, and I didn't have anything better to do." She shook her head and her unruly curls fell onto her cheeks. "Now you know how bad my social life really is."

"I never heard of that club before. Who started it?"

"It's a national club, but this is a local chapter. They call it the Gavel Club. It was started by one of the inmates, Mr. Harris. He says you know him. You should hear him talk, he could be a motivational speaker."

I smiled. *Nice to hear he is already doing something positive.* "What did Mr. Harris talk about?"

"Responsibility and changing your life. It was so powerful, I even started looking at my life and where it's going... or not going, in my case. I can't remember how the whole speech went, but by the looks on the faces of the other inmates, I could tell he got'em thinking. You should go sometime and listen to the inmates give their speeches. I bet you would really enjoy it."

Not long after, I had the opportunity to talk to Mr. Harris when he came in for his annual physical. "I hear you've started a speaking club on the yard." I said. "How has it been going?"

He rubbed his hands together and his eyes brightened. "I love it, and I know some of the guys are really getting a lot out of it as well. I even had a new guy start this week who has a terrible stutter. With the club's help, I'll bet we can get him squared away."

"So tell me, how did you get a club like that started here, and why?"

"Well, I first heard about Toastmasters and the art of speaking from one of the teachers in the college program. They explained all the benefits you get from learning how to communicate well in a public setting. Like assurance, self-esteem, getting your point across and persuading people."

He clapped his hands. "And then it hit me, Dr. G. I saw how it could help me and the other guys get our lives on track. I'm not just talking about speaking well when we're in front of the parole board, but like when we go on a job interview, or meet new people, or anything we have to do on the outside. The more I thought about it, the more excited I got. So I decided to see if I could get a club like that started here."

"That must have been quite an undertaking. How did you pull it off?"

"I had to get a staff sponsor and approval from the warden. Let me tell you, it was not easy. But once I set my mind on it, it all fell into place."

"Who did you get as a staff sponsor?" I asked.

"The college teacher, Ms. Silva. She's the one who told us about Toastmasters and how much it helped her." He put his hands on his knees and leaned forward. "Would you believe she even helped me get a mentor on the outside? He's a philanthropist who helped me get the club started."

"That's wonderful, Mr. Harris. What do your old friends think about

245

the new direction your life has taken?"

He sighed and ran his hand through his thick brown hair. "They're giving me shit. They think I'm just manipulating the system. It's one thing when the officers and free staff are suspicious of you, but it's hard when it comes from your own friends. You'd think I'd get some encouragement somewhere. But if anyone's ever going to pat me on the back, it will have to come from me."

I smiled and stood up. "Mr. Harris, I think you've just defined self-motivation, but allow me." I gave him a little pat on the shoulder.

He chuckled, and pulled a folded note from the pocket of his faded blue shirt. "I know you're busy, Dr. G., but I wanted to read you this quote by Steven Covey before I go."

Intrigued, I nodded.

He cleared his throat and read: "We all see the world, not as it is, but as we are. We look through the frame of reference, the pair of glasses, the paradigm of our whole past background and experience. If you want to make major improvements, shift your paradigm."

"The system and the inmates would both have to shift their paradigms, wouldn't they, Mr. Harris?"

His eyes sparkled. "I knew you would understand, Dr. G." He shook my hand. "Sometime when you're not busy, you have to come in and see what we're doing."

"I'll keep it in mind."

A few weeks later, I convinced Coley to come into the prison and check out the club with me. The inmates had the use of a classroom in the old building, and I looked with nostalgia at the space that had been my original little clinic with its twenty beds. *Times have changed.*

I was surprised by the mix of the group when they started filing in. Black, white, Latino, Native American... and I even spotted a psych patient.

Mr. Harris stood up, thanked everyone for coming, made introductions and explained how the meeting would be run. It was the first time I had heard of the sandwich method. The person designated to give feedback on the speech was to say first what was good about the speech, then give constructive criticism, followed by something positive.

By the time Mr. Harris explained the timekeeper's role of giving a 30-second warning before the speaker's time ran out, I was wishing he was helping run state meetings.

A muscular, black inmate sweated profusely as he was introduced as the first speaker. He had written his speech on lined paper, which shook in his fist as he started to read. "M-m-m-my name is Va…va….va…Val Tobbins. I-I-I…I'm th-th-th-thirty." He stopped and wiped his brow with the back of his hand.

A few guys in the room started murmuring. "It's okay buddy, you can do it." Tobbins continued despite his stutter, and by the end of two minutes I saw something in the inmates' faces that I had rarely seen before on the prison yard: empathy.

A few more speakers rose and shared their stories. Long before Harris spoke, I had decided that the club was worth supporting. Then Harris rose, walked back and forth in front of the room, stopped, and raised his arms over his head. When he started speaking, he immediately owned the room.

"When I was a kid," he began, "I committed crimes to survive and for the thrill of it. I committed crimes to cover my ass after spending the rent money on my addictions. Those decisions cost me the most productive years of my life. I literally prevented myself from coming to terms with who I had become, because I had no respect for myself or others." The room muttered in agreement.

"Each of us must understand why we've committed a crime," Harris went on. "The events leading to my own criminal behavior may be different from yours. You decide what led to your incarceration, and what changes you must make. For me, the change had to be acceptance. I had to accept the fact that resorting to crime is not an option, because its consequences are more than I can afford to pay. I had to accept that the cost of my addictions was more than I could afford to pay." More murmuring from the crowd. I looked around and saw many of the men nodding and shaking their heads in agreement.

"When I chose to accept the facts, I made it possible for myself to learn about the tools that would help me change my life." Harris paused, looked around the room and let out a deep breath.

"For those of us who return to prison again and again, it may seem like it's too late to change. By the time we've broken out of the rut of self-deception, many of us have practically spent our entire adult lives confined. But when you begin to be honest with yourself, you can also begin to listen to the people that offer solutions for change. Once you learn to listen, then you can start applying the solutions."

"It's *never* too late to change!" he exclaimed, to another murmur of agreement. "We don't have to stay the same. Inside of you, you have the tools you need to change those aspects of your life that brought you to prison."

I felt my eyes getting misty, and as I looked around at the faces of the men in the room, I saw something beautiful: hope, and belief. *Is this really happening? They look so... happy.*

Harris continued: "We must do everything necessary to come to terms with ourselves. We have to understand the reasons for our incarceration. We need to utilize every resource at our disposal, including talking to prison counselors and getting help. There's nothing wrong with asking for guidance."

"There's no way to hold onto destructive behaviors and expect to achieve any type of long term success. We have to think of ourselves as vacant lots. Break down the old structures, and build something new. But before you can build, you have to get the foundations down. Once you accept the fact that the old foundation will never support your efforts to succeed, you will be ready to build a new one."

He paused and took a breath. His tone resonated with power. "We need to rid ourselves of those selfish old behaviors. *They are robbing us of the freedom every one of us deserves.*"

He raised his right index finger in the air. "I leave you with this thought from Glenn Van Ekeren: 'The toughest thing to change is our *approach* to change. Expect change: it is inevitable. You must decide whether it is to be by consent, or by coercion.'"

The room was silent for a second, and then erupted in applause.

I heard someone in the back yell, "You tell 'em bro!"

I looked at my husband Coley, who was looking around at the inmates in the room with a smile on his face. When he turned back towards me, I leaned forward and put my hand on his arm.

"Coley, at the break Mr. Harris asked me if you and I can become sponsors for this club. It seems the current sponsor is moving away. Are you up for it? It's only every other Sunday night."

He looked at me over his glasses, smiled, and shook his head. "The things you get me involved in."

I patted him on the arm. "If you can't make it, I can come on my own. I know how much you enjoy teaching in the college program, but think about it, that's only for the guys who can pay. Just think how worthwhile this program is, and it's for everybody. You don't really have to do any work. We can just come in and enjoy hearing their speeches, and watch them develop."

Coley rolled his big brown eyes and chuckled. "Okay, so now besides teaching and supporting their VVA chapter, I'll be coming in on Sunday nights."

I smiled and squeezed his arm. "Every *other* Sunday night, and you're not doing anything anyway that night except watching television." I waved my arm around the room. "Why watch stories when you can be part of them?"

249

Coley and I sponsored the Toastmasters club for over ten years. I considered it one of the best free programs I had ever witnessed. The inmates developed it, were responsible for it, and supported each other's growth in a group that included all ages, races, religions, and educational backgrounds. Plus, they developed a skill that could open doors for them when they left the prison.

Mr. Harris was responsible for not only founding the first Toastmasters club in the prison, but also for starting the first literacy program in the system. Many people benefited from the programs he started, and I enjoyed hearing about their successes.

After he left, I heard Harris began a career in marketing. One of the inmates sent me a newspaper clipping of him winning a state award for his speech; another inmate in the club told me that because of his talent for public speaking, his church had helped him become a motivational speaker.

After ten successful years of meetings, a new warden decided to stop the program. It did not cost the state anything, nor did we ever have a custody officer present, but an officer complained that it was too much work to let inmates in and out of their units for meetings. The men in the club, as well as Coley and I, petitioned for the club to continue, but the new warden was not program- or education-minded.

"Isn't a shame?" I said to Coley after I told him of the warden's final verdict.

Coley rubbed his chin. "It would be nice to keep that club going," he said, "but no warden can take away what the inmates accomplished for themselves. I like to think some lives were changed, don't you?"

"Yes, I do." I smiled. "Maybe nothing lasts forever, but some of those men will never see themselves in the same way, no matter how the world treats them."

"Right," he agreed. "Some of those guys will bring goodness into the world, and they'll create more of it. And just think, it all started with one guy who wanted to be a better father to his daughter."

PART

THREE

Karen Gedney, MD

20. Fired Up

The alarm went off and I grabbed my cell phone. I was about to say, "This is Dr. G.," when I realized I didn't have to dispense medical advice in my semi-conscious state. I hit the snooze button, laid back, and tried to remember how many times the prison had called that night and what I had actually said. *All right, I don't remember anything too crazy.* I stretched, remembering that the alarm was set for a reason. *What am I getting up for? Oh yes... a breakfast meeting on my day off. This better be good. I could sleep another eight hours.*

The meeting was being put on by a networking organization in the next city. They brought in a motivational speaker once a month, and it was usually worth the trip. For me, being surrounded by positive people who wanted to improve their lives and the lives of others was a counterweight to what I experienced in the prison, and I needed it.

In the large, colorful meeting room, two hundred people were smiling, shaking hands and hugging one another. Once a month, it felt as if I had stepped onto another planet where I felt less gravity pulling me down. I stood in line to get my buffet breakfast, piling on the blueberries, strawberries, pineapple, and melon. I thought about the inmates: they were lucky if they received any fresh fruit, and if they did, it was a apple that went to the men who didn't have teeth.

By the time I had finished my breakfast, the host was introducing Mr. Aric Bostick: a young, trim white male with blond hair who immediately started engaging his audience.

"Come on, get up on your feet! Find someone you don't know in the audience and ask them: 'What fires you up?'"

I stood up, hoping someone would approach me. Aric shouted out, "The late great hockey coach Fred Shero said, 'Success is not the result of spontaneous combustion. You must first set yourself on fire!'"

All right. I'll walk over to the young woman in the purple dress and ask her. "Hi. My name's Karen. What fires you up?"

"Ahh... I'm not sure. I mean, I like my job, but you know, I wonder if it's what I really want long-term."

I took a small step closer. "Okay then, tell me what makes you so excited that you can't wait to do it again."

She nibbled her lower lip. "Traveling to another country. I went to Spain last year and I really want to go to Portugal next. How about you?"

What does fire me up? Helping, healing, teaching, making a positive difference in other people's lives, learning, overcoming obstacles. That's why the universe put me in prison, but the system certainly seems to be conspiring to put out my fire.

I was about to answer when Aric shouted out over the babble of voices. "Okay, give your person a high five and tell them they are AWESOME!"

I did as I was told, chuckling. *This would never happen in prison.*

When we sat down, Aric told us about his upbringing, which sounded reminiscent of the upbringing of a lot of my inmates had. His father was an alcoholic and his mother was an illiterate bipolar who abused him in every way possible.

I sat up straighter and started taking notes. *What circumstances and thought processes separate this man from the men I took care of?* From what I could tell, Aric grew up in a good neighborhood, went to good schools, had some good teachers, and got a lot of therapy to help him forgive his mother. He also learned to look within himself and let go of his neediness and his expectations. *Well, those things certainly aren't common among the inmates.*

Aric shared his acronym: FIRED UP! As he detailed it, I realized it contained ideas that I could easily teach the inmates in my life skills class, "Health Related Recovery."

The acronym, used here with Aric's permission, is as follows:

FUEL: What Fuels Your Tank?

INVENTORY: Take Stock of Your Life

REFRAME: Shift Your Perspective

ENERGIZE: Exercise, Get R&R, Eat Well

DECLARE: What's Your Mission?

UNDERSTAND: Step into Someone Else's Shoes

PRESENT: Live Here and Now

By the end of his presentation, Aric was so fired up that he ripped off his shirt to expose a Superman shirt and a red cape. His right arm went up in the air as he yelled, "Are you ready to be FIRED UP for today and for the rest of your life?"

I've got to get his book, I thought, *and have him dedicate it to the inmates*. A short paperback, it was perfect for the guys in my class.

I read the book that night, and summarized it in a one-page hand out which I brought to work the following week. As the clinic was shutting down for the evening, I was getting ready to bring the FIRED UP lesson to my class.

Dr. Alie walked out of the medical building with me, carrying her little lunch cooler. "Hey, did you do anything exciting over the weekend?" she asked.

"Yeah, I went on a twenty-mile hike after I heard a motivational speaker that actually motivated me. In fact, I'm going to share his talk with the inmates in the camp class tonight. How about you?"

"I went out and did some target practice. You know I keep a gun in my house, just in case. I want to learn how to use it."

"Just in case of what? I once asked Coley about keeping a gun in the house. He said that if you didn't practice all the time with it and always have it on you, it would be more of a liability than an asset."

Alie wrinkled her nose. "Well, I feel safer with it."

"If guns really keep you safe, I certainly haven't heard it from anyone that's worked in the prison. And all I remember are the tragedies."

255

"What do you mean?"

"Well, let's see. We had one nurse at Max that fell on bad times and shot himself in the head. Two different officers did the same thing over the years. Then we had a nurse here who liked to talk about his gun and mess around with it. One day he dropped it and shot himself through the chest. He missed his heart by two inches. Oh, and there was the first officer I worked with. He had a young son who played with a gun and blew off his hand."

"Okay, okay, I get your point." Alie shook her head. "But I'm keeping my gun."

I let it drop, and we talked about other things as we walked the remaining distance to the gatehouse.

"See you tomorrow, Alie," I said as the officer buzzed us out.

"Have fun in class."

I got into my car and smiled. I truly enjoyed teaching in the camp, much to the consternation of my fellow staff who mostly preferred to leave work as quickly as possible.

The minimum-security camp was only a mile or so from the main prison yard. It held about three hundred and fifty inmates, who worked on fire crews or on the ranch. When I got out of my car, I took in the pungent aroma of manure. It brought back my childhood growing up in the countryside, and lightened my mood. I could see some guys playing basketball on the court outside the gym, and remembered my days of shooting baskets with my sister off the backboard on the garage.

I knocked on the door to the camp gatehouse, and Officer Tranowski let me in. He smiled. "So, what are you going to teach the guys tonight?"

I was going to say, "I'm going to get them fired up!" Instead I said, "How to become self-motivated and successful."

The other officer behind the counter laughed. "If you can figure out how to teach those bozos how to do that, you can have a go at my seventeen-year-old daughter."

"What do you call that class again?" Tranowski asked.

"HRR. It stands for Health Related Recovery."

"Oh, yeah." He hit the button on the console, which broadcasted his announcement to the camp. "Listen up. HRR will be held in the culinary. Everyone needs to be dressed appropriately with their shirts tucked in." *A stirring call to action,* I thought.

At the entrance to the culinary stood a small stone monument, and I stopped for a moment to pay my respects. It had been carved by the inmates, and was dedicated to Harold Green, the officer who had started the Incarcerated Vietnam Veterans chapter and so many other positive programs. He had died suddenly, leaving behind countless changed lives. Years earlier, he had written a grant with the Bureau of Alcohol, Tobacco, and Firearms to start a substance-abuse course. When the course was a success at that facility, the incarcerated vets on my yard convinced me to start one. Over the years, the HRR program turned into a life skills course, where addressing substance abuse was just one of the topics.

When I opened the door of the culinary, the smell of onions greeted me. An inmate was just finishing mopping the floor with a bucket of brown water that rivaled the smell of the onions. He spun around and cautioned, "Watch your step, Dr. G. It's wet in here."

I opened up my briefcase and took out the one-page handouts as I watched the men arrive. Some came over to me, asking for free medical advice. I had to remind them every week that I was in camp as a volunteer teacher, and they had to put in a kite like everyone else to get medical attention.

I watched them choose their seats around stainless steel tables bolted into the floor. The seating pattern had remained constant over the decades. The black inmates sat closest to the doors. The Latinos sat toward the back. The meth addicts sat in the furthest corner from me, and the whites sat the

257

closest. No seat was safe, though, because I would wander the room and pick on them wherever they sat.

At six o'clock, I raised my voice over the din of forty chattering male voices. "Okay guys. Quiet down so I can get started with class."

They quieted, and I scanned the room. The attentiveness on their faces was more or less proportional to the distance they sat from me.

"My name is Dr. G., and this class is called Health Related Recovery. How many of you are new in class tonight?"

Six men raised their hands, glancing around the room.

"For those of you who are new, let me explain who I am, what this class is about, and how it will benefit you. Some of you know me as the doctor on the yard, but when I come to this camp every Wednesday, I am coming as a volunteer on my own time. Years ago, men like you asked me to come out and teach a substance abuse class. I did that at first, but it became clear very quickly that what you really want to learn are the life skills to heal, cope, succeed, and live a life without depending on drugs.

"I believe that people can change if they want to, and if they have the right tools, knowledge, and support. That's what this class is about. Some of you might have been told by the other guys that you can get meritorious credit for the class, so you get a few days taken off your sentence. That is true, but I don't teach this class for that reason and you shouldn't take it for that reason. You should come to this class because you want to have a different and better life that isn't spent in and out of institutions." I paused and my tone went up. "AND you have to be willing to believe that it is possible, and willing to work for it."

The room was quiet, and quite a few men were looking down at their tables instead of at me.

"As many of you know, I like to share things with you that I think will help you have a life that you and your mother can be proud of." A ripple of laughter went through the room.

258

"Last Friday I listened to a motivational speaker named Aric Bostick, who I think some of you can relate to. Please raise your hand if you didn't have a father, or didn't have a good father because they valued their alcohol or drugs more than you."

Ninety percent of the hands went up.

"Okay, now raise your hand if you had a parent who had mental health problems and abused you emotionally, physically or sexually." Seventy percent of the hands went up.

"Well, this guy had two parents like that too. He could have used drugs or made decisions that put him in prison, but he didn't. Have you ever asked yourself why some people who have every strike against them can still succeed in life, and others born with tremendous advantages never go anywhere and fail?"

A few heads nodded.

"I ask myself those questions all the time. There is a saying that the quality of answers you get depends on the quality of the questions you ask. Let me give you an example. Which question is more powerful: 'Why am I a failure?' Or, 'What do I need to do to succeed?'"

A muscular black inmate with a shiny bald head raised his hand. "What do I need to do to succeed?"

"That's right. Tonight I'm going to share with you what this speaker said about getting fired up and becoming successful in life. So first, you need to know what it means to be "fired up." It means that you are on fire for life. You are excited about it and can't wait to wake up every day."

I pointed at a young white guy with a confused look on his face. "You. What fires you up? What is something that gets you out of bed in the morning because you're excited for it to happen?"

"Uhh, I don't know," my victim said.

The old, fat man with a pockmarked face sitting next to him laughed.

259

"Winning the lottery," he said and the room chuckled.

I raised my hand to quiet the laughter. "Let's take a look at that answer. Do you know that there has been a lot of research done on people who have won the lottery? It turns out that two years later, most of them are broke and more miserable than they were to begin with. Why do you think that happens?"

The inmate with the shiny bald head raised his hand again. "Because his old lady spent it all and his good for nothin' relatives came out of the woodwork and asked for handouts." The guys at his table started laughing and one of them gave him a high five.

I nodded and asked for his name. "It's Thompson, ma'am," he said with a huge grin.

"That's a common story, yes. Or, they spend their money on material things, and after a short time they realize that they are still unhappy, unfulfilled, and now they don't even have the illusion anymore that money would make them happy.

"Happiness can come from external sources, but it doesn't last. Think back to the time you really wanted some material thing, like a pair of fancy sneakers or a car. Initially it probably made you happy"—some of the men chuckled knowingly—"but that type of happiness didn't last. Did it?"

"No ma'am, it did not," piped up a voice from the chatter.

"I know it is hard to believe, but happiness, inspiration, and excitement for life comes from within. You create it yourself. And if long-term happiness doesn't come from the things you get in life, what is it from? Any guesses?"

I noticed that the men at one of the tables were talking among themselves and I walked toward the table. They quieted and looked in every direction except at me. "It is from what you *give*," I said, putting a hand on the table.

"Let me tell you what fires me up. What fuels my fire is helping other people. I can do it as a doctor, or as a teacher, or a mentor. It's important to me, because it gives me a purpose, and because I have to constantly listen and learn in order to do it well."

I walked back toward the front of the room. "I want everyone of you to think about what fuels your fire. Let's start with you, Mr. Thompson. What fuels your fire?"

His dark eyes twinkled. "Well... in mixed company, I would say to be a good father to my son."

"That's a great one. Everyone think back to when you were a child. Think about what a good father would look like to you. Raise your hand if you can describe him."

A toothless, thin middle-aged man raised his hand. "He wouldn't come home stinkin' drunk and beat on me and my mom."

"I agree. From now on, I want all of you to concentrate on what you *do* want, instead of what you *don't* want. You didn't want an abusive, alcoholic father. So, what you wanted was a sober, loving father, right?"

An older Hispanic inmate raised his hand. "I wanted to be with my papa. He was never home."

I smiled. "So, a good father would spend time with you. What would you have liked to do with him when you were growing up?"

"Fishing. I like to fish."

"Okay. Now, how many of you in here have children?"

The majority of the class raised their hands.

"How many of you want your children to grow up and use drugs that will put them at risk for becoming addicted?"

All the hands went down.

"How many of you want your children to grow up and go to jail or prison?"

261

They all looked at each other, and no one raised their hand.

"Mr. Thompson, how do you think children learn?"

"They copy their peers."

"They certainly do, and who else do they copy?"

The Hispanic man raised his hand. "They copy the adults around them."

"That's right, they do." I stopped and picked up a copy of the handout. "I want all of you to look at your handout now and read what each letter in the phrase FIRED UP means."

The room filled with the sounds of shuffling papers and voices. I led the men through each letter in the acronym, discussing the meaning of each concept and how it applied to their lives. As I did, I could feel the room warming up to the conversation. They began to respond more naturally, to laugh with me, and to hang on my words.

We had come to the last letter: P.

"The 'P' stands for 'present,'" I said. "As in 'living in the present.' I have watched a lot of men in prison who sit around and think their life will start up again when they leave. A short time later, I see them again on their second, third, fourth, or fifth intake exam. Let me show you: Everyone who has been sent to prison more than once, stand up."

The sound of men standing up bounced off the grey concrete walls.

"Look around you. More than half of you have been here before. I know some of you have come back multiple times. Now, sit down if you have come back to prison fewer than five times."

There were seven men still standing. I knew most of them.

"Mr. Tace, would you like to tell everyone how many times you've come back, and why?"

I had seen Tace three weeks ago during intake day, and had warned him that if he attended the HRR class again I was going to ask him to speak about his actions.

Tace had hollow cheeks from his recent meth use, and his once-muscular body now looked old and weak. He hung his balding head. "I knew you were going to pick on me." He looked up and his grey eyes met mine. "This is the seventh time I've been sent back, and I don't know, I'm just a drug addict."

"Thank you for sharing, Mr. Tace. All the rest of you can sit down now while I ask Mr. Tace, whom I have known for many years, some questions."

He shifted his weight from one foot to the other and put his hands in his baggy jeans.

"Mr. Tace, I've seen you in this class a number of times, and from interacting with you I know you're not 'just an addict.' I know you're a father, a construction worker, a motorcycle rider, and a leader. What else would you like to add to that list?"

"Uhh, I don't know."

I pointed to the man sitting next to him. "You're friends, aren't you? What else would you say about Mr. Tace?"

The other man rubbed the tattoos on his neck and smiled. "He's a hell of a tattoo artist." The guys in the class laughed, and I thought I heard one of them say, "He's a good meth cooker too." I put my index finger to my lips to quiet them.

"Mr. Tace, would you agree there is more to you than just being a drug addict?"

He nodded.

"Then why do you think you said you were just an addict, when I asked you why you came back to the prison?"

He pulled up his pants, which had started to slide down his thin hips. "I didn't know what else to say."

263

"Thank you, Mr. Tace. You can sit down now." I walked toward the back of the room and turned around. Most of the faces in the room followed me.

"When someone tells me they're an addict—that addiction caused their behavior and actions—I ask them two questions. First, if you were an addict and you wanted your drug, would you steal money from your best friend?"

I looked around the room and saw a lot of men nodding their heads.

"Most of you nodded your heads 'yes.' Next question: What if you wanted your drug and there was no way to get it AT ALL without selling your two-year-old child to a child molester. Would you do it?"

There was a collective chorus of consternation and more than one "what the fuck?" before the room quieted.

"I gave that as an example because I want you to actually think about where you would draw the line that you would not step over to get your drug. Now, how many of you know addicts who *would* sell their kid to a child molester?"

Several hands went up.

"If someone sold a child to a child molester to get money for drugs, would his excuse of being an addict change the way you felt about what he did?"

The guys squirmed in their seats and I heard many variations on "Hell no" and "I'd kill the motherfucker."

"This may sound harsh to many of you, but I think if you say 'I'm just an addict,' you are giving yourself a pass. You are not taking responsibility for your actions.

"Think about those powerful words we were talking about earlier. If you don't want to return to prison, what is more powerful? Is it 'I'm just an addict', or is it something like 'I am someone who is worthy of a life outside of prison, and I am willing to do what I need to do to get it, including getting help for my addiction.'"

I took a deep breath. "Remember, I am a volunteer. If I didn't believe that you were worth it, I wouldn't be here. You can have a different life. Even if you're a slow learner and come back seven times."

The class started laughing and many looked at Mr. Tace, who was being slapped on the back by his friend.

I walked toward the door to make sure no one was going to slip out. "I know class is almost over, but before I hand out the homework, we're going to do something different. Stand up."

They all stood up and looked at each other. I heard a few groans and laughs. "Mr. Thompson, come up here and do this exercise with me," I said.

He puffed out his chest, and the guys at his table started laughing and slapping the table as he walked toward me. He was trying not to smile and wiping his sweaty hands on his jeans.

I raised my hand to quiet the class. "Mr. Thompson, we're going to show the class what they are about to do. Everybody is going to turn to the guy next to them and ask them, 'What fires you up?' After they answer, you give them a high five and say 'You're awesome.'"

I ignored the awkward groans of the class, and turned to Mr. Thompson. He stood a head taller than me. Looking up into his face, I asked. "What fires you up?"

There were catcalls and suggestions among the laughter and Mr. Thompson had a hard time keeping a straight face. His eyes twinkled and he said in a deep, loud baritone: "To be an outstanding father."

I breathed a sigh of relief.

"You're awesome!" I said, and gave him a high five. He turned around and bowed as the class started hooting and clapping.

"Now it's your turn. You're not getting out of the class until you tell

265

someone next to you that they are awesome and give them a high five."

Once they got into it, they really got into it. I had never seen them so alive and with such big smiles. Before I gave them their homework, I had to quiet them so Custody wouldn't come in to the culinary and investigate why there was so much noise.

When they left with their homework, my hand was a bit sore from all the high fives I had received.

I had purchased two of Aric Bostick's books, and lent them to two inmates in the class on the condition that they return them the following week. They not only returned the books, but both had written thank-you notes to Aric. I was so impressed with their letters that I mailed them to him, along with a copy of my handout, a few representative homework assignments, and a thank-you note.

A few weeks later, I received a box with fifty books in it and a wonderful letter written to the class. I'll share with you the final paragraph of Aric's letter:

My only wish for you is to be free despite the walls and bars around you. You are not a prisoner in your mind. You are a free man with a life that is just getting started and so much left to live. Set yourself free today from within and know that you are enough and you can and will overcome this. I hope to meet you someday and speak at your camp but until then, know that I am your brother and I send you strength as you grow one day at a time toward being the man that you already are. Awaken to it!! Your best you is inside of you already! You just have to let it out!

21. Angler

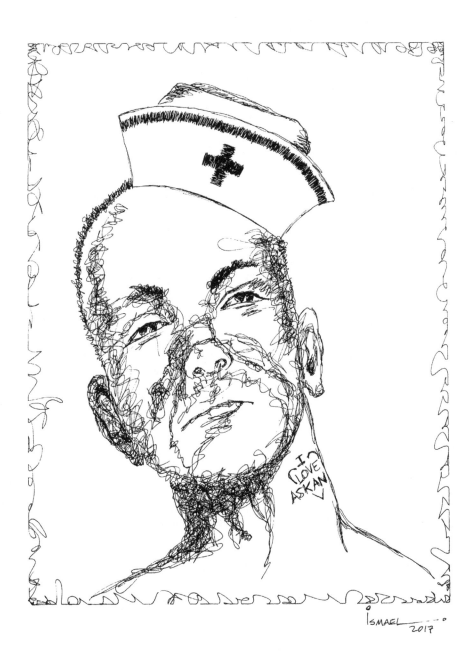

I sat down in my office with my mug of coffee and looked at the large calendar on my desk. *Good, no meetings or court cases to interfere with my schedule.* I closed my eyes, and was appreciating the comforting aroma of coffee when the phone rang.

"Regional Medical Facility, Dr. G. speaking."

"Hey, good morning. This is Dr. Becker. I'm sending over one of my favorites today, and I want to give you a heads up on the guy." Dr. Becker was a portly ophthalmologist who had come out of retirement for financial reasons, and was working as a physician in a nearby prison.

I shifted the phone to my other ear and grabbed my favorite black pen. "From the tone of your voice, I'm guessing you're not heartbroken over this."

He chuckled. "The staff will probably throw a party the second the asshole leaves. He must hold the record for filing the most grievances at this place."

A "grievance" is a form an inmate fills out when he believes he has an issue that has to be addressed that day by someone in authority. In the medical department, handling grievances fell on the charge nurse or the director of nursing. They were only supposed to be used if it was urgent, but depending on the perspective of the inmate, grievances could range from serious to silly.

"Does this particular individual have a name, and why am I so lucky?"

"His name is Mr. Angler, and he's a manipulating sicko. He filed enough lawsuits to get the attention of the attorney general's office, and drove them crazy enough that they finally cut a deal with him." He paused and cleared his throat. "Angler said he would drop the suits if they transferred him to the Regional Medical Facility, and they nominated you to give him an objective medical evaluation."

I pulled over my scratchpad to write on. "What kind of medical problems does he have?"

"Claims he has Crohn's so he can get special food and a private bathroom. The gastroenterologists in town scoped him a year ago and found nothing. It didn't stop him, though, from talking one of the doctors into giving him medication and food supplements. But I put a stop to that months ago."

Crohn's disease is an inflammatory bowel disease that can cause serious trauma to the digestive tract. Not an easy one to falsify. *I wonder what this Angler is up to.*

"When is Mr. Angler coming our way?"

"Today, I hear, and he'll be a direct admit into the infirmary."

"Lovely," I said, and recapped my pen.

I stood up, stretched, checked the time, and decided to make a quick stop in the infirmary to tell the nurses about the patient coming in.

Suzy looked up at me and tapped her long manicured silver nails on the counter.

"What's up, Doc?"

"We're getting an admission today from Dr. Becker over at Max. The attorney general's office wants an objective medical examination done here."

Suzy's forehead wrinkled and she leaned on her elbow. "Well, that's a new one. Who are we getting, and why is the AG's office involved?"

"His name is Mr. Angler."

"Oh, God," she said, and rolled her eyes.

"So you know him. What can you tell me about him?"

She shook her faded blond hair and snorted. "I knew him for years when I worked at Max. He was some act. He loved to split staff, play one off the other and..." She looked up. "Let me give you an idea how slick he is. One of his games is putting ads in newspapers requesting female pen pals. Then after he sweet talks to them for a while, he gets the dummies to send him money. Some were stupid enough to even bring him drugs. If I were you, I wouldn't believe anything that comes out of his slimy mouth."

I straightened up and gave her a nod. "Thanks. I'll keep it in mind, Suzy."

I returned in the afternoon to the infirmary, which smelled like buttered microwave popcorn. My stomach growled as I flipped open Angler's chart and studied his unremarkable blood tests, colonoscopy, and consultation reports from a year ago. I checked again to make sure I hadn't missed anything. There were no recent tests or procedures, and I was glad I was accustomed to reading Dr. Becker's nearly-illegible notes.

I turned to the thickest part of Angler's chart, which was the section where they kept the kites. A kite is a green form on which the inmate writes his name, ID number, the unit he lives in, and the nature of his request to see Medical. Sometimes kites were short and non-specific ("I sick"). Some struck me as funny ("I don't know if they are himrods or herrods, but something is coming out of my ass"). And some were in the category of Mr. Angler's: lengthy, condescending and grandiose.

> Dr. Becker, I understand you have a hard time keeping up in medicine as you were never trained to take care of general medical problems, let alone complex ones that require a team of specialists including a gastroenterologist, a pharmacist, a dietician, and others. When you took me off my Purinethol and caused me to deteriorate, I hold you responsible. You supercilious little munchkin.

I shut the chart, closed my eyes, and rubbed the back of my neck with both hands. *Okay Karen, don't let Dr. Becker's or Suzy's comments prejudice you. You need to be objective and not miss anything.*

"Dr. G., the inmate from Max is in the exam room when you're ready," the officer said shortly afterward. I headed for the exam room.

When I opened the door, Angler's bright powder-blue eyes glanced up, then darted away. I studied his gaunt, pale face, decayed teeth, and thinning shoulder-length brown hair—and decided he didn't look as animated as his writing.

"Mr. Angler, my name is Dr. G. I understand you were sent to my facility for an evaluation."

His eyes flickered up for a second, but he was still avoiding eye contact as he began to talk.

"Before I tell you what happened," Angler said, "I want you to know that I could have picked any doctor in the system, but I chose you. The last prison misdiagnosed me, took away my medications, withheld the extra food that I needed to survive on, and caused me undue suffering." He took a breath and slowed down his speech. "You see, I'm not saying the last doctor was bad, he just didn't know what he was doing. We also got off on the wrong foot, and no matter what happens to me, he feels I have nothing coming. I know you'll be objective. You have a reputation in the prison for being a real professional who cares about her patients."

I hope he doesn't spread it on any thicker, I thought as I sat down on the stool and opened his chart to a blank progress note. "Mr. Angler, why don't you explain to me what medical problems you have, and what I can do for you."

He stared at my pen and wet his lips. "It's a long story." He gave me a furtive glance and continued. "I was fine until I came back from having a rectal fistula fixed years ago. A few days after the operation, I was in so much pain I thought I was going to die. They thought I was just scamming them for more narcotics. By the time they finally brought me back to the hospital, I had peritonitis and ended up with a colostomy."

I searched his face. "Do you know what caused the rectal fistula?" He shrugged his bony shoulders. "They thought I was taking it up the butt. They found it funny. I don't know, maybe it was because of all the diarrhea I was having from the slop they pass off as food."

"You don't have a colostomy now. When did they take it down?"

A slight smile crossed his lips. "I forced them to hook me up a year later. It was their fault and I held them responsible."

"How did you do after that surgery?"

"I still had diarrhea off and on, and sometimes would pass blood. They always told me it was because of my hemorrhoids. Finally a decent doctor showed up for a while, and he gave me some medication to try. It helped, and they diagnosed me with Crohn's."

"How did they diagnose you? Did they do any procedures or biopsies?"

"They didn't have to do any of that because I responded to the medication and the special diet. If Dr. Becker hadn't taken me off of everything, I wouldn't be suffering now."

"In what specific way are you suffering?"

"My belly is killing me all the time. Cramping, diarrhea, blood in the stool. I need a private cell. No guy wants to keep crapping in front of another guy all day long. I'm losing weight and I don't have the energy to do anything anymore, and no one will listen to me. I need special food and the meds I had before."

"Mr. Angler, I'm listening to you. After we finish talking, I'm going to examine you and order the tests to diagnose what is going on. Is that okay with you?"

He nodded his head.

The tests began shortly after, and to the surprise of many in the clinic, the specialists did diagnose Crohn's in his small intestine. Worse, it had gone on so long that they were unable to control it. The small intestine had developed abscesses that were so bad, they had created their own passage from the intestine, through the abdominal wall, to the skin. In medicine, this phenomenon is called a fistula. Angler had five of them, constantly draining greenish-brown intestinal fluid through the skin on his abdomen.

After a year of attempts and failures to control Angler's illness, it was decided that he would need surgery to remove part of his intestine. *This is a long shot,* I thought, as I wrote a different regimen of complicated intravenous medications, including TPN (total parenteral nutrition), which were barely keeping him alive. Then I stood up to see him for the hundredth time.

I peered through the window of Angler's cell and saw him sitting on a commode chair next to his bed. He was now too weak to walk the five steps to the toilet in the corner of his room, and had to slide his body onto the white plastic chair with the bucket beneath it. He had become almost unrecognizable to me in the last year: he looked like a large, grey marshmallow. He was bent forward, holding his abdomen and staring at his naked, fluid-filled feet. A blue knit cap sat high on his head and a worn grey blanket was wrapped around his shoulders.

The click of the key opening the door caused him to turn his head slightly. He sniffed back a few tears. "This isn't living. I can't even get off the crapper long enough to fall asleep, and if I eat or drink anything, it comes right out of me. I know the stuff you're pumping into me is supposed to help, but it doesn't matter. I'm dying. I'm so tired. I can't do this anymore."

I touched his cold hand and noticed how even the slightest pressure made an indentation into his puffy skin. "Mr. Angler, I know you feel miserable now, but I've convinced a surgeon to operate on you. They didn't want to attempt it at first because of all the risks involved, but we've run out of options. All of the doctors who've seen you feel it's your only chance."

The once-bright eyes, now dulled with pain, made eye contact for a few seconds. "I could always just die, Dr. G., save the state money and make a lot of people happy."

I smiled ruefully. "That doesn't sound like your style."

The surgeon who did the operation was a specialist in complex gastrointestinal issues. He could only salvage about two and a half feet of Angler's small intestine, but he survived the surgery. Angler returned from the hospital and spent several weeks recuperating in the infirmary. Eventually, he seemed to be improving.

"How's our favorite patient doing, Suzy?" I asked, reaching for the clipboard with his vital signs.

She leaned back in the swivel chair, which creaked. "He's driving me nuts, so he must be getting better."

"What's he up to this time?"

"He's been bribing the inmate porters to sneak in tobacco so he can smoke in his room. Every time a porter gets caught, Custody gets rid of them and we have to train a new one. And every time we write Angler up, he turns around and writes a grievance on us."

She huffed. "How are we going to discipline him? He's too sick for us to kick him out of here. We can't take away his ability to buy food out of the store, because you say he needs it. We took away his T.V., but all that did was give him more free time to write grievances and lawsuits." She tapped her nails on the counter. "You know, if you hadn't made this building non-smoking, we wouldn't have this problem."

"I know. Instead, we'd have the problem of the men on oxygen treatment singeing off their eyebrows, or the senile guys falling asleep while smoking and setting themselves on fire."

Not pleased, Suzy stood up and walked down the hallway. I went to see Angler. When I opened the door, the smell of cheap tobacco smoke assailed my nostrils. Before I could comment, he said, "I know, I know, but I have so few pleasures in life." The brightness in his eyes was back; their piercing gaze reminded me of a bird of prey.

"I'm suffering back here," Angler said. "You have no idea how much smoking helps me with everything. If you actually, truly cared about patients, you wouldn't arbitrarily make them suffer."

Well, he must be feeling better. "Is there something else I can do for you today, Mr. Angler?"

He reached toward the stack of papers next to him, and handed me some printed articles on Crohn's disease from the Internet. "I know you're not a specialist in Crohn's, and you seem to refer me to doctors who don't know much either. That's why I've decided to do the research on my own and advise you on the best way to treat me. First of all, from now on, to reduce my stress I need a room all to myself. Forget ever putting me in a dorm or with a roommate. Second, the prison serves nothing but slop. I need to be given good protein, not that grey slime they pass off as baloney. And oh yeah, I need supplements. Like this thing they call glutamine. I've also read about some new medicines that are out. They are expensive, but you need to give them to me as well."

Well, now I know he's back to his old self again. "Mr. Angler, I'm glad you're taking an interest in your health, and I advise you not to believe everything that is posted on the Internet." I paused and riffled through the articles he handed me. "You've got quite a few articles here. Who printed them off for you?"

He waved his hand dismissively. "I've got girlfriends on the outside. They send me what I ask for."

"How fortunate for you."

A month later, Angler was transferred to a unit with a private cell and twenty-four-hour access to a toilet. His comfy new lifestyle gave him the time to write more grievances, lawsuits, and long letters of complaints. It irritated me that instead of being appreciative of all the complex care he had received, Angler chose to spend all his time complaining and suing the medical department that was responsible for saving his life.

One afternoon, Nurse Wilma, an older woman with bronze parchment skin from a lifetime of smoking and sun, handed me yet another large envelope from Mr. Angler. "Good God, that sicko gets me twitchin'. Dr. G., why the hell did you have to go and save his skinny ass? All us nurses are never gonna forgive you for that one."

"I know. Some days after I read the grievances he puts in against me, I wonder what all the trouble was for too."

Karen Gedney, MD

I turned and headed to the break room to make myself a cup of hot tea. Inhaling the steam of a black, earthy tea made me feel better. I grabbed the plastic bag containing my salad and fruit out of the refrigerator, and headed down the hall to eat with Dr. Alie in her office.

Alie was warming her hands around her mug. She pointed to the envelope. "Don't tell me Angler's written you another love letter."

I opened the letter and took out ten yellow, lined pieces of legal paper. Each page was filled with handwritten script that any teacher in the 1960s would have shown to the rest of the class to demonstrate perfect penmanship and spelling. I scanned the first page and shook my head.

"Listen to how Mr. Angler starts this one: *You came to mind not because you care so little, but because, well, let's say you have an amalgam of limitations.*"

Alie burst out laughing and almost choked on her tea. "He's creepy. Let me take a look at what he's written."

She flipped through a few pages, and horizontal lines started to march up her forehead. Then she put the papers down and tapped her finger on them.

"You've got to promise me you're not going to see this guy alone. He's a grandiose narcissist and probably delusional on top of it." She wrinkled her nose. "He's got a thing for you. Read this part." She passed a page back to me and pointed at a paragraph:

Where I've written of you with boundless enthusiasm, at this moment it is with tedium. I want to blame you because you inspire me repeatedly simply to drag me down with the absence of substance your inspiration has, but that would be wrong. You spread yourself thin.

I leaned back. "Why don't you see him instead of me?"

"I'd rather be shot dead than see him, and besides, you're the internal medicine specialist and you know his entire history."

I sighed. "I probably know too much of his history. When we all thought he was going to die, I told him to write down his thoughts. I wanted to give him something to do. Before he went to the hospital, he gave me seventy-six pages of material of what his life was like when he entered Max at nineteen. He went into great detail about riots, killings, rapes, and drugs. I wonder if he wishes he hadn't told me all those things."

I also knew from his writings that as a child he would set fire to things and hurt animals. He had what the psychiatrists call an antisocial personality disorder, which included deceitfulness, impulsive behavior, aggressiveness, and lack of remorse. I had once asked one of our psychiatrists what he thought caused the disorder, and he told me that usually people developed this type of disorder because they never bonded with a human in childhood.

Giving medical care to someone with an antisocial personality disorder is difficult on multiple levels. It took a significant amount of effort to keep treating someone who cried wolf a hundred times for no objective reason. In Angler's case, he had already been doing just that for years at the other prison, which was why they didn't believe his complaints when he developed a real illness.

He also was, as Alie suggested, narcissistic. I knew his exaggerated feelings of self-importance, coupled with his history of aggression and impulsivity without remorse, could be a problem for me. *I've been down this road before.* I didn't think about the incident with Moth every day anymore, but it was never too far from my mind. I wasn't going to get into another situation that could be dangerous for me.

Angler's letters continued to arrive, and oscillated from praising to vilifying me:

> *Dr. G., if I were a bug attracted to light, the dimness of your mediocrity would repulse me. Look into my eyes and do it with your own two hands. Your continued ineffectiveness bores me. Coward.*

I continued to treat him professionally, and ignored his manipulative

277

behavior. A few months later, I heard that Rosa, our new nurse who worked on graveyard had been fired. What was surprising was the reason she was let go: she had been telling nurses and inmates that I was killing patients and falsifying medical records to hide it.

I had never met Rosa, and at first I was flabbergasted; but the director of nursing told me that she had been "compromised" by Angler during the night shift. She had been spending more and more time in his room, and eventually Custody, suspecting a romantic relationship, found that she had been bringing him contraband and drugs from the outside. Rosa was walked off the yard and fired.

Angler had compromised the new nurse into doing something he wanted, with no regard for what would happen to her. He deceitfully made her believe that he loved her, and he deceitfully made her believe atrocious things about me. It was easy for him to do: she had never met me, was new on the yard, and was gullible. Angler had used Rosa to bring him contraband and engage in illegal activities on his behalf, and he had no remorse when she lost her job as a result.

I felt sorry for Rosa, but I was relieved that the rest of my staff had stood up for me. I was even more deeply relieved when Angler was sent to another prison, and I did not have to interact with him further. I didn't know if I could treat him with consistency and objectivity in the future.

People who are deceitful by nature still deserve the same quality of medical care as anyone else. As a medical professional, I had to always remind myself to give my patients the benefit of the doubt—even if many people around me had given up doing that a long time ago.

22. Cancer

279

Lucy walked into my office and handed me a thick chart as she sat down across from me. Over the years, and as our prison population aged, Lucy had found her niche as the primary nurse working with cancer patients. Whenever I saw her, I could usually guess what she wanted to talk about.

She launched right into it. "Mr. Lynch is having a real hard time with the cisplatinum. He vomited for three days, and the Zofran hasn't touched him. Do you think you can write for that new drug, Emend, and we can see if it stops his vomiting?" Lucy asked.

I looked up from his chart. I could see the concern in her hazel eyes. "I haven't used that drug before, what's your experience with it?"

"I've seen it used on cancer patients that don't respond to Zofran. It seems to help them. I also think that Mr. Lynch will refuse any more chemo if we can't reduce his nausea and vomiting. He's already lost fifteen pounds, and he's only had one cycle of chemo. And you know he was a thin guy to begin with."

"I'll read up on it and see if the pharmacy can get it for us. Is there anything else you think I can do for him?"

She pressed her lips together. "He says he could get down some jello and canned fruit, but I haven't been able to get the nurses in the infirmary to get them for him. Do you think it would help if you talked to them?"

I smiled. "You know how difficult it is to get things like that from the culinary. Maybe I'll send you over there to see if you can pry it out of them personally."

She smirked. "I bet you would, but I'd probably get fired. Then who would do the chemotherapy?"

"Lucy, you know I wouldn't be able to take care of these cancer patients without you. We've been doing this so long that I can't even remember the first case we did together."

She leaned forward and put her hand under her chin. "I do. Remember

Karen Gedney, MD

that guy with that horrible lung cancer we had in the old infirmary?" She shuddered. "He had lumps on his chest from the cancer spreading."

His case came back to me in an instant. "Yeah, now I remember. Mr. Babbit. Boy, that must have been twenty-five years ago. You know, something about that case still makes me feel a bit guilty."

Lucy tilted her head, and the morning light coming in through the window made her red hair glow. "Guilty? There was nothing we really could do for him but keep him comfortable."

"I know, but it had to do with his last wishes."

"What do you mean? He knew he was terminal and didn't want to be resuscitated."

I shook my head. "No, it didn't have to do with those wishes. It had to do with what he wanted done with his body. He wanted his family to fly his body back to Arkansas and bury him in the family plot."

A wrinkle appeared between her eyebrows. "I've never heard of the prison doing anything like that. I thought they only cremated bodies."

"That's the standard protocol. But if the family wants to bury the body, the system will release it as long as the family incurs the expense. Mr. Babbit's family agreed with his wishes until they found out how expensive it was to ship a body in a plane and pay for a funeral. His mother and sister both called me and told me that it would take all their savings, and that they would have to put second mortgages on their homes to do what they had promised. You can't imagine how distraught they were when they talked to me. They felt they couldn't deny him the thought of being laid to rest with his family, but they also felt that the cost of their promise would financially destroy them. Then they went into all their guilt regarding his molestation of one of the little girls in the family, and it didn't get better from there."

"What did you do?" Lucy asked.

"I told them to let him think that his body would be buried in his home plot, and they could pay the mortuary to send his ashes to them after he was cremated at the prison's expense."

I leaned back in my chair, remembering how desperate his sister sounded on the phone. "I think they called me because they wanted someone else to make the decision. It just seemed to make the most sense to me. He died content with the thought he was going home, and the family wasn't destroyed financially in the process."

Lucy checked the silver watch on her wrist and stood up, smoothing down her green scrub top. "At least he got to go home. So, do you think you'll have time to see Mr. Lynch today?"

"I'll see him after I take care of these charts. Don't worry about the culinary. I'll see if I can sweet-talk them into sending us some jello and fruit."

A few minutes later, I walked up to the door of the treatment room. The room held an exam table, emergency medical equipment, and a counter with cabinets. Today it was being used to give Mr. Lynch his chemotherapy.

Lucy was checking his vitals, and looked up as I entered. Mr. Lynch was sitting comfortably on the reclining exam table with his eyes closed. He had lost all his hair, and his pale skin sagged on a once-virile face.

"He isn't asleep, Dr. G." Lucy said, and Mr. Lynch opened his hazel eyes.

"Hi Mr. Lynch, you looked like you were taking a nap. How are you feeling today?"

"Mostly weak. If I'm not sleeping, I'm puking. I don't know if I can do two more of these treatments, if I get as sick as I did last time. Do you really think they'll help me? It feels like they're making me worse and I think they're killing me. What if I just stop them till I get back my strength?"

"I know you feel miserable now, Mr. Lynch, but that's because the drugs are killing off cancer cells. The specialists feel enough of those cells are still in your system that we need to continue treating you."

He picked at the worn grey blanket Lucy had draped over him, and

Karen Gedney, MD

muttered, "But I thought they got it all. My scans didn't show anything else after they took out my bladder."

"The cancer specialist feels that people with your condition have the greatest chance to stay cancer-free if they do this chemotherapy. They are concerned that scans don't show cancer cells that could be in your body now. I'm told the only way to make sure those cells don't grow is to kill them off now, before they set up in your organs or your bones and cause you to die."

He pulled the blanket up to his chin. "What if I don't have those cancer cells in me now, and all this poison kills me off? What would you do, Dr. G., if it was you?"

My stomach tightened. *I wouldn't make a good patient if I was puking all the time and spending my days thinking about the pros and cons of cancer treatment.* I rubbed my chin. "You're fifty years old and could have a long life ahead of you, if you beat this cancer. If I was fifty, and knew that I would have to put up with feeling miserable for a few months to give myself the greatest chance of getting back to who I was, I would do it. I knew you on the yard before you got sick. You are going through this tough period to get back to that man. Think about what he would want you to do."

I looked Lynch in the eyes and held his gaze. "You have the other half of your life to live, and it is your decision how much you want to fight for it. The patients who fight for their life with everything they've got, and believe that they are going to beat it, always do the best. Those are the ones that survive."

Lynch turned toward Lucy. "What would you do?"

She glanced at me and back at him. "I'd take one day at a time. Dr. G. is helping me get a medication that I think will really reduce your vomiting. It's more powerful than what we tried the last time. I'm also going to have the other nurses give you more IV fluids, so you won't get dehydrated." She patted him on the shoulder. "Just one day at a time. You'll see, pretty soon you'll be finished with the chemo and you'll start feeling good again."

283

He nodded, sighed, and closed his eyes. Lucy and I looked at each other and I winked as I left the room.

I walked back to my office to pick up the stack of charts on my desk. Balancing all the charts under my left arm, I unlocked the door to the clinic with the switch key. Immediately, I heard the irritated voice of one of the new nurses coming from the med room to my right. The room had a window on the clinic side for orders, and a second, secure window that faced the prison yard. Twice a day, inmates came to the outside window to get medications that they could not keep, like psych meds or medications that had to be controlled. They had to bring their identification, wait in a long line, and then swallow the medication in front of an officer. The entire process tended to make the inmates, the officers, and the nurses grumpy.

I continued walking down the hallway, past the empty psychologists' offices, and to the nurses' station where I put my stack of charts in front of my nurse, Suzy. She was wearing a dark blue scrub top with a parade of zoo animals on it. It looked one size too small for her ample figure.

"Cute animals. So, Suzy, is it going to be a zoo in here today?"

She smiled and looked down at her top. "Yeah, they are cute aren't they? And it's always a zoo in here, unless Custody locks down the yard." She brushed back her light bangs. "Oh yeah, before I forget, one of the night nurses wanted you to see Mr. McKesson before the other patients come in. He's in the holding cell and doesn't look so good. You want to see him now?"

"For sure. Let me see his chart while you do his vitals."

Suzy handed me his chart, and I went into the exam room to see if anyone had charted on Mr. McKesson since I had last seen him. No, there was my progress note from one month ago discussing his metastatic melanoma and the fact that he hadn't responded to any of the new oral medications. McKesson was terminal, but when I'd last seen him, he was not emotionally prepared to come into the infirmary for hospice care.

The door opened, and the officer led in a very pale McKesson.

"You want the chains off him, Doc?"

"Yes, the belly chains too, and you don't have to stay."

He nodded, and began unlocking the cuffs behind McKesson's back. "Geez, these cuffs are hard to get off."

I looked at the edema in McKesson's arms and wrists, and wondered if the officers had access to extra-large handcuffs. He was going to need them.

"Mr. McKesson, take a seat on the chair so we can talk."

He lowered himself slowly, wincing as he repositioned his left leg.

"It looks like the mass in your left groin is bothering you more, Mr. McKesson."

He rubbed his wrists, where the cuffs had left a deep indentation, and didn't say anything.

"It must be difficult for you, having to deal with all the changes that are occurring in your body." I studied his face, which had aged ten years in the last month, and noticed that his blond hair had turned into a faded wisp.

"I'm okay," he said and his voice cracked. His jaw trembled, and his grey eyes filled with tears. He put a hand over his eyes and bent forward, bracing himself with his other hand on his swollen leg.

I handed him a box of tissues, and waited as he wiped his eyes and blew his nose. "Mr. McKesson, why don't I examine you and then we can talk some more. Okay?"

He nodded, and slowly took off his shirt. When he tried to get off his pants, he needed my help because his leg was so swollen.

I examined the grey lump in his left groin, which was now the size of a football. It was a mass of lymph nodes involved with a metastatic melanoma, which had started from a lesion on the back of his left calf years ago in another prison.

He touched the lump. "The medicines aren't helping. Isn't there any

285

way it can be cut out?"

He asked the same question every time I saw him. "It wouldn't help, Mr. McKesson. The scans show that your melanoma has spread throughout your body. The only reason you have such a large lump in your groin is because that's where your body is putting up the biggest fight to hold it back. Taking the lump out won't change what's going on throughout your body."

He rubbed the corners of his eyes. "Why isn't the medicine working? My sister looked it up on the Internet and said it's the new wonder drug, and it's curing people with my type of cancer."

"You're right, it is a new drug. It can help a small number of patients, but I'm sorry to say you are not in that group."

"My sister said the pill I'm getting is about $1,000 per day. That can't be true, can it?"

"Unfortunately, it is. That's why some people say medical care is so expensive in the United States."

He sniffed. "It's crazy. If I spent that much money and it did nothin' for me except make me feel like shit, I'd ask for my money back."

I smiled. "I wish we could, Mr. McKesson. Maybe then we would see better treatment options. But let's talk about you. Have you put in the paperwork to try to get a compassionate release?"

He nodded his head slowly and bit his lower lip. "Yeah, I filled it out and gave it to the caseworker. How long does it take to get an answer?"

I sighed. "It can take a couple of months if everything goes well. I sent my medical letter and the cancer specialist's letter to Central last month. Remember, I told you then that I could only recommend a compassionate release if I felt you had less than six months of life left, and would not be a risk to society. I hope you beat those odds, Mr. McKesson. I would love for you to prove me wrong. I know you want to be with your family now, instead of..." I could feel the tears start to sting behind my eyes, and breathed deeply until my emotions settled.

He started to cry again. "Shit..."

I touched his shoulder. "It's okay."

He gulped a few times. "I don't want to be weak, a punk... and oh God, my poor daughter. I don't want her to come in the prison and see me like this."

Inside my chest I felt a vise squeezing and twisting.

"Mr. McKesson, is there anything I can do to help you deal with all the emotions you are going through now? Everyone is different in how they deal with the situation you are in. Some of the guys want me to call someone in the family and talk to them. Others want to talk to a psychologist or a chaplain, and some people want their family to visit them in the infirmary. Is there anything that I could help you with?"

He shook his head.

"I hear from my nurses that you are having more pain, and that the pain medications aren't helping you. I can't give you a patch or long-acting narcotics on the yard, because of the custody issues. If you come into the infirmary, I can keep you more comfortable and we can give you more care. Would you like me to admit you to the infirmary today?"

"No," he sniffled. "I can handle the pain."

"All right, I won't admit you today, but you have to promise me that if you get too miserable you'll let my nurses know. Is that a deal, Mr. McKesson?" I put out my right hand.

He looked at it, shook it, and then held onto it for a few seconds until he had to swipe the tears off his face. I helped him back into his clothing and went to find the officer to chain him up and get him back to the unit.

When I put his chart in front of Suzy, she said, "He looks like hell. Why didn't you admit him? Custody will be pissed off if he dies in that unit, because they'll have to treat it as a crime scene."

"He's not ready. I'll make sure the med nurses know to notify me if he takes a turn for the worse. Right now, I'm thinking about what's best for him."

"Hmph. What's best for him and us is that he doesn't drag it out. Is it my imagination, or is everyone around here getting cancer now? The inmates say it's the food and water here. What do you think?"

"I think it's a combination of their lifestyle choices and the fact that the population is getting older. But you're right; I'm seeing more and more cancer. What this system really needs is a hospice unit. It's horrible to see them die alone in the infirmary. You know, a psychologist and I tried to get a hospice started in the past, but it never got any traction. The prison director and the warden really have to be behind it, and that hasn't happened yet."

"Yeah, I doubt it will," Suzy said and stood up. "So, you going to lunch? You look like you need some food to cheer you up."

I smiled. Food didn't cheer me up like it did Suzy, but I was ready for a break. I walked to the other side of the building, where the nurses congregated for lunch. The room had two microwaves and a refrigerator, and in the center was a large, square wooden table surrounded by chairs. The chairs were filled with nurses, who were all laughing so hard that I almost started laughing with them for no reason at all.

June turned toward me and pounded her fist on the table. "Dr. G! Do you know what Lisa found in her coffee this morning?"

Lisa was the director of nursing. I couldn't imagine who, or what, would willingly cross her. "Something funny, I guess?" I replied, which started another wave of laughter.

June gulped and giggled. "She left a mug of coffee on her desk last night, and found a dead mouse floating around in it this morning. You should have heard her scream. I guess he couldn't take the prison anymore, and he committed suicide."

One of the LPN's added, "Lisa couldn't handle it. She made me find Officer Kranzi to dispose of it. You should have seen the look on his face, he was

288

probably wondering if he had to write up an incident report or something."

"If I know him, he'll probably insist they fumigate the whole place and fill it with rat poison. That poor mouse probably just wanted to get out of the cold and find something to eat. Maybe you guys should be careful of stashing your cookies and candies in the drawers and cabinets in the clinic," I said, and took my hot water out of the microwave.

"Ooh, you would go there, Dr. G.," June said, and reached for her bag of chocolate chips.

Poor mouse, what a way to go, I thought as I walked out of the room. Turning the corner, I almost ran into Lucy.

Lucy jumped back, avoiding the hot water that splashed from my cup. "Sorry, Dr. G., I didn't see you coming. Hey, have you seen Dr. Tiernan today? I wanted to ask her about a patient I just found out about, a lung cancer patient the jail sent over as a safe keeper. She admitted him over the weekend. Do you know anything about that?"

"Dr. Tiernan's on vacation this week. Why don't you join me for lunch in my office, and we can talk about him."

"That would be great. I've got some paperwork on him. I'll bring it."

I walked back to my office, sat down in my comfortable, padded grey chair, and reached into the plastic bag that held my salad and container of fruit. I took a sip of tea, and turned to look at the poster hanging above my computer. It was of a calm blue lake at dusk, surrounded by gentle, rounded mountains. It reminded me of the Catskills, where I grew up. I found landscapes relaxing, though I smiled thinking about Alie Tiernan's posters that all sported biting declarations. She had one that said *Life is hard. It's harder when you are stupid*. I couldn't disagree with that one.

Lucy came in, sat down across the desk from me, and handed me the paperwork on the new inmate. I read it and shook my head.

"There's got to be a better way of handling these types of cases," I said, putting the paperwork down.

"Why didn't they just let him go home and die? He hasn't even been convicted yet. With that cancer, he probably won't last another two months. Why did Central let the jail send him to us?"

"I want to say it's because the system is stupid, but I've never really got a straight answer from Central on why we take on the medical cases that the jail system can't handle."

"You'd think the judge wouldn't put someone in jail who only had two months to live."

"I would think that, but when I asked that question, I was told that sometimes a terminal inmate is considered more of a threat because they have nothing else to lose."

She sniffed. "That's crazy in this guy's case. He's on oxygen and can't even stand up on his own. When I talked to him, he said that the last few months of chemotherapy and radiation almost killed him, but he thinks he's going to get better."

I tapped the paperwork next to me. "Did anyone tell him his follow-up scans showed that his lung cancer has metastasized everywhere?"

"I don't think so, or if they did, it didn't register with him." She bit into her sandwich and chewed slowly.

I leaned back in my chair. "So I'm going to be the bearer of bad news. I can always present his case at the tumor board and try an alternative regimen of chemotherapy, but I've never seen it work in these types of cases. When you were giving chemo on the outside, did you ever see it work?"

"Never on lung cancers that failed the first regimen and look as bad as his. When you go back and see him, you'll know he doesn't have long. Maybe you should ask the new chaplain to see him."

"The last time I asked him to see one of the cancer patients, he asked me if they wanted fire insurance."

Karen Gedney, MD

Her red eyebrows came together and she pulled back. "What does he mean by that?"

"It's his way of saying that they want to be forgiven for their sins so they don't spend a lifetime burning in hell."

"Is he really that cynical?"

"I think he's probably desensitized," I said, thinking back to the kind chaplain who had served here for decades and helped countless men before retiring. *I don't suppose that's an easy job.*

I once did a survey in one of my classes, in which I asked the inmates to rate who they would want to interact with before they died. Their choices were family members, a psychologist, a chaplain, or a dog. The dog beat the chaplain and the psychologist every time.

"Lucy, I often find that the Christian inmates don't even want to speak with the chaplain. Why do you think that is?" I asked, knowing that Lucy believed in God and had a family involved with missionary work.

Lucy looked at her freckled hands and twisted her wedding ring on her finger before she answered. "I think Catholics would want to speak to a priest, but if you're a Protestant and believe in Jesus, I don't think they all feel that there's a need to go through someone else."

"I know you spend a lot of time with the cancer patients when you are giving them chemotherapy. Do you talk with them about dying and things like God? I must admit, when I see an inmate is dying and I can't do anything more, I tend to distance myself emotionally and spend less time with them." My throat tightened. "It takes too much out of me to watch them die, especially the ones that I've known for years."

Lucy's hazel eyes darkened. "This place needs hospice. It's so sad that they have to die all alone. You know that poor man they sent to us last year, with that horrible esophageal cancer? He didn't have any family or visitors, and was so lonely that I told him to envision Jesus sitting in the chair next to his bed and that he should just talk to him like he was sitting there. I think it

291

helped him."

I remembered that tragic case. "Lucy, I really appreciate everything you do for the cancer patients. I've never felt that comfortable talking about dying and death with them, but I know that if they believe they are going to a better place, it's easier for them to let go. I feel bad, though, for the ones who are afraid of death. Often they don't want to let go, and it seems to prolong their suffering."

Two months later, Lucy came into my office and said, "Hey, did you hear that Mr. McKesson passed away this weekend?"

I put down the pen I was writing with as tears pricked my eyes. *Poor Mr. McKesson.* "I wasn't on call this weekend, but I knew he was sent out with an acute abdomen on Friday. It doesn't surprise me that he didn't make it."

"Do you think he died from the chemo treatment they were trying on him, or the cancer?"

"Well, when we get back the autopsy report, we'll find out."

She cocked her head. "Why would they do an autopsy on a terminal cancer patient?"

"Last year the state legislatures decided to do autopsies on inmates who died, regardless of the reason. I'm not sure what prompted that decision, but it's a bit problematic at times."

"What do you mean?"

"Well, you remember the old guy in the back, Mr. Renkin? "

"The guy who had severe dementia in his eighties and wouldn't eat, no matter what we did?"

"That's the one. They listed his death as starvation."

"Oh...."

"Anyway, speaking of having a hard time eating, how is Mr. Lynch doing?"

"Actually, I think he's turning the corner. I checked on him this morning, and he had eaten the fruit cocktail they got for him and was trying a bite or two of the pancakes."

"That's great. Let's hope all the suffering he went through will be worth it."

"I've got my fingers crossed," Lucy said as she walked out the door.

Thankfully, cancer doesn't always win. Luck was on the side of Mr. Lynch. He beat his cancer and left the infirmary after completing his chemotherapy and regaining his strength. I hoped he made the most of his second chance at life.

23. Mind Your Thoughts

294

I got out of my car and pulled up the collar on my long black coat. The smell of fresh snow was in the air, and I could see a line of footprints in the fresh-fallen powder. They led to the gatehouse, where Wilma was pounding on the door with her red mittens.

"How long have you been out here?" I asked, and started to walk toward the black phone attached to the side of the building.

"They ain't answerin' the phone, I just tried it." She wheezed and pulled her scarf up to cover the bottom of her face. "God, I'm gettin' too old for this. I need to move in wit' my sister in Florida."

It was 6:30am, and pitch black. The light from the towers at the end of each fence line highlighted the fresh snow covering the coiled razor wire and chain-link fence. It reminded me of a painting I had seen in a museum in Germany.

"What are you smilin' about Dr. G? We're freezin' our butts off out here."

"Wilma, we're in luck," I laughed. "I see the officer coming."

She stomped her white furry boots and muttered, "It's about time."

The officer had an electric heater at full blast in his small caged area. Wilma and I handed him our bags, took off our heavy coats and laid them on the counter, and walked through the metal detector. The machine was temperamental today, and my hair clip made it go off. I reached up and took it out, and my long hair fell down my back. As I was putting it back up, I watched Wilma try to slide through the scanner so the underwire on her bra wouldn't set it off. She didn't succeed, and the officer had to come out of his cage and wand her down.

I grabbed my coat off the counter, thinking how silly this daily charade was. *Anyone could have anything in his or her coat, but let's make the officer get out of his warm cage and wand a woman's breasts.*

When we were finally on the yard, Wilma launched into a discussion

295

on a patient who she felt needed to be seen before the clinic opened.

"You know Mr. Lear, don't ya?" she asked.

"Yeah. He's an old guy with a bad heart. He doesn't seem to come in much."

"He gives me the heebie-jeebies."

"Why? He doesn't complain, and he hardly ever bothers the medical department."

She turned her head quickly. The hooded parka covered half her face. "You know what he did, don't ya? He raped and kill't a young woman and cut her up into bits when he was eighteen. God, it's disgusting. He's been in here for probably over fifty damn years. He got a death sentence and I dunno why they haven't kill't him."

Wilma stopped, wheezing a little. "Ya walk too dang fast, Doc. Why don't you just keep goin' and I'll see ya in the clinic."

I stopped and looked at the two-story medical facility, which was only a hundred yards away. "I'm not going to leave you out here in Siberia by your-self. Besides, I'm in no rush. I don't think a lot of guys will come in today any-way."

She cackled. "Yeah. Can't you see them old guys gettin' up here today? They're probably lookin' outside at the snow and sayin' fuck it, and rollin' right back over." She started walking again.

When I walked into the exam room a short while later, Mr. Lear was sitting in a chair with his thin, pale face cocked back and his eyes closed. Sparse, thin white hair, matted from being under his hat, stuck out at odd an-gles from his head. I wondered what it would have been like to be on death row at eighteen, and what would possess someone to do such a heinous thing. Custody did not consider Lear to be a threat now, so I was in the room alone with him, with no other patients waiting.

"Mr. Lear, my nurse who saw you this weekend was concerned about the swelling in your legs and your shortness of breath. Can you take off your clothes and sit up here on the exam table?"

He took off his wet, thin sneakers and tried to get the socks off his swollen feet. He was breathing hard with the attempt.

"Mr. Lear," I said, "why don't you try to slip down your pants a bit, then just sit up on the exam table and I'll help you get out of your wet clothing."

I helped him up, and had to pull his pants down with care because his legs were so swollen and shiny with edematous fluid that I thought his skin would rupture. His feet were puffy, and his toes had a bluish tinge.

"Mr. Lear, have you been taking the medications for your heart?"

He looked down and pushed down on his thigh, leaving an indentation from his finger. "I ran out five days ago and the weather's been so bad that I haven't been able to come up and get more."

"Have you been able to get to the culinary to eat?"

He looked up, but his eyes did not engage mine. "Too cold to stand in line all that time, so I've just been eating Ramen."

I sighed. "The swelling you have now is due to the salt from the Ramen soup, and the fact that you haven't been taking your medications. You have congestive heart failure, and you really need to take those medications and stay away from salt. The nurses have already done your EKG, and it hasn't changed. I can get the fluid off of you with medications and a low-salt diet, but I recommend you come stay in the infirmary so we can turn your heart around before it gets into more trouble."

He hung his head. "I have a good spot on the yard. I don't want to lose it. Can't you just give me some medications now? I'll be all right and I won't eat my soups either. I promise."

Wilma tapped on the exam door and pushed it open. "Dr. G., The officers want to know if you're gonna admit him in the back. If you do, they're gonna have to make some bed moves, 'cause we're out of beds. Seems everyone and their brother decided to get sick this weekend. We're jam packed." She grimaced and rubbed her lower back.

"Tell them not to make any moves yet. Please ask Lucy to come in and draw some blood on Mr. Lear and put in an IV. Oh, and can you call and tell them to bring Mr. Lear up some breakfast? He hasn't eaten in a while."

Wilma nodded and disappeared.

"Mr. Lear, I'm going to see if the medications I give you will work. If you have to pee, I want you to go in this bottle, because I need to see how much fluid I can take off of you this morning. The nurses will look in on you, and if you need anything, I'll be back in a few hours, okay?" I positioned the exam table so his legs would be elevated and he could lean back and rest.

"Thanks for not putting me in the back, Dr. G. I don't want to cause any trouble."

I headed to the infirmary. The smell of pancakes and syrup greeted me when the officer opened the door that led into the infirmary. I continued down the hallway to the nurses' station, and glanced to my left as I passed the double cells. I could look through the safety glass to see two men in each room, most of them eating breakfast or curled up under grey wool blankets. I reached the nurse's desk and picked up my list for the day.

June was looking at the computer screen and tapping her red-and-green nails on the counter top. "Hey, Dr. G. The weather report says we're going to get another two feet today on the valley floor, and who knows how much the mountains will get." She swiveled in her chair to face me. "Did Dr. Tiernan come down off the mountain today?"

"No, she didn't, so I'm the only doc here today."

"Well at least you don't have to see any walk-ins in the clinic. The officer just told me they locked down the whole yard. It's snowing so hard, the officers in the towers can't see anything."

I looked at the list of patients I needed to see in the infirmary, then at the clock. *As long as there are no emergencies, I bet I could get through most of this list before lunch.*

Lucy kept me up to date on Mr. Lear, and I saw him again in the afternoon after seeing the infirmary patients. We had taken a few liters of fluid off of him by this time. I sat down in the chair after examining him, and realized I had some free time to talk with someone who had been in prison for over fifty years. *I probably won't have an opportunity like this again.*

"Mr. Lear, you've been here many years. I bet you've seen the medical department change quite a bit over the years. What was it like here decades ago?"

He leaned back, looked at the ceiling, and squeezed his eyelids shut. "There was this old doctor back in the sixties. He had this horrible shaking. He must have had Parkinson's or something. I had a bad shoulder, and he wanted to give me a cortisone shot. He was shaking so bad the officer had to hold me down for him to do it. That was the worst pain ever, I guess he couldn't find the spot."

"You must have been very young when you came to prison."

He pursed his lips and opened his eyes to gauge my expression. "I was eighteen, sitting on death row with no radio and no TV, and I couldn't read." He closed his eyes again. "I had a lot of time to just think."

"What did you think about?"

"I thought about how I got to where I was, and how come I was always so angry."

"Why do you think you were so angry?"

His eyes were still closed. "I'm not sure, but I remember when I was three or four years old and me and my brother were being watched by a babysitter. She had her sweater on a chair, and I guess me or my brother pushed the chair too close to the heater and it caught fire. She really beat me

Karen Gedney, MD

for that."

"Did that make you feel angry?"

He shrugged, but didn't open his eyes. "I guess."

"How did you get along with your parents?"

"My father was a liar. One time he told my brother that I broke his bike. My father was the one who bent the wheel when he backed over it in his car. He lied about everything."

As he went on, Lear did not mention physical or sexual abuse in his home, but it was clear that he was in no way connected to his family. The night he ran away from his home in anger and killed the woman, it was after he had heard another lie from his father. I wanted to understand why his anger was directed at her, instead of his father.

"Do you remember why you entered that woman's home that night?"

He shook his head and his eyes squeezed tighter. "The paper made it out like I knew who she was. I didn't, it was just the first house I saw the light on, and I wanted to hurt someone."

"I understand you also raped her." He opened his eyes with a start. "It wasn't about sex," he said. "I just wanted to hurt someone. It could have been anyone."

"What did you do afterward?"

"I went home and went to bed." He said it with no more emotion than someone saying they went to bed after watching TV.

"Did you feel anything afterwards?"

He leaned back and rubbed his chin. "It was like a fantasy or something surreal. I wasn't quite sure if I had done it, or just imagined it."

"What did you do the next morning?"

He shrugged. "Nothing. It was only a couple of days later when I heard a car come up the driveway. You know, in those days you could hear the difference in the alternator of a police car. When I heard it, I knew it really happened, and then I ran."

"How did they know it was you?"

"I took an expensive camera from her house and pawned it. That's how they found me."

No remorse, no emotion. *I wonder if he felt any emotion for himself, sitting alone in a death row cell with no TV, radio, or ability to read.* "What did you do all day long in your cell?"

"I just would think and sleep, until this guy taught me how to read with comic books." He opened his eyes, looked at the ceiling, and smiled. "The first book I read front to back was this book about an English and German soldier in WWII. I remembered reading that they shared a cigar." He looked at me and his eyes brightened. "I could actually smell it."

"Reading must have opened a new world for you. Did you ever read any of the religious texts, like the Bible?"

He rubbed his neck and his nose wrinkled. "Yeah, I read the Old Testament. All that killing God did, just because people didn't do what he said. He was very cruel. I couldn't understand how an all-knowing God could be like that, so I don't believe in it."

That was not the response I expected. The majority of inmates I dealt with were very attached to the concept of a God that would forgive their sins if they just believed in him and asked him.

"What do you think happens to you when you die?" I asked.

His narrow shoulders hunched forward. "Well, you just go to sleep and don't wake up." No fear, no regret, and no belief in the concepts of Heaven or Hell.

"When you were on death row as a teenager, did it ever get so bad that you contemplated taking your own life?"

He looked at his swollen legs and rubbed his thigh. "Yeah, I did try hanging myself once. Another time I took some pills and ate some ground glass bulbs, but none of it worked. So I stopped trying."

"Did you worry about being executed?"

"No, I knew I wasn't going to be executed."

"Really? How come?"

He pushed his thin white hair off his forehead. "I just knew. I'm an optimist."

I tried to reconcile the angry, violent young man of his youth with this thin, old man with swollen legs sitting in front of me with hardly any emotion—anger least of all.

"You seem to have gotten over your anger. How did that happen?"

"I stopped blaming other people and became responsible for how I felt."

"Do you think, if they ever let you out, you could be violent again?"

This time he didn't answer so quickly. He closed his eyes again, and I could almost feel him going through the possibilities in his mind.

After a moment, he straightened up and looked at me. "Maybe, if someone else was being threatened."

Wilma tapped on the door just then. She cracked the door open and asked, "Is Mr. Lear dun' ready to head back to his unit? They shoveled out the path, and I can take him over in the cart now befor'n I go home."

I looked at Mr. Lear, who was already sliding off the exam table and putting on his pants. "That would be great, Wilma. Make sure he goes with all his medications, and we need to see him back tomorrow to check his vitals and weight. And, Mr. Lear?"

He looked up, but his eyes didn't connect with mine.

"If you have to eat Ramen soup tonight, don't put the seasoning pack in it, okay?"

He nodded, and followed Wilma out into the hallway.

I stood at the nurses' station and wrote my progress note, then turned to see the psychologist Jake walking toward me. He cocked his head in the direction of Wilma and Mr. Lear.

"What did you think of him?" he asked.

"I'm not sure. Why do you ask?"

He put his palms on the counter and stretched his back. "Just wondered what you thought. I did his psych review. You know, he was in an institution at fifteen for trying to strangle and rape a girl his own age, and they let him out after eight months. Apparently he's always had fantasies like that, as long as he can remember. He told me that after he did the crime, he didn't even know whether he had really done it or just dreamed it. Did you know he cut up her body and put it in different parts of the room? Even cut off her head and took out her heart."

"I heard about that. It reminded me of one of the schizophrenic inmates, the guy who cut off his father's head and put it on the dashboard and drove around town with it. But that guy was put on psych meds. Was Mr. Lear ever medicated?"

"No. He's just a psychopath." Jake said.

"Hmm. I've heard different definitions for being a psychopath, but what were you taught?"

He stroked his short grey beard. "It all has to do with core deficits in empathy and conscience. Typical psychopaths are ruthless, fearless, and have a lot of self-confidence."

"Sounds like investment bankers, or some of the political leaders on the world stage today."

His laugh sounded almost like a bark. "You've got that right. Cold-blooded murderers and psychopathic leaders are only separated by the context, plus the degree to which they have those traits. Mr. Lear appears to have

303

had no conscience or empathy, and for whatever reason, he only fantasized about hurting someone. It reminds me of the old adage that you become what you constantly think about."

A few weeks later, I saw Mr. Tennison, a seventy-one-year-old white male who exuded vitality and did not make anyone's skin crawl. He was wearing a tight blue back brace from a major back surgery a couple of weeks previous.

"How are you doing, Mr. Tennison?"

He raised both his arms over his head, punched the air with his fists, and smiled. "One hundred percent better."

Tennison had been physically fit all his life, and in prison he had taken great joy and pleasure from pushing his body to the limit. When he was in his thirties, he was the guy on the weight pile benching four hundred pounds and squatting eight hundred. That type of lifting, though, takes its toll, and when he hit fifty he decided to work on finesse. So he started learning karate and jujitsu from some of the other inmates. Over the years Tennison had shared his thoughts on his study of Zen and martial arts with me. I will always remember his explanation: "Dr. G., it took me a while to realize that I needed to think like a dragon and not react like a tiger anymore."

Now, he stood up and faced me. "Doc, I want to know when I can start exercising again. I've been walking, but after a while I have to stop because I tighten up and feel burning down my right leg." He lifted up his right leg and, balancing on the other, started to throw some quick punches in the air.

My eyes widened. I was about to jump up and steady him, when he put his foot down with a wince. "I guess I should get out of the brace before I do that again," he chuckled.

I agreed, and skimmed his chart looking for the report from the neurosurgeon. "Mr. Tennison, you left the infirmary the day after you arrived from the hospital, and never asked for pain meds. Most of our back surgery patients pressure us for meds, and feel victimized if they don't get their narcotics. What's different with you?"

He snorted. "You can't teach a victim not to be one." He paused, then his blue eyes lit up. "Do you know Ronnie Lott?"

I shook my head.

"He was a famous football player who got took out of a game because he mangled a finger and couldn't hold the ball. He told them to cut off the part that was in the way, taped it up, and finished the game," he said with a grin.

"I can see you identify with that mindset. I'm curious. You've been in the prison for over forty years. Every time I see you, you appear to have a positive outlook, and you do what you can to take care of yourself physically and mentally. What do you think accounts for that?"

He looked at me with a face that was open, alive, and twenty years younger in appearance than his real age.

"When I first came in, someone told me I had two choices. I could be a victim, or make victims. I stayed away from gangs, but I was a hot reactor. After a while they stayed away from me, because they knew I would fight and I had nothing to lose." He shrugged. "When I got into martial arts and Zen, I learned to think before I react. Now I tell the young guys, 'Do what you can live with.'"

"Well, I wish more people would think before they react. It's a good philosophy to live by, and I'm glad you're teaching it to the young guys on the yard. I know how many of them respect guys like you. "

He cocked his head and his brown eyes twinkled. "It's like they say: 'when the student is ready, the teacher appears.' It took me fifty years to be ready to learn about Zen, and to be honest, it just happened because my body couldn't fight every time anymore."

"Well, the important thing is that you learned that lesson." I smiled. "It looks like you are healing nicely, and your right leg seems a little stronger. Are you glad you went through the surgery?"

He got up, pulled his shoulders back, and flexed his biceps. "I'll know when I can really start exercising again. When do you think that will be? I'm going stir crazy."

"Whoa tiger, remember you need to think like a dragon. You only had the surgery a few weeks ago. Your back needs to be completely healed and stable before you really get back into exercise. You will have to take things far slower than you want. You'll see the neurosurgeon in three to four weeks, and he'll tell you when he thinks you can work out again. In the meantime, just walk—and keep your brace on."

"I knew you were going to tell me that, Doc, but you're still raining on my parade."

"I'd order you an umbrella, but Custody would think it was a weapon."

A month later, I happened to meet another long-timer, Mr. Randall. To my surprise, when I walked into the room, he was sitting straight in the chair with his eyes closed, hands resting on his thighs palms-up in a slightly curled position. He was breathing in and out slowly. His belly moved forward with each deep breath, causing a strain on the buttons of his clean, faded blue shirt.

"Mr. Randall?" I said softly, and let the door close slowly.

He opened his grey eyes, arched his back, and exhaled. "Hi, Dr. G."

"Where were you?" I asked, and sat down on the stool next to him.

The corners of his mouth curled up, and the wrinkles around his eyes deepened.

"I wasn't in prison," he replied.

"I could see that. It looked like you were meditating. Do you do that often, or just when you have to wait on a doctor who's running behind schedule?"

He leaned back in the chair, stretched out his legs, and rubbed the greying stubble on his chin. "I've been practicing meditation since I became a Buddhist. It's not the easiest thing to do in here, because you can never find a quiet place where the guys won't mess with you."

"How long have you been a Buddhist?"

He looked at the white ceiling above him. "About twenty years." He put his hands palm to palm, bent his head forward, and touched his lips to his index fingers. "So -I had just got out of solitary confinement for the umpteenth time and I knew I just couldn't do it again. I was so tired of hating, fighting, and blaming everyone, and just creating more problems for myself." He lowered his hands and exhaled. "I wanted peace, and when I looked around, I noticed that old man Dent seemed to be the only con on the tier who looked like he had it. I watched him for a while, and then asked him to tell me his secret. He's the one who taught me how to meditate. It actually helped me unwind. Later, he taught me about Buddha and gave me books to read. You know Buddha was a prince? He could have had anything he wished for, but he left that world when he saw suffering. He spent his whole life trying to understand suffering and help people."

Randall paused and took another deep, slow breath. "When I was a kid, I prayed to God to have him stop my father from beating me and my mother all the time. It didn't help. One night when I was only nine years old, my father bashed in my mother's head and killed her. I couldn't do anything. I ended up in the foster system, bouncing from one place to another. The only emotions I ever felt back then were anger and hatred. Now I truly understand that my suffering had to do with my attachments."

"What do you mean by that?" I asked.

He turned his head toward me and smiled. "I was attached to the thought of having a loving father and mother. That wasn't my life. I learned to let it go, and I don't suffer like I used to. The meditation really helps me. One time I experienced a feeling that I can't even describe. It was like I was one with everything. I knew I would be all right, no matter what happens in my life."

"Thanks for sharing your story with me, Mr. Randall. I've read of the

307

medical benefits of deep breathing and meditation. I wish there was a way of teaching the inmates here."

He laughed. "So, why don't you teach them?"

I opened his chart. "Let's talk about your labs instead, so I can get you out of here before count time."

My day was a long one, and when I left the medical facility that night, I saw the full moon come up and soften the lines of the squat grey buildings on the empty prison yard. I noticed all the pigeons huddled on top of one of the units facing the culinary, and wondered idly if that unit had a warmer roof for some reason.

The full moon was huge that night. I knew that some of the staff in the mental health unit believed that moods fluctuated with the phase of the moon. *How many beliefs to explain behavior have come and gone over the centuries? How many tactics have been used to try to change people's behavior? Isn't that what every religion, law, and philosophy has tried to do since the dawn of human history? And do prisons change their inmates' underlying beliefs and behavior?*

After watching the inmates for over twenty-five years, what did I see? In honesty, I saw that some of them did succeed and change their behavior. But to do it, they had to take individual responsibility for their actions—not blame their circumstances in life, no matter how horrible those circumstances were. They had to ask themselves some basic questions that caused them to think, not just react. They had to ask themselves if they wanted a different life and what it would take to get it. They had to decide whether they could commit to changing themselves, and whether they could remain consistent no matter what happened.

Many people, especially the ones in custody, believe that people can't change. I choose to believe they can.

Had Mr. Lear changed? If he was free, would he commit a heinous crime again? He had no remorse, no empathy, and did not seem connected to

308

anyone—not even to himself. I doubted he had ever asked himself whether he *could* change. I wondered what anomaly in the brain caused that, and whether it would someday be treatable.

Had Mr. Tennison changed? It seemed he had, out of necessity. *He got older and wiser, started asking different questions, and now he thinks like a dragon. Nothing wrong with changing yourself because you have to, especially now that he's mentoring young guys.*

Had Mr. Randall changed? It seemed his change had come from within, because it was too painful to keep on being a victim and acting out in a way that was only hurting himself. He had been lucky to find a belief system and technique that helped him cope.

As I reached the outside gate, the yipping of the coyotes interrupted my stream of thoughts. I looked up at the moon again and smiled. *So you were responsible for my questions and thoughts tonight.*

24. Senior Grit

I opened the door of the exam room and a scrawny, elderly white male stood up and took off his blue baseball cap off. "Good morning Dr. G. How are you?"

"That's supposed to be my line, Mr. Drew."

He grinned, showing grey, stained teeth. "I keep telling you, Doc, you need to call me Scrappy."

I tilted my head and smiled. "It fits you, but I feel more comfortable calling everyone by their last name. So, Mr. Drew, what can I do for you today?"

"I didn't want to bother you, but Jenny asked me to make an appointment so you could look at my knee."

"Jenny really looks after you guys in that unit. How do you like the new senior program?"

His light blue eyes sparkled. "You have no idea what a godsend that program is for us old guys. Jenny's the first psychologist who has ever really helped us in this place. She calls it diversion therapy and programs, but I call it a miracle that will help a bunch of old guys live again."

"Sounds interesting. Why don't you tell me about that after I examine your knee. Have you had swelling in this knee before?"

He touched his right knee. "Well, it got messed up in Vietnam and really swelled up. But it seemed to heal, because it didn't stop me from a boxing career."

"Is that why you're called Scrappy?" I asked as I put his knee through a range of motions.

He nodded. "I got that nickname when I was a professional lightweight boxer, but that was a long time ago. I'm lucky now if I can make it to the chow line with this knee. Sometimes it just seems to lock up and I can't even get out of the unit. The other guys look out for me, and that's what's so great about this program, but Jenny thinks I need a wheelchair so I can get to the culinary."

There was no heat or redness in his knee, and the history of it locking up made me concerned about a medial meniscus that was now getting stuck in the joint, or arthritic changes that impaired movement. I looked through his chart and saw no previous X-rays or recent labs. The rest of his exam was unremarkable, except that he was underweight for his size.

"Well, Mr. Drew, I'm glad the guys in your program are looking out for you. But if you can't get to the culinary on your own, I think a wheelchair for now is a good idea. I'd also like to get some X-rays on your knee and check your labs to see if we can do anything that would help you out."

"Okay Doc, but don't worry about me. I couldn't be happier in the Senior Grit program, it's given me back my life."

"In what way?"

"Well, Jenny cares about us old guys. She wants to help us and makes sure that we really do the work. Her programs deal with things that a lot of us guys haven't dealt with in the past, like sexual offenses. In groups, she makes sure everyone knows what's expected of them. Everyone signs a contract, and if they aren't respectful or don't participate, they don't stay in the program. It's a beautiful thing. The guys look out for each other now and deal with their shit." He looked up. "I mean, I haven't seen guys let down all their defenses and come clean like that in a long time." He shook his head. "I've seen a lot of tears, and you know as well as I do that you can only allow yourself to feel emotions if you feel safe."

"Wow, that sounds impressive."

He rubbed his gnarled hands together as he continued. "It's not just the programs. Jenny knows we have to do something and feel like our life matters." He snapped his fingers. "For example. She somehow got yarn donated, and a bunch of us are learning to crochet. We're making cat baskets and they're being donated to the Humane Society."

"I'm impressed. Who's teaching you how to crochet?"

He laughed. "Hey, some of us know how to crochet, and we're teaching the other guys who want to learn. Some of them are making hats and socks and even animals. All of it is donated to organizations. You see the beauty? We get to do something where we're actually helping people or an animal. I love it."

I stood up. "It's great to hear you so excited about the program. I hope it continues to do good things for you. Why don't you get dressed, and I'll have the nurse take you down to X-ray and do your labs."

"Do you think I can have a wheelchair for now?"

I turned around. "There will be one waiting for you after the tests. I want you to use it only when you really need it. You don't want to let your muscles and balance systems to get weak."

He folded his arms and chuckled. "There's a reason they call me Scrappy, Doc. I'll probably just lean on it when I hobble over to the culinary. I don't want to end up in a wheelchair full time."

I walked out to the nurses' station and handed Wilma the chart. "Mr. Drew will need an X-ray, some labs, and can you see if you can find him a wheelchair."

Wilma scratched the side of her wrinkled neck and rolled her eyes. "You're gettin' too soft, Dr. G. Them old guys are just playin' ya. I'm tellin' ya, they're startin' to think if they just complain to that psychologist, she can call you up and they can get on the schedule." She pushed herself out of the chair and pointed at the list. "Lookie here, three of them old farts from that same unit are on your list today."

"True, but you know we had room on the schedule to fit them in before lunch."

She sat down with a huff. "That's not the point. Them old farts need to put in a kite just like the rest of 'em."

"Hmm. Don't worry, I'll talk to the psychologist about it." *So it's my day to see the old farts, is it? Might as well get started.*

I entered the next room to see Mr. Reyes, whose voice trembled when he asked, "Is the news bad?"

"I'm glad to say that I have good news for you today, Mr. Reyes. Take a deep breath, relax, and I'll tell you what the cancer specialist has recommended for you."

He inhaled deeply, and some of the worry left his brown eyes.

"So, all your pathology tests are back now and the cancer they removed from your colon didn't spread. All the lymph nodes they sampled are free of cancer. That means the cancer specialists feel you don't need chemotherapy and should do extremely well."

The breath Reyes was still holding came out in a sigh. He slumped forward a little, putting his hands on the knees of his worn blue jeans.

"We will be following you with tests and colonoscopies in the future, but for now you should consider yourself very fortunate and enjoy your life." I said with a smile.

Reyes leaned back, closed his eyes, and chuckled, "I was ready to hear the worst. I thought I was a goner."

"You were very lucky that you came in when you did, and that we were able to remove it before it spread."

He looked at me and cleared his throat. "I'm lucky that Jenny got me in to see you. You know, the other doctor told me I just had an irritable bowel. If it wasn't for her, I probably would have died."

"Jenny's good at sending me cases that benefit from a second opinion. So Mr. Reyes, I just talked to a guy from your unit who says he loves the Senior Grit program. What about you?"

He smoothed back his dark hair, which had a few streaks of grey in it. "You should come over sometime and see what goes on there, Dr. G." He smiled. "We have three different bands now, and I'm the lead singer for the

314

doo-wop group. I never thought I'd be singing in a band again. On the outside, I made my living that way. There's a bunch of us in the program who were musicians on the outside, and now we can start jammin' again."

"I didn't know that was going on. Where did all the musical instruments come from?"

His face lit up and ten years fell away. "You ever hear of Wayne Kramer and Jail Guitar Doors?"

I shook my head.

"Well, he's a famous musician who did some time in prison and he now donates guitars to inmates. Can you believe it? We got ten guitars, rhythm, bass, cords, amps, everything. You've got to come out to the unit and hear us sometime."

"I'd like to. I'll talk with Jenny and see when it would be a good time to come over. Do you have any other questions before you go?"

He stood up. "No, I'm good. Thanks for the good news, Doc. Just come over sometime and hear us play."

"It's a deal."

We both walked out of the room. I picked up the thick chart on the counter, and entered the next exam room.

"Good morning, Mr. Toney. How are you today?"

He looked out the door and asked, "How's Reyes? We're all worried about him. Is he going to be all right?"

"Yes he is. Are you in the Senior Grit program as well? Aren't you only fifty-four?"

"Yeah I am, but I feel like I'm in my seventies."

I didn't doubt that. Toney was a hundred pounds overweight, had diabetes, gout, hypertension, arthritis, and stage three kidney disease. He was in on a sexual offense, which made his life miserable on the yard—and the other men calling him "Baby Huey" didn't help.

After his exam was finished, I asked Toney what he thought of the Senior Grit program. *He always sees everything in a negative light. Let's see what he has to say about this.*

To my surprise, a small smile appeared on his round, pale face. "I like the diversion therapy. I'm teaching some of the guys how to crochet, and you should see some of the arts and craft things we are making. Yesterday one of the guys showed me a box he made out of coffee grounds, and it looks like he made it out of wood. He painted an owl on the top. It could be a great jewelry box for someone."

"Sounds nice. What else do you do in the diversion therapy?"

"Well, some of the guys do puzzles and, you know, dominos and play bridge. We are even doing an exercise program now for the guys in wheelchairs."

I nodded. "I understand Jenny has developed programs addressing the guys' problems that put them in prison, like addictions and sexual offenses. Are you in any of those programs?"

He hung his head. He knew that we had discussed his sexual offense in the past. As a child, he had been molested by a neighbor who had given him attention he hadn't received from his mother.

"Yeah, I'm in the S.O. program," he replied. "Jenny makes sure it's safe. If anyone just keeps making excuses for their behavior and can't see the victim's point of view, they don't stay in the group. It's hard to let yourself feel anything in here. You never know what can be used against you. But I'm starting to feel a little safer now."

"I'm glad to hear that, Mr. Toney. I hope you continue doing the work you need to do. Before you go, we need to do some labs on you today. Okay?"

As Toney got up to leave, I watched how he used the arms of the chair to push himself up, and then stood for a few seconds before he could hobble the twenty steps to the treatment room.

Wilma caught my eye and pointed at the clock. "I hope y'all don't want anythin' more than labs, because it's gonna be count time soon."

I looked at the clock, then back at Toney, still wobbling down the hallway. "You're right. He's got ten minutes to get back to the Senior Grit program, and it's in Unit Three. He'll never make it in that amount of time. I'll tell the officer to put him on out count."

Wilma cackled. "Maybe you wanna give him a wheelchair too."

I smiled. "You know me, Wilma. If they're overweight and can still move, I want them to move. He's not going to waste away like the other patient if he misses a few meals in the culinary."

I walked down the hallway toward the administrative side of the building and lunch with Dr. Alie Tiernan.

On the wall behind Alie's desk was a poster which read *Never argue with an idiot, he'll drag you down to his level and beat you with experience.* There were two large stacks of light-green charts sitting on the edge of her desk. I sat down and began opening my lunch.

"See anything interesting this morning?" Alie asked.

"I was seeing a bunch of old guys who were all happy and excited about what they were doing over in Unit Three. Have you heard about the Senior Grit program yet?"

"No, but it certainly describes some of the clothing they come over in."

"Ha, you would say that. A lot of those old guys are veterans from the Vietnam and Korean wars. They think of grit as toughness and strength of character."

Alie laughed. "Well, they may have been tough at one time, but now they're a bunch of whiners."

"The three guys that I saw today seem to be less interested in whining

317

and more interested in what they're doing in the program. It's a welcome change. Who knows? It may decrease their sick calls, because they'll have something else to do besides sit on their bunks."

"I'm all for that. What are they doing over there anyway?"

"Would you believe they are crocheting, doing wheelchair exercises, making crafts, and they have three different bands with instruments?"

Alie's forehead wrinkled. "How did that all happen?"

"When I see Jenny, I'll have to ask her how she got that program going. I thought I was the only one who was into programs."

"Maybe Dr. G. has competition for the Saint spot," Alie said, and laughed.

"I hope so. It would be great if there was another person with a target on their ass," I chuckled.

A few days later, I was in the medical records room pulling charts when Jenny walked in.

"Have you seen Dana?" Jenny asked, looking into the small side room where the medical records coordinator usually sat.

"She called in sick today. Is there anything I can help you with?"

She sighed and rubbed her forehead. "Dana told me yesterday that she had the paperwork I need to help one of the old guys get help on the outside when he leaves. Today I found out from the caseworker that he's leaving tomorrow." Her usually bright brown eyes looked tired. "He's eighty, and I was trying to see if I could get him into a nursing home. He has no family on the outside and can't take care of himself."

I leaned against the wall. "That's crazy. Didn't the caseworker know way ahead of time when he was scheduled to get out, so they could help him?"

She sat down on the chair next to the wall. "You'd think so, but Central figures out the time, and caseworkers don't always get much warning."

"So they're just going to drop him off at a bus stop and give him his twenty-one dollars?"

Jenny put her hands behind her head, clasping them and arching her neck backward. "I heard it's twenty-eight dollars. I also heard that amount was picked forty years ago, because it was the amount needed for a bus to take them to the next state."

"I've heard that story as well, and it figures. That amount of money won't get them anywhere. I did have a guy last week who got out, spent it in a bar, and was back in custody in less than twenty-four hours. When I saw him on intake, I asked him what he was thinking. He told me he had nowhere to go and would rather be in prison than under a bridge freezing that night."

Jenny finished stretching and shook her head. "It isn't right, especially with these old guys. They need real discharge planning so they don't end up in an emergency room or the morgue."

"The inmates tell me the Senior Grit program is really helping them on the yard, though. How did you start it? I've been here a lot longer than you, and it seems we're the only two people who believe that programs are worthwhile and are willing to run them."

"Not the only two. Did you know that Director Jackson asked me to come up from the prison down south and start a program like this?"

"Really? Now that I think about it, it makes sense. When she started here, she was the first prison director who ever called me over to her office and talked to me about what I was doing with the programs. The director before her canceled the Toastmasters program I had been running for over a decade, and didn't even give me the courtesy of telling me why. Thank god we have a new prison director now who isn't one of the good old boys."

"I know what you mean," Jenny said with a half smile.

"I loved it when she started the Puppies on Parole program at Max. I just wish it could have been on this yard."

"That program is a real win-win scenario," Jenny agreed. "I've always felt that there's nothing like the unconditional love of a dog to heal someone." The program united dogs at the SPCA who otherwise would have been euthanized with inmates volunteering to train them.

"Seems you're healing some of the guys with your programs in Unit Three. I even hear you're running a group for the sex offenders. How did you get involved with that one?"

"Back in the seventies, I started as a parole agent and I had to develop programs for the sex offenders I had as parolees. It sort of became an area of expertise for me. It interested me so much that I got my Master's in psychology to pursue it."

"I always hear people say you can't change a sex offender. What do you think?" I asked.

"They can change their behavior, but they have to come clean and be able to empathize with their victim. They have to do the work, and many don't want to. It's like an addict. You can change their behavior, but they have to do the work, and they need support." She paused. "It's also tough with the old guys, because some of their behavior occurs when their brains get disinhibited. The classic is the guy with Alzheimer's in the nursing unit, saying and doing inappropriate sexual things."

I nodded in agreement and flashed back to a number of mentally ill or demented patients who annoyed the nursing staff with their off-color remarks and masturbation displays. "I've had a variety of those guys, and I know what you mean. Anyway, besides the programs that you are doing, I wanted to thank you for getting all those wheelchairs and walkers donated. That really helped the medical department."

"Thanks for saying that. You know, I got in trouble for it. Central asked me why, and I told them we didn't have enough wheelchairs for the old guys and it would save money."

"Well, I appreciate what you did. Whenever we ask Central for more equipment or supplies, they tell us the money isn't in the budget. They don't seem to understand that the inmates are getting older and sicker. They will cost the system a great deal more money than they are allocating for."

"Sometime you have to come over to the unit and see what we're doing in the program. The first Saturday of every month we bring in the therapy dogs and one of the bands plays for us." She giggled. "You should see Mr. Drew dance. He was gyrating so much, I thought he was going to fall over and I grabbed his hand to steady him. Would you believe one of the officers wrote me up for dancing with him?"

"I'd believe it, if it was Kranzi." I replied.

"How did you know?" she asked as she stood up.

"Because he'd write up his own mother," I said, and waved goodbye.

On the ride home that night I thought about Jenny, and how one individual in a system could create a program that could change lives for the better. But we could only accomplish it with the help of someone in power, like the new prison director, who believed in the value of programs. The downside of programs like Jenny's though, was that they were at risk for falling apart, if the person who started them left and they had not become institutionalized with people who were ready to take it over.

When I started in the prison, there were hardly any old men in the population. Now this yard had become geriatric. Part of it was due to the fact that the system had built the regional medical facility here, but part of it was also related to the length of the inmates' sentences. The lifers and the men with long terms did not go home. They just got older and more frail. They also experienced accelerated aging related to their prior lifestyle choices and living in an unhealthy environment.

I was glad Jenny had taken on the old men and given them something else to do, other than sitting around and getting debilitated and demented. The yard was not ready to deal with hundreds of debilitated, demented men. The system barely had two bathroom facilities on the yard that were ADA

321

compliant. The prison system was not built with the thought that it would have to house a large population of nursing-home patients.

When I had started, decades earlier, I saw a need in helping the younger men with their addictions and lifestyle choices. Now those same men were middle-aged and complaining about the 'youngsters.' No one stays young forever. How to stay vital, active, and able to be an asset to society as long as possible—this was not only a question for the outside world, it had to be addressed on the inside of a prison as well. Jenny was trying to give the men a way to be active and still contribute, even if it was with simple crocheted products and crafts. She was doing all this with volunteers, and with her own time and money.

I thought back to all the volunteers who had given their time to teach in my life-skills course, Health Related Recovery. *How many years have I been running HRR? Wow, almost twenty-five years, and I've taught a class in camp or on the yard almost every week for all that time. How many did I help? I have no idea. But I know I tried.*

When I trained to be a doctor, I didn't realize that the word comes from the Latin verb *docere*, which means "to teach." In prison, I found that I loved teaching patients and inmates what they needed to know in order to heal and thrive. I had some remarkable success stories, and will never forget them. Nothing else came close to the feeling I got from helping inmates improve their lifestyle choices and how they viewed the world.

25. Health Related Recovery (HRR)

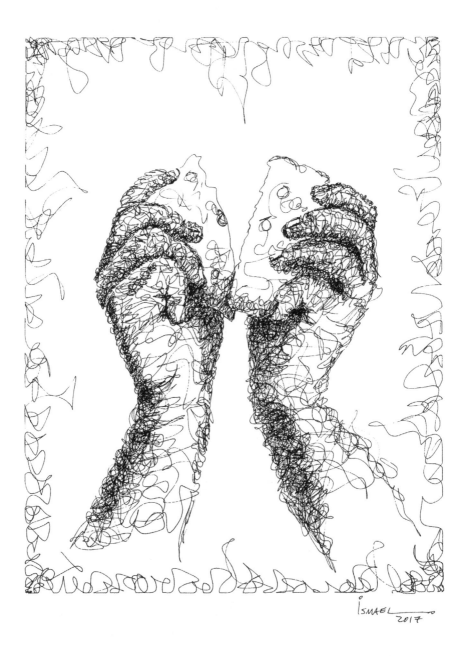

Coley picked up a piece of sushi and dipped it into the small porcelain cup of rice vinegar. He pushed the bottle of soy sauce away. "See? I'm being good tonight."

"Your blood pressure will appreciate it," I said, and took a forkful of crab off his Godzilla roll.

He pushed back the cuff of his black shirt and checked his watch. "Do we have to pick up anything at the store before the graduation tonight?"

"No, I've got Mom's cookies in the car, and the inmates still have enough coffee and creamer from the last HRR graduation."

"How many of your speakers are going to make it tonight? Is Gino going to be there? I haven't seen him recently."

"Well, you saw him four months ago at the last graduation, and you know he wouldn't miss the opportunity to tell a couple of jokes."

Coley took a sip of hot tea, and I could see him contemplating whether he was going to order another sushi roll.

"Go ahead and get another one, if you're still hungry. I'm full."

His smile made him look younger than his age, and he laughed, "That's because you ate all the crab off my Godzilla roll. So. Besides Gino and us, who else is coming?"

"Harry. Remember, you met him once. He's the big guy with grey hair and glasses who is heavily involved with the local AA chapter. At first he was a bit timid as a speaker, but he's really enjoying it now and he told me how much he appreciates the opportunity to make a difference. Lorraine will be there as well. She said she was going to bring in some fliers for halfway houses and job opportunities on the outside. Did I tell you she's trying to start a program to help guys when they leave?"

Coley shook his head and took another sip of tea.

"It seems she already put together a support group for them on the outside. It's run by ex-inmates who are running their own successful businesses."

Coley's eyes lit up. "I'll have to talk to her about that, and incorporate it into the business classes I'm teaching at Max."

"How's the teaching going out there?" I asked, watching Coley eat the remaining pink ginger off my plate.

"Couldn't be better. Custody is really supporting programs since that new prison director was hired."

"Yeah, she's program-oriented, and it is so much easier to run them now. You know how much trouble I had trying to keep the program going with the last director."

"I know. I also know how much the volunteers enjoy coming out and making a difference in the inmates' lives. At the last graduation, Gino told me that even though he only teaches two classes in a four-month course, he looks forward to them for weeks. He misses being a teacher and a counselor since his retirement. This gives him an opportunity to use his skills."

"And an opportunity to tell his jokes to a new audience every four months."

"Yes, there is that," Coley chuckled, and waved the waiter over so he could pay the bill.

When I entered the gatehouse, the officer stretched his neck to peer at the two large, clear plastic boxes filled with cookies. I handed him the piece of paper giving me approval to bring them in. "Would you like some?"

"You have the ones with the powdered sugar on them?"

"Sure do," I said, and opened the lid on one of the boxes so he could take some.

He put them on a piece of paper next to his coffee cup and chuckled, "I made the mistake of telling my mother that I had the best cookies I ever had in my life in prison. So, you got any more guests coming in?"

"No, that's it."

As I walked through the mailroom, I turned my head to make sure Coley was following me with the other box of cookies, and saw the officer wiping powdered sugar from his lips.

Gino, a Sicilian man with silver hair and the type of skin that didn't age, caught up to us and clapped Coley on the shoulder. "Did you hear the one about the Irish guy who ordered three shots of whiskey?" Coley rolled his big brown eyes and looked at me. They had known each other for years and enjoyed teasing each other.

On the walk over, Gino stopped and bent over to pick up a little clump of feathers from the side of the path. He placed them in the pocket of his jacket.

"Gino," Coley asked, "are you making some dream weaver catcher thing?"

I smiled, thinking about what inmates told me about their dreams after Gino's talk on dream analysis.

When we entered the medical facility, the four inmates who comprised my steering committee were getting the large classroom in order and making coffee. I handed the boxes of cookies to Carl. He and Ken would be dividing them up and putting them on forty paper plates. It was important that each inmate in the class received the same amount and types of cookies. They always passed them out during the break, and the inmates could eat them in the second half of the program. They were not allowed to take any cookies when they left. An officer had to check them before and after class to make sure they did not leave with anything they hadn't come in with.

I watched the steering committee swing into action, and thought back to the original group of incarcerated Vietnam veterans, including Harold Green, who had made this class possible for so many other men.

The inmates valued and took pride in the course. They protected it by not doing anything that would compromise it. This resonated with the guest teachers, who volunteered their time out of belief in the inmates' capacity to change.

Marcus, a handsome young black male who was the newest member of the steering committee, was getting coffee for the speakers as I entered the tiny steering committee office. I also saw John putting together the graduation certificates. A quiet, unsmiling white male, he reminded me of a stoic cowboy.

"John, can you give me a list of the supplies we'll need for the next class?" I asked, and opened the supply cabinet.

He reached over and handed me a printed list. "It's all there, Dr. G. We're going to need more ink cartridges for the printer."

I picked up the graduation certificates, the attendance list, the agenda for the night, and the evaluations of each speaker. He had those in a spreadsheet, which also incorporated all the data from the forty men in the class.

"John, how do you keep up with all of this? I know you work full time in prison industry, take college classes, and do this as a volunteer twice a week."

His grey eyes showed a trace of sadness. "So do all the guys on the committee, Dr. G. All we have is time."

"Well, I really appreciate what all of you do for this program."

Soon, the officer gave me a thumbs up to indicate that all the inmates were in the room and accounted for. I walked into the room and surveyed the faces of the inmates, who were all excited at the prospect of graduating—and getting some of my mother's cookies, which had garnered quite a reputation on the yard over the years. My four guest lecturers—Coley, Harry, Lorraine, and Gino—were sitting in chairs on the right side of the large room, next to the wall. The inmates were sitting behind their desks. They started to quiet down as I walked in the room and held my hand up.

"Tonight is graduation night."

The inmates started cheering and clapping. I raised my hand and waited for the silence.

"Tonight, is also the night I can thank and honor the people that help me teach this class. My steering committee: Ken, Carl, Marcus, and John. Without them and their knowledge of how to get things done in the prison, I wouldn't be able to run this program. They believe in the program, and they conduct themselves in a way that keeps this program above reproach. That means they keep me out of trouble."

The inmates started to laugh and one of them said, "Yeah, they've gotta protect Dr. G.'s ass."

"That's true, and all of you have to conduct yourself in a way that will keep me out of trouble as well." The laughter quieted down. "I consider the men in the steering committee as heroes. Do you know why?"

A few of the inmates looked at each other, and the rest looked at the steering committee members standing at the left side of the room.

"When I talk about a hero, I am talking about the type of hero from myths and legends of the ancient past. A hero's journey in that time included surviving hard, dangerous times that the gods threw at them."

"A hero chooses to pursue something noble, and never gives up in his pursuit until he achieves it. He learns and becomes wise from his trials, and when he returns, he shares his wisdom and noble pursuit. You might wonder what I'm talking about, but ask yourself: has a hero's journey really changed that much from ancient times? "

"Have *you* survived hard and dangerous times? Are *you* pursuing something noble, like being a positive force in this world? Do you give up when it is difficult, or do you never give up until you achieve it? Did you become bitter and angry from what happened to you in your life, or did you become wiser? When you return to the outside world someday, will you become that type of hero? We do not have control of what is thrown at us in life, but we do control what we do with it."

I turned to my right, and looked at my guest speakers. "Harry, Lorraine, Gino and my husband, Coley, are all heroes in their own right. I know they've shared their backgrounds with you and told you why they come out here and teach you. They believe in a person's ability to learn, grow, and be a positive force in the world. They are champions of the underdog. Don't let them down."

I gave each one of my steering committee and guests a certificate of gratitude with a picture and a special quote just for them, which I read out loud. When I called Gino up, the inmates started chanting, "Joke! Joke! Joke!" Gino raised his hands and looked at me with a grin. "My audience wants it."

The inmates quieted down, and Gino squared his shoulders. "Have you ever heard of the man who had sex with a chicken?"

I felt a few inmates' glances slide toward me. Gino raised his hand to his mouth, coughed—and out of his fist, feathers flew.

The class howled in laughter. Some were laughing so loud that I thought the officer was going to come in and check on us to see what was happening. Gino's brown eyes were shining like a kid who rounded home base.

I called out each man's name and they walked up to shake my hand as they received their certificate. Each certificate was in a plastic holder, with two extra copies. My steering committee had advised me on the importance of giving extra copies of the certificate, because many would send a copy to their mother or family to show what they had accomplished. Others needed it to show the courts that they were involved in programs to help them with their problems.

On the drive home, I asked Coley, "So what did you think of my little speech tonight?"

"Well, you left them with a sense of hope and purpose. You know, I think the worst thing you can do in life is to crush someone's hope. I've watched over the years how Custody deals with the inmates. Most of them are professional. They just want to do their job, and they don't see it in their job description to crush anyone's hope for a better life. There are a few of the old yard dogs, though, that take pleasure in bullying the inmates. The problem is that the harm they inflict is disproportionate to their number."

I tried to read Coley's face, but he kept his eyes on the road.

"Coley, remember the first time I dragged you into the prison?"

He glanced at me and I could see a smile forming. "How could I forget? Now look what you've done to me. You turned me into a good person."

Over the past twenty-five years, Coley had taught college classes in five different prisons, been a guest lecturer for my HRR class, and acted as staff liaison for the incarcerated vets group and the Toastmasters group with me.

"I always held out hope for you." I said with a sly smile.

He shook his head and started laughing. "You know, before I set foot in a prison, I just thought lock 'em up and throw away the key. But now..."

I thought about that comment. *What did I believe before taking this job? I suppose I never thought about prisons before I stepped into one.*

"What do you think now?" I asked.

"I don't think we should waste human potential that way. I've taught in the community college and I've taught out here, and I find these guys are more committed. I've seen them succeed in the outside world against all odds, so it only makes sense to me to give them the tools they need. Education is what it's all about, whether it's school, a program, or learning a new skill."

"Anything that works and can help them stay healthy and out of prison interests me. It seems to me that if the system wanted a solution, they would approach it in a scientific manner. You study what works, what doesn't, and what it costs. Like Puppies on Parole. I love that program; I just wish it was on my yard. When I was over at Max, I got to see some of the dogs and how the inmates were being trained to take care of them. Almost all of the dogs are pit mixes, and considered unadoptable because of their behavior. Just think about it. There are people who love animals enough to give a dangerous, violent dog another chance by exposing it to consistent love and direction. But when you talk about doing it with humans…"

"Hmm, I know what you mean. I've seen a change on the yard with those dogs. The inmates as a group protect them, and the yard has become less violent. One of the guys in my class told me that an officer tried to provoke an incident with a dog, and the other officers and the inmates wouldn't let it happen."

Officers and provoking incidents. I remembered the horrific story my first prison director, Director Sumtin, had told me. He had said that when he started working for the system, the Max yard was overrun with feral cats. So he told the officers to take care of the problem. The officers chose to round up the cats, put them in burlap bags, and bludgeon them to death in front of the inmates.

When Director Sumtin told me that story, his concern was that the officers' actions could have incited a riot. All I could think about was how someone could do that to an animal—and in front of someone who probably considered those cats to be pets.

"I'm glad the inmates didn't let someone ruin the dog program. You know, if they feel a program is worthwhile, they tend to protect it. That can mean not doing anything that an officer would find fault with, or keeping the inmates who are troublemakers out of the program."

"So, what's going to happen to your HRR program when you leave the prison someday?" Coley asked as we pulled into our driveway.

I rubbed the back of my neck. "I'm grooming one of the new speakers, who might be interested in taking it on. He's retired and already is coming out as a volunteer with a religious group. We'll see." I yawned and opened the car door. "Boy, am I going to sleep tonight."

26. Unintended Consequences

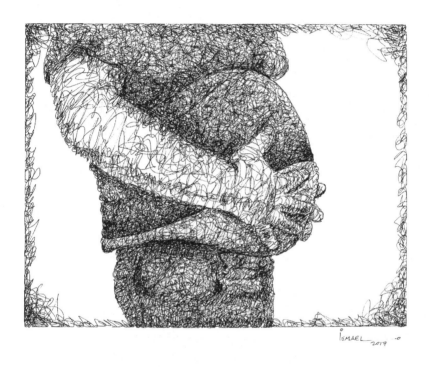

Warden Bimbit didn't last long. A few months later a new warden by the name of Damerin was hired. The changes he made on the yard had not gone over well with the inmates or with many of the staff. It wasn't long before the changes started to cause things to unravel.

I frowned when I saw Mr. Whalen waddle into the first exam room. He was built like a sphere, had no neck, and no interest in changing his lifestyle.

"Mr. Whalen, how are you today?" I asked, and looked at his most recent lab. His glycohemoglobin, which reflected how well his diabetes was controlled, was atrocious.

He was short of breath just from trying to get up on the exam table. "I feel like shit all the time, and the meds aren't helping my diabetes." He pointed his finger at me. "You told me I'd feel better without smoking, and fuck it, I gained twenty pounds. I feel even worse. If they hadn't taken it off the yard, I'd start smoking again."

"Stopping smoking can affect your metabolism and even your weight at first, but if you want to avoid your next heart attack, nothing will be as effective as not smoking." Whalen snorted, and loosened the button on his pants.

"You've already had two heart attacks and have gone through angioplasty twice and have two stents. Do you want to avoid a third one?"

His small brown eyes glared at me. "What do you think?" he muttered.

I waited a few seconds. "I think you don't want to have another heart attack, or complications of diabetes like losing your legs or ending up on dialysis. But I'm not sure you're committed to make the changes you need in your life."

"Well, how the hell do I eat what you want me to eat, when they just feed us shit? You see what they are giving us now for lunch. We're getting four pieces of white bread and that green, slimy baloney." He started to get red in the face. "And we get the same goddamn lunch every day. And yeah, those diabetic diets. They give us the same crap they do on the main line, except for

333

the only decent thing on the tray, which is the dessert."

"I understand the diet isn't the best, but one of the nurses pulled your canteen orders and you use your money predominantly to buy potato chips and honeybuns."

His eyes widened, and then narrowed. "Look, they took one of my only pleasures in life away, and that was smoking. I don't care what you say. I'm not going to give up the only thing left that gives me pleasure in this rat hole."

"Mr. Whalen, you're maxed out on the medicines that I can give you for your diabetes and cardiovascular issues. If you have no interest in changing your diet, you could try to walk a little more. I heard that you now have someone pushing you in a wheelchair to the culinary."

"Ahh, give me a break. Ever since the warden changed us to controlled movement, I can't walk fast enough to get into the culinary to eat. You know the deal, controlled movement on a medical yard, what horseshit. They make us guys with medical problems walk the long way around the yard."

He hit the side of the exam table with his pudgy fist. "Some of those old guys just go once a day to chow now, because they can't do that long walk. And I ask you, how are we supposed to get exercise when he is forever locking us down? Before that asshole came, we could get out almost every day and get some air and move around."

"I understand your point, but you need to concentrate on what you can do for yourself, not get angry over what you can't change."

He licked his chapped lips. "I'm going to sue all their asses."

The conversation didn't improve. In fact, it seemed that everyone I saw that morning was irritated and threatening to sue. The inmates were upset that they were locked down almost all the time—and it was unclear to me why the warden had made that change, because there had been no increase in violence or changes in staffing.

In the past, and ever since I had been on that yard, the inmates had the freedom to do a variety of things in a week: call their families, put in their laundry, go to the law library, go to the inmate store or canteen, the gym or weight pile, walk on the track... Now, because they were locked down so much of the time, they had to decide which activities were most important. The decisions they made about skipping those activities had unintended consequences.

Many inmates cut out getting any physical activity, which not only affected their health, it affected their mood. Putting off doing their laundry affected other people's moods... and the list went on. Locking up people for more time, in cells or dorms with little to do, when it hadn't happened on that yard for decades, did not make any sense to me. When I asked what reason was given, I was told that the new warden wanted to put his mark on the yard.

I was glad when the morning was over, and I headed to lunch. The break room was packed with staff loading up their paper plates with potluck food. I placed my water in the microwave to heat it up for tea and asked Alie, "What's the excuse for all the food?"

Alie rolled her eyes. "It's for one of the psych nurses who's leaving. Aren't you going to get something?" She put some chicken wings on her plate.

I shook my head. "I'm happy with the lunch I brought."

Alie laughed. "You eat nothing but rabbit food. Why don't you indulge sometimes and eat something yummy?"

I smiled. "I do, but not here. It's the principle of the thing."

She put some potato salad and a biscuit on her plate, and eyed the chips and guacamole. "You'll have to enlighten me on that one when we get to my office."

I grabbed my hot tea, and we walked to her office to eat. She took a bite of her chicken wing and asked, "Why do you have such an issue with fat people?"

I speared a piece of broccoli in my salad and looked at it. "It's not the

335

person, but what obesity can medically do to a person. Have you noticed how every time we turn around we're diagnosing another diabetic?"

She licked her fingers. "Yeah, we do have a lot."

"What you don't realize is that twenty-five years ago, we hardly had any diabetics on this yard. Part of it now is due to the aging of the population, but I think that's only a piece. When they stopped nicotine on the yard, I couldn't have been happier, but I didn't consider what the inmates would do to replace that addiction. For the most part, they replaced it with a different addiction, and for the majority of them that was sugar."

Alie savored her biscuit. "Yeah, but the breathing treatments for the lungers have gone down, and all that hawked-up yellow phlegm on the pavement has decreased."

My nose wrinkled. "I know. Now I don't have to be looking down all the time to avoid stepping on globs." I snapped my fingers. "I've got to read you something one of the inmates gave me last week. It's on my desk. I'll be right back."

In my office, I grabbed the little blue booklet titled *Razor Wire* from my desk, and walked the few steps back to Alie's room.

Alie tilted her head to get a look. "What's that?"

I showed her the stippled art work on the front, and opened it to the page I wanted. "It's a collection of poems from the creative writing class on the yard. Their teacher publishes this little book every year. Listen to the title of this one: *Felonious Phlegm*."

Her head rocked backward and Alie burst out laughing. "Okay, you've got me. Read it."

I cleared my throat and read.

Felonious Phlegm

The prison yard is dappled with it

like a shooting range where

the ejected dead cartridges lie everywhere

at first I thought it was the chain

smoking, the harsh hand rollies

congesting the lungs

or maybe something hanging in the barbed air

where the desert banshees howl sand into

silent open mouths

or even (God forbid) the food, until years later

impoverished by this abundance of time

and the futility of words,

I realize it is just the Spartan language

of the powerless.

Alie put her chin in her hand and looked at me. "Very nice. Speaking of powerless, did you hear that our medical director is no longer our boss?"

I felt my muscles tighten. "What do you mean?"

"Well, it seems our esteemed leader decided to let the wardens of each institution supervise the doctors."

I felt the heat rise to my face. "That can't be right. How can a warden supervise a doctor? They have no medical training, nor do they know how to run a medical department. Who told you that?"

"The medical director himself. Seems the situation with the doctors down south was becoming a political problem, and he was pressured to do it by the higher-ups."

I had heard about the problems with the doctors in the southern part of the state. They had not been working the hours they were supposed to, and as salaried employees, they didn't punch a time clock. It came to a head when

337

one of the inmates had to be sent to an outside hospital because their prison doctor was not there. The doctor in the hospital who took care of him was— guess who—the prison doctor, who was working two jobs at the same time. That did not go over well, and the rest of us prison doctors were painted with the same brush. I was particularly annoyed, because I not only worked more than my hours, I also ran all the inmate programs I created on my own time.

"Why do people and systems react with a bomb, when a laser would do?" I asked. "I'm telling you, Alie, this is going to be a nightmare for us."

"How bad can Warden Damerin be? We're working our hours, and they should be paying you overtime. This place runs fine and we're taking care of all of the worst cases. What could he do to us?"

"The yard was running fine as well, until he arrived. Look what he's done to it and to the inmates. Don't you think that turning this into a max yard is just making it harder for us to take care of the old and sick?"

"Yeah, that's true, and they certainly are bitching more." She looked at her watch. "Geez. Do you have patients this afternoon in the clinic?"

I nodded.

"Well I don't, so I'll head to the back and start seeing the patients in the infirmary." She threw her soggy plate in the wastebasket and took a last sip of tea. "See you back there."

My first patient was Mr. Webster, a 37-year-old black male whom I had been seeing for hypertension and prediabetes. "Mr. Webster, I see you've lost 24 pounds in the past year, and your labs and blood pressure look great. What have you been doing to get such wonderful results?"

He smiled, his straight white teeth complementing his fine features. "I decided that I didn't want to get old and fat and take all those pills, so I did what you said and started to exercise and buy protein powder in the store in- stead of cookies and popcorn."

"Well, I'm proud of you. You've lost the fat around your abdomen, and you've put on some muscle. What type of exercises are you doing now?"

He sat up straighter and tightened his abdominal muscles. "I do my own kind of HIT training. You ever hear of it?"

"Not hitting someone, I hope."

He chuckled. "No. It stands for high intensity training. A bunch of the guys in my unit have seen the results I've been getting, and they asked me to teach them how to do it too."

"That's great. You will probably have more success than I in getting people to change their habits. Everyone needs an example. They need to see that it is possible to change."

He nodded and looked out through the exam window. "Not everyone believes that people can change."

"Well, I know that I have to believe it, otherwise I wouldn't be able to continue working here."

He tilted his head. "Do you think this current warden will change, or are we stuck with him turning this into a max yard?"

"I don't know. He's made a lot of changes. What do the guys on the yard think about him and the changes he's made?"

He exhaled forcefully. "They think he's a rainmaker."

"What do you mean by that?" I asked, expecting a more derogatory response.

"A rainmaker is someone the higher-ups bring in to make things so bad that all hell breaks loose and you have to bring in the reinforcements. It's a way to get more money, more staff, more power from the legislature."

I felt slightly nauseated, hoping that was not the reason. "What do you think?"

He shrugged. "You know, I knew him when he was a guard in the old days. He wasn't such a bully then. Maybe it's like that old saying about how power corrupts, or maybe he's just following orders and turning this place into a maximum security yard." He looked up at me. "Sort of seems crazy to me. This yard is mostly made up of old guys now. The worst they can do is run you over in their wheelchair."

"I know what you mean. This yard has the only regional medical facility, and all the other prisons dump their old and sick on us. Some of the old guys are complaining to me that they can only get yard time twice a week now, and many are afraid to go out because Custody won't let them back in if they have to go to the bathroom. If that's true, it doesn't make any sense to me. A lot of these old guys can't control their urine or bowel movements well. Does that actually happen now? I don't remember them ever restricting guys from coming back into their own unit."

His lips pressed together. "Every time we get a new warden, they put their own mark on the place. I just hope this one doesn't stay long."

I feel the same way, I thought to myself.

At the end of the day, Alie and I walked out of the medical building and across the prison yard. There were no inmates on the yard at all, where in the past I would have seen some walking, others lifting weights, and some out on the field playing soccer or softball.

I looked down as a chubby squirrel crossed our path and tried to go through the wire fence. I stopped and touched Alie on the sleeve. "Look at that squirrel, his butt is so fat he can't fit through the fence."

Alie snickered. "Don't tell me you have something against fat squirrels too."

"Alie, I've been on this yard for over two decades and I've never seen an obese squirrel. I bet the inmates are feeding him the white bread they get from that god-awful sandwich at lunch." The squirrel's butt was stuck, and his plump hind legs were digging in the dirt to push him through. "Do you think we should give him a push?" I said.

She put her hand over her mouth and laughed. We both looked at each other, wondering who was going to bend down and give him a good push, when finally his massive butt wiggled through.

As we watched him lumber off, I said, "I bet that poor squirrel has diabetes. Do you know that white bread has a higher glycemic index than pure sugar? "

Alie looked up at the sky. "So?"

"It means that feeding the inmates white bread all the time is going to give a lot of them diabetes and make them fat. Look what happened to that squirrel."

She shook her head. "You're crazy."

Maybe I was crazy, but I couldn't help notice how much the inmate population on this yard had changed over the years. Gone were the days of tough young inmates. It was about twenty years since the medical facility was built, and this yard had become a dumping ground for the old, obese, and infirm. *When it was built, I don't think anyone envisioned that consequence.* The system certainly was not prepared to take care of a growing geriatric population. Now we had a new warden who was taking away inmates' mobility, and I wondered what consequences his actions would have.

I didn't have to wait long to find out. The following week, the doctors were ordered to appear before the warden. We were given an ultimatum— which I won't detail here—that affected our schedules and our lives. In the process, our only dentist, a physician assistant, and a psychiatrist all chose to leave. Another prison in the north lost its only doctor, and the southern part of the state fared worse.

If the intent of this new policy was to improve medical coverage, that did not happen. If the intent was to get rid of all the doctors and privatize the medical department, that did not happen either. Over the years, I had seen medical privatization attempted at a few prisons in the state. Privatization meant that the state would pay an outside company to take care of the medical needs of the inmates, including staffing the medical providers. I had not seen it work, or be cost-effective. The state eventually gave up on it.

The warden's behavior toward Medical created an unexpected change in heart for Alie. She started empathizing more with the inmates—something I had done through the years, which she always gave me a hard time for. That was the only interesting thing I noted about working under the new warden. Soon it was not only the inmates and Medical that complained to me, it was also the caseworkers and Custody.

Every morning I walked into the prison, I started to feel tense and on guard. Our medical director had quit, our complaints went nowhere, and the warden had more than once called me into his office and yelled at me to the point where I felt physically intimidated. To make matters worse, the prison clamped down on educational programs, and my Health Related Recovery class was terminated.

I wondered if I could stick it out. I had always promised myself that if the prison changed who I was, I had to leave.

27. Phasing Out

"You look tired," Coley said as he got up from the sofa and turned off the television. He hugged me, and I slipped my cold hands under his sweater and held on to his warmth longer than usual. "What's the matter?" he murmured.

"It's just getting more frustrating all the time, and I don't know if it's worth it anymore."

He took my hand, sat me down on the sofa, and asked, "So what's going on now in the nuthouse?"

I grabbed a soft brown pillow and held it in my lap as I sunk down, closing my eyes. "I've seen a lot of wardens come and go, but this has got to be the first time that the inmates and Custody feel the same way about a warden. The inmates hate him. They keep complaining to me about him taking away all their programs, locking them up all the time, and limiting their ability to get to the culinary so they can eat. There's also a lot of the Custody who hate him because they think he's a reactionary bully and making the yard more dangerous."

I kicked off my shoes, put my legs on the wooden coffee table, and arched my back to stretch out my legs. "You know as well as I do that when the inmates aren't involved in doing something positive, they create more problems for everyone."

He patted me on the thigh. "Yeah, I remember how the violence decreased at Max when they implemented all those programs. I really enjoyed teaching over there in those days, and I liked the support I got from the captain and assistant warden."

I turned and put my legs on Coley's lap, hoping he'd rub my feet. "I found it hard to believe those guys supported programs. They seemed like hardasses to me."

"Well, I remember both of them telling me that they saw the positive impact the programs were having on the number of incidents and injuries on that yard. Once they saw the change, they were converts. I also think it made a difference that they were both combat vets."

"What do you mean by that?" I asked, and nudged his thigh with my foot so he would start rubbing my feet.

"If you were in combat like we were in Vietnam, you would know what I meant. When you're in a war, you realize how easy it is to lose the things that hold together a civil society. You find yourself doing things that you would never have believed of yourself... and then you have to live with what you did. It gives you a new understanding of the saying 'there for but the will of God go I.' And one of the things you never wanted to do was to leave another brother in the field."

I looked at Coley's brown eyes and tried to imagine what he looked like at twenty-four as a platoon leader. I remembered the story he had told me of chewing out his squad leader who didn't look after his men, and later that day holding the same man in his arms as he died. "What happened to the captain and the assistant warden?" I asked. "Did they retire or something?"

"No, it had to do with the wind starting to blow in the other direction when they lost that progressive prison director."

I knew what Coley meant. *How many sea changes have I seen in the last three decades? How many prison directors and wardens have come and gone? Am I on my eighth or ninth warden now?*

I sighed. "Well, the wind has definitely started blowing in a miserable direction for me. I don't know if I have it in me anymore to wait till it blows the other way again."

Coley finally started rubbing my feet. "You know," he murmured, "you don't have to work there anymore. You've put in enough time."

I closed my eyes. *I don't want to think about leaving yet.*

I slept deeply that night, and when my alarm rang at four AM, I actually felt awake to hit the gym. The workout made me feel like I had energy again... until I walked into my office, and saw a lawsuit on my desk. *Not anoth-*

er one.

I was used to the occasional lawsuit from a disgruntled, entitled inmate, but in the last two years the number had gone up. How much of it was due to the changes on the yard making them want to lash out? How much was from other variables? It was hard to tell, but I was getting tired of spending my day answering interrogatories for the attorney general's office instead of taking care of patients.

I looked at the beige metal file cabinet that stood next to my open door, and opened the bottom drawer. *I know I had some extra coffee in here for emergencies.*

My first patient was Mr. Kelner, an intelligent inmate with eyes like a bird of prey. When I entered the room, he said, "Dr. G., I hear that you might be leaving us soon. Is it because of our current warden? I hear he's the reason we lost the dentist too. You know, I've been here over thirty years and that dentist was the best one we ever had. Remember the old dentist we had that was so old he got lost just getting to the medical department?"

Yes, I did remember him. *I also remember that before him, we didn't have a dentist for over a year and I had patients with severe dental abscesses that compromised their airways.*

I gave Kelner a half-hearted smile. "Yes, I remember him, and it will be difficult to replace the last dentist we had."

"So is that warden going to run you off too, Dr. G.?"

"If I leave, it won't be just because of him. I'm getting tired of the lawsuits, the grievances, not being able to be involved in programs anymore, the hospital not wanting to take our patients..."

I came up for air and found Mr. Kelner studying me. "Dr. G., did I ever tell you that when you started, we had a bet going on the yard for how long you would stay?"

"Who won?"

He shrugged his shoulders. "I don't remember, that was so long ago, but none of us thought you'd last this long. You must be close to thirty years by now. You can retire with full benefits now, right? I mean, why would you stay anymore? I know you. You probably have things already lined up, like traveling around the world."

"Well Mr. Kelner, since you know me so well, let me ask you a question I've always wondered about. I know you work in the law library and have quite a reputation in there. Why haven't you ever helped the inmates sue the medical department?"

His thin lips broke into an easy smile, showing his small teeth. "It's because I'm only interested in helping the PUMAs get a reduced sentence or their sentence overturned if they didn't get a fair trial."

"What's a PUMA?"

"It stands for poor, underprivileged, mentally incapacitated and addicted. I cherry-pick the cases after I check out all the information, and see if there was something done wrong in the case or something that wasn't pursued that would have helped or cleared the person. You ever hear of Bobby Helstein?"

"No, is he an inmate?"

"He used to be, but he's out now. He was in on a murder charge. When I went through his case, I found out that the defense attorney had made no attempt to contact or track down witnesses that could have cleared the guy. When I got it back in court, the judge overturned the sentence. I live for those cases."

"What else do you live for?"

"I loved helping guys write grants to start programs. But if the outside world sees that something good is happening for an inmate, it can be the kiss of death."

"What do you mean?"

"Well, remember when we had the culinary arts program?"

I nodded my head. *How could I forget that one?* It trained inmates to be sous chefs, a marketable skill. "That was a great program."

"Well, we had a graduation ceremony happening on the yard, and a news channel came in and filmed it. The warden sent some pastries over from the culinary arts program, and you should have seen what happened the next day. We were told that a person of substance saw 'perpetrators of heinous crimes' eating fancy foods on the government's dime, and that killed the program."

I rolled my eyes. "People should be more interested in whether the programs reduce violence in the system and recidivism, instead of an inmate getting a pastry. But it never ceases to amaze me how many decisions are made on an emotional basis." I looked down at his chart and realized that I hadn't yet asked him why he had come in. "Sorry, Mr. Kelner, for getting off track. Was there something I needed to do for you today? "

He smiled and brushed back the grey stubble on his balding, sun-damaged scalp. "You already have, Dr. G., and I'm going to miss you." He put out his hand and I shook it, feeling a sense of sadness as I wondered if I would ever see him again.

I saw another dozen patients before my nurse Suzy came up to me and bristled, "Kranzi didn't let me know we had another patient to see, and the poor old guy's been sitting in the waiting room for the last four hours." The nurses only knew who was in that secure area when the officer gave them the inmate's kite. Suzy did not think well of Officer Kranzi, and his name made my neck muscles tighten. There were officers who did their job well, and there were ones who seemed to go out of their way to make bad situations worse. I thought Kranzi was one of the most unprofessional officers I had ever seen working in the clinic, and wondered why the warden had let him stay in that position even though the nurses had put in multiple complaints about him.

When my eighty-year-old patient walked in, I said, "I'm sorry you had to wait so long, Mr. Robinson. My nurse didn't know you were in the waiting room."

He waved his age-spotted hand in front of him and gave me a lopsided smile. "That's okay, I'm used to it. I know it wasn't the nurse's fault, it was Kranzi."

"Maybe the officer just forgot," I said, doubting my own words.

He snorted. "Naw, I saw him take the kite and toss it."

"Why would he do that?"

He laughed and grinned. "Because I know who he is."

I was intrigued. Mr. Robinson had been in the system over forty years, and I found him to be reasonable and intelligent.

I couldn't help myself. "So who is he?"

He sat up straighter in his chair and leaned forward. "Twenty years ago when I was at Max, Kranzi was a puffed-up new officer. Arrogant, mean, and petty." He paused a few moments. "One day, someone beat the shit out of him. He was too afraid to walk the yard after that. They put him up in the gatehouse where he never had to interact with an inmate again." He sighed and leaned his bowed back into the chair. "When Max closed a few years ago, Kranzi was sent to this prison and he had to work with inmates again." He looked up and almost sounded cheerful when he said, "Us old guys know about his beating and that's why he just tries to give us the blues."

It doesn't sound like that beating did the trick, I thought, but instead I said, "Let's talk about you. Have you had any flare in your symptoms since I tapered down your medication?"

Fortunately he hadn't, and after examining him I told him, "I'd like to taper down your steroids even more, and in two months I'd like to see you again." I thought about it and added, "I'll make the follow-up on a Monday; Kranzi doesn't work that day."

He gave me a little smile and his grey eyes twinkled. "Don't worry about it, Dr. G. I'm used to his type."

When he left, Suzy came over to me and asked, "Can't you help us get rid of Kranzi? We're getting more and more behind on seeing patients, and if he doesn't work with us, we're going to lose some of our specialists. Did you know that Kranzi wouldn't allow the guys from the camp to be seen by Dr. Myros? He said we couldn't mix security levels. I mean, give me a break. Custody does it all the time. Dr. Myros brought in his echo tech and everything, and he wasn't able to see the patients I had scheduled with him. He isn't happy and can't wrap his head around why that officer acts so differently than the others."

"I gather you've already talked to the director of nursing about this," I said.

"You know I did, and all he said was that the warden didn't want to move the officer, and we just have to deal with it. Kranzi is a liability. It's only a matter of time before someone gets hurt. I mean, you're the doc here, can't you talk some sense into the warden?"

"I wish I could, Suzy, but..." I didn't want to go into detail about my own problems with the warden. "I'll talk with Dr. Tiernan at lunch and see if there's something else we could do."

Alie hadn't even started eating her lunch before she said, "Hey, about the complaint we brought to Personnel about the warden." It was the first complaint I had ever put in, and Alie was the one who encouraged me to do it.

"I try not to think about the warden while I'm eating. Why? Did you get a response from them?"

"No I didn't, and I wondered why it's been taking so long. So I called them up today, and they told me that nothing's going to be done about it and we're not going to even get a response."

"That doesn't surprise me."

"Well, I'm pissed," Alie said, and stabbed her salad with enough force that I wondered whether her plastic fork would make it through the meal. "I didn't expect them to do anything, but they should have at least sent us a letter saying they looked into the situation. All four of us complained that we felt physically threatened by the warden, and there's only two of us left. I knew we were in trouble when that director made the warden our boss. I'm telling you, they're going after us first. If they break us, no one else in the state will fight back."

"I don't know if it's worth a battle anymore. One of the things my husband always told me over the years was that you never go into a battle unless you're going to win the war."

"Well, I'm going to protect myself and you should too. I'm keeping copies of all the correspondence and emails at my house, because I don't trust them and what they'll do. ...And the way he treated you, after all you've done for this system." Her hand tightened into a fist around her fork.

I looked at her fist, and thought back to the fist the warden had made—and his red, threatening face when I wouldn't sign the paper he pushed in front of me in his office.

I felt spent and decided I wasn't hungry after all. "Alie, what really bugs me is that they're going after us, when the problems are really with the doctors in the south. Instead of dealing with the problem, the director overreacted and put the wardens in charge. We just happen to have a bully as a warden."

I sighed to relieve some of the tightness in my chest. "Do you know, the last time he called me into his office to yell at me, I told him that I found his behavior threatening. I said it reminded me of what happened to me as a hostage."

Alie's fork stopped midway to her mouth. "What did he say?"

"He didn't say anything, and I think it may even have shocked him. But I'm just letting you know that I'm never going to see him again without someone else in the room."

351

She put down her fork. "Did you put that in writing? I'm going to do the same thing."

I nodded and picked up the lawsuit on her desk. "So, have you responded to this lawsuit yet?"

"Oh give me a break, I haven't finished my lunch yet." Alie said. She took out the plastic clip that held up her dark, shoulder-length hair, and let it fall. She had worn her hair on top of her head, in a sort of Shih-Tzu look, since the prior warden put out a memo instructing all the women to cut their hair or wear it off the collar. I had played along for a while, but wearing my near-waist-length hair on top of my head all day long was sometimes annoying, and when that warden left, I reverted to the occasional ponytail or braid.

Every warden seemed to want to put their own restrictions on the place, but they tended not to last—and I had a hard time taking them seriously when they didn't make sense to me.

"So, do you have any clinic patients this afternoon, or are you heading to the back?" Alie asked.

"Suzy told me they're bringing over some guys from the camp for me to see and—oh, I said I would talk to you about Kranzi."

"Kranzi? What has that idiot done now? Did you hear that last week when you were gone, he wouldn't let Mr. Stanley go to the bathroom and..." She started laughing. "You know Mr. Stanley, he's that crusty old Italian diabetic who doesn't put up with any BS and..." Alie's brown eyes were filling up with tears of laughter. "He pleaded with Kranzi to let him use the bathroom, and when Kranzi wouldn't let him, he pulled down his pants right in the entranceway and took a dump."

She wiped the tears from her eyes. "You gotta love it. Mr. Stanley might be twice Kranzi's age, but I'd put my money on Stanley if they ever squared off."

"I wouldn't bet against you," I laughed, as I picked up my lunch containers and left her office.

Suzy already had my exam rooms filled, and was lecturing one of the obese patients about whether a large bag of potato chips was a wise food choice. She had a hand on each hip and stood in front of him like an army sergeant, and I could see him squirm. I avoided his pleading look, and walked into the first exam room.

Mr. Beele, a fifty-year-old, chiseled heroin addict, stood up and handed me a piece of paper known as a C-4. "Sorry to bother you, Dr. G., but the camp said you had to fill this out because I got hurt on the job. I was out on a fire yesterday and stepped into some damn gopher hole or something, and twisted my knee." He touched his right knee and I could see that it was more swollen than his left. "It's not bad when I'm walking on level ground, but going up and down those mountains is a bitch. Maybe you could give me a few days off till the swelling goes down."

I examined his knee; it was swollen, but his range of motion was normal and he had no laxity in the joint.

"Let me see that form, Mr. Beele. I'll fill out my part and give you off till Monday. I can also give you a packet of Ibuprofen if you would like."

"I don't take any pills or anything like that anymore, Dr. G." His brown eyes were serious, and I noticed he carried himself with an assurance that I had not seen two years ago when he had started attending my HRR class. I knew from his history that he had a lengthy history of drug use, ever since his older brother shot him up with heroin when he was six years old.

"Mr. Beele, you've changed over the past two years. I know from reading your homework assignments in HRR that you are thinking differently as well. What happened to create that change for the positive?"

His chapped lips compressed a little and his gaze dropped a fraction. "Oh... well, I first started to wonder if another life was possible. Then after attending your classes a while, I asked myself why I didn't care about my life when someone like you did care about me. It got me thinking. And you know, I feel stronger and better now than I ever have in my life. I can't go back to that old life again... I just can't."

"When you leave the prison, do you have a plan that will support you in your new life?"

The left side of his mouth curled up in a small smile. "I'm going to go to NA meetings and get myself a sponsor, get myself a CDL, go to a place where no one knows me or my old habits, and yeah, go to a gym and get more education."

"Anything else?"

He laughed. "Oh, that's right. I'll get myself a plant, and if it lives a year I'll think about moving on to a fish."

I rubbed my nose and grinned. "I'm glad you remembered the lesson about developing relationships slowly, but I actually was thinking about eating nutritious food instead of junk food."

"Dr. G., I know what to do, I just need to do it. I don't know how to explain it, but somehow I now have hope." He looked down.

After a few moments, I touched his knee and said, "Hope is the first step. When someone believes it's possible, when they consistently work at it and never give up, it will happen. Remember all those stories I told you guys about people who beat the odds? Be one of them. Everybody loves the underdog story."

The rest of the afternoon was filled with disgruntled inmates, and I was relieved when Alie and I walked out of the medical building and across the yard on our way off campus.

Alie pointed to a spot where there had recently been a few metal benches for the inmates to sit on. "Can you believe it? The warden had them removed. Now the old guys don't have anywhere to sit. What possible reason could he have had for doing that?"

"I don't know, and I can't imagine it was a good one."

"It's crazy. They're dumping more and more old and sick guys on this yard, and he's making it harder and harder for us to take care of them. One of the inmates told me they were going to put together an ADA class action suit on his fat ass, and I hope they do."

I chuckled and glanced at her. "Alie, you're starting to side with the inmates now."

"Well, I never really paid all that much attention to their whining until we started to be treated like shit," she said, and pushed back her sunglasses. "How much longer do you think you can take it?"

We turned the corner at the weight pile and I saw the gatehouse in the distance. *How many times have I walked down this path?*

"Hey," Alie said and hit me on the shoulder. "How much longer? Because when you go, I go."

"I haven't decided yet. I've got to talk to some people first."

"God, I know you could retire, but what would you do?" she said. "I've never not worked. I wouldn't know what to do with myself. I know you've got all sorts of plans, but don't you want to see that warden out of here before you leave?"

I did, but I didn't know if that was worth it anymore.

As I drove through the alfalfa fields and into the hills, I realized my decision was made. It was not a question of "if," but "when." *I'll miss the inmates and staff that made me laugh; the people who helped me be able to function as a doctor in a world behind bars. But the rest...no.*

28. Saying Goodbye, and Lessons Learned

Dylan Pearson knocked on the open door to my office. "Hey Doc, do you have some time to talk before you go home?"

Dylan had been one of my favorite nurses, who had transferred to become the director of nursing at a small prison a few miles from us.

"I always have time for you, Dylan. How are you doing at your place?"

"Can't complain. The warden is great, and you'd love seeing the dogs and how the inmates train them over there. In fact, I was hoping to ask you to come over and help us catch up with medical appointments. I don't know if you've heard, but the part-time doc they hired for our place keeps calling in sick, and we're really falling behind. If you came over, Custody wouldn't have to transport inmates to your place for consultations."

"I don't know. Alie and I are barely able to keep up here, and I don't think she'd appreciate it if I left her here by herself too often."

Dylan pushed his glasses back and smiled. "We'd only need you one day a week, and you and Alie could alternate weeks. Just think, every other week you could get out of this place and walk onto a yard where you'd be appreciated."

I smiled. "You'd make a good salesman, Dylan. I'll talk it over with Alie and let you know."

Dylan leaned across my desk. "I know it's bad over here. I've heard some rumors from the nurses that you're thinking about retiring. Is it true?"

I leaned back in my chair and sighed. "I am thinking about it."

"Well, if you do, you'll be sorely missed. When you make that decision, we need to have a big retirement party."

The thought made me uncomfortable. I had seen enough retirement parties over the years, and it often felt empty and hypocritical. Someone in power would say words they didn't mean, and that would be that. The thought of having a party where I would have to interact with individuals like that was too much for me.

357

"No, when I leave I don't want a party or anything."

Dylan's face fell. "But you *are* the medical department. Your whole career has been here. The staff will want to do something for you."

I stood up. "There's no need, Dylan, and I'm not gone yet. I'll let you know when Alie or I can pinch hit for you."

When he left, I thought about what he had said. *If the staff wanted to do something for me, what would I want that to be? Something that's important to me, and that would positively impact the prison...* I had it. *When I decide to retire, I'll let my staff know that if they want to do something for me, they can donate to Big Brothers Big Sisters.*

Coley had started as a mentor with that organization over fifteen years ago, and now he was mentoring four young people. Two were now in college, one was graduating high school, and the youngest was in grade school. Three of them had fathers who were or had been, in prison, and all the children were doing extremely well.

Big Brothers Big Sisters claimed that if a child had one parent in prison, that child's chance of ending up in a prison was sixty percent; but if they had one good mentor in their childhood, it dropped to ten percent. What better way to impact a prison than to reduce the young people ending up there in the first place?

Seeing my husband's success with the children at highest risk for going to prison made me interested in becoming a mentor as well. When the prison terminated my Health Related Recovery class, I decided it was my turn to become a mentor. I had been working with a ten-year-old girl. She had issues, but tremendous potential as well. If I could help her believe that it was possible to have a different life than the one she saw around herself, and if I could give her the tools to achieve it, she could have a future she could be proud of.

I looked at my watch, and grabbed my briefcase to leave so I wouldn't be late for dinner. I had made plans to meet Lucy and see how she was doing with her own recent retirement. She had left the prison a year ago, leaving a void—as well as a lack of qualified chemotherapy nurses.

Lucy's red hair was cut in a new style, and she looked younger when she hugged me in the restaurant.

"Lucy, you look great. How is retirement treating you?"

"I love it. I'm keeping busy with the nursing board and playing with my grandchildren. I hear through the grapevine that it's getting ugly at your place. They say you're thinking about retiring as well. So what gives?"

"Well, I certainly miss you, but you know I've survived ugly times in the prison before. Remember Hannah?"

"That witch. Whatever became of her?"

"I have no idea. If she's still alive, she'd be pushing ninety. Do you think she's still wearing that bright red lipstick?"

Lucy shuddered. "Ow, don't remind me. Those were miserable times."

"They weren't all bad. Remember that inmate porter, M.C., who was always joking around and making everyone laugh?"

"How could I forget him?"

"Well, do you remember when I used to give talks for the drug companies about the new HIV drugs as they were coming out?"

"Yeah, I remember some nice dinners when they held those up here in town. What does that have to do with M.C.?"

"Well, I once did a talk in Las Vegas for one of their big conventions, and who do you think I ran into?"

"No. Really? What was he doing there?"

"He wasn't at the convention. You have to picture this. I was walking down one of the streets off the strip, talking with a doctor from Ohio, when this big black Mercedes screeches to a stop. All these black guys with heavy gold chains pile out of the car and head straight toward us. That poor guy

Karen Gedney, MD

from Ohio almost peed in his pants. Then the driver of the car got out, and it was M.C. He was jumping up and down, pounding one of his friends' backs and yelling, 'I told you it was her.' Turns out he hosts what they call a player's ball in Las Vegas."

"What is that? Is it legal?"

"It is. It's a ball that showcases... let's say, the players and the escort services they run. They pull in rappers and celebrities and make money off of it."

"You think he'll stay out of trouble?"

"I think he will, because he's doing something he loves that he happens to be very good at." I remembered one of my conversations with M.C. in the prison, where he was explaining his wheeling and dealing. I had asked him if there was a way he could do it legally. He didn't answer, but that day I saw a different light behind those blue-grey eyes.

Lucy picked up a piece of warm sourdough bread and spread butter on it. "So... what did you love doing in the prison that you'll miss when you retire?"

"Hmm. Good question. I think it will be my ability to positively affect someone's life after society has given up on them. I always was a sucker for the underdog."

"Well, you can still do that when you leave the prison," Lucy said, and took a bite.

"True, but it isn't the same, is it? It's not only that society has given up on them. It's that a prison can be a system that keeps kicking them when they're down. I know a lot of the prison staff over the years have called me 'pro-inmate' or other choice words, but what I really am is an advocate for programs, education, and skills that keep the inmate from coming back to prison. I'm also the type of person who believes that there are better ways to change people's behavior than making their lives more miserable than they are."

360

"You know I agree. Let me ask you, how many of the people behind bars do you think can really be helped?"

"I don't know, but I remember John, one of my inmates on the steering committee for HRR, telling me that one third of prison inmates would never come back no matter what happened to them; one third would always come back no matter what you did; and the other third were the ones that could be tipped either way depending on what happened to them on the inside. I think his percentages were simplistic, but I agree with his assessment."

Lucy dabbed her mouth with her napkin. "It's like medicine, isn't it? Some are going to live or die no matter what we do, but sometimes we make a difference."

I took a sip of water and thought, *yes, there are a lot of parallels between the two fields: corrections and medicine. Too much money spent on the tail end, and not enough on preventing the problem from starting in the first place. Both fields plagued by not believing or knowing how to effectively change the human behaviors that created the problem. Both a necessary, and costly, last resort. Both plagued by industries that make money off the problem and aren't invested in looking for solutions.*

I enjoyed my dinner with Lucy and we promised each other we would keep in touch. "Just let me know if you decide to retire, okay?" she said as we were leaving. "I want to be the first to celebrate with you."

When I arrived home, Coley was watching the news. He patted the seat next to him on the couch. "How was dinner?"

"Interesting."

"So what did you and Lucy talk about?"

"My views on the prison. She asked me how many inmates I thought could be helped. What do you think? You taught them for years. Did anyone ever call you 'pro-inmate?'"

Coley snorted and turned to me. "I'm not pro-inmate. I'm anti-

Karen Gedney, MD

stupidity. You know, some of the inmates over the years asked me why I treated them like I did. I told them I saw no reason to disrespect them or treat them as an enemy, when they gave me no provocation to do so. You can't take any animal that is aggressive, treat them badly, and expect them to be less dangerous. That's stupid, and I consider humans the most aggressive predators around. There's a reason we're on top of the food chain."

I snuggled close to him and looked around at the pictures of wolves he had on the walls of the den. *He would know.* "So how do you gentle an aggressive wolf?"

"They only respond to love and kindness," he said, and kissed me on top of the head.

The next day during lunch, I talked with Alie about going over to the other prison, and she was all for it. Then our conversation drifted to what was on her mind.

"Have you set a date for leaving yet?" Alie asked.

"No, but I'm thinking about it all the time. My life won't be the same when I leave this place. I might have to start watching television or something, instead of experiencing life for real."

"Huh? What are you talking about? You're not the type. I know you. You won't be able to sit still. You'll be off tilting at windmills."

I looked out Alie's window at the grey clouds, which were becoming darker. "Each administration affects the climate of a yard. I just wish they would learn from the past what works and what doesn't."

Alie put down her mug of tea. "So, what do you think worked the best?"

"Without a doubt, the administration that believed in programs and supported them. The greatest change was over at Max prison. They had a warden over there who I thought was a bit rigid. But after he saw how the programs reduced violence and cost and made it easier for his staff, he was all in. It was like a light had been turned on over there. I remember some of the inmates telling me that the officers started treating them with respect and consideration. They started joking that they must have had to go to the warden's 'Kindness Classes.'"

Alie shook her head. "Can't imagine having anything like that under this warden."

"I told you before, that's where they started the dog program. But they started so many other programs around the same time. They had a program that used inmates to transcribe literature into Braille for the blind on the outside. They had a veteran's group that offered a lot of classes. An NAACP group that helped inmates get housing and employment for release. They started meditation classes, planted flowers, had a quarry where they carved rocks for people on the outside. They raised money for the United Way, in fact I remember it even made the papers. It was after 9/11. Would you believe that yard, which had only seven hundred inmates, raised almost $10,000?"

Alie's smile was winsome. "How do you remember all that stuff? I can't remember one day to the next."

I chewed on my lower lip before answering. "I suppose I've chosen to treasure and remember the good stories over the bad. I think that's what has kept me here so many years. I love it when I've helped people beat the odds or exceed other people's expectations. I know most people pay more attention to the bad versus the good in life, but I don't think it should be that way. I've always believed in the maxim, 'first do no harm, and to the best of your ability, help people heal and become whole again.'"

Epilogue

As my last day behind bars drew to a close, I decided to slow the pace of my walk through the yard and remember it. There was no movement on the hardened brown soil, except for a few seagulls battling the wind as they landed. They were hundreds of miles away from the ocean and their home—just like many of the inmates housed in the squat grey buildings, who fed those birds their baloney sandwiches. The wind kicked up, and I thought about sea captains, who could plot a course and survive the squalls, gales, and perils at sea.

What course will the prison take next? I wondered. I had seen it improve in a variety of ways over the years, when the wind was blowing in the right direction, filling the sails. And with a captain at its helm who could chart a course that passengers and sailors both believed in.

I shook my head. *Captains and wardens both wield power at the helm, but they do not control which way the wind blows.* The latest administration was more aligned with the "lock them up and throw away the key" mindset, instead of education and programs that were known to decrease recidivism. The wind was controlled by the legislatures and politicians who decided what to fund, and what type of administrators would set the tone and course they wanted for the prison system.

I studied the largest unit on the yard, which stood across from the medical facility behind its own fence system. I remembered the day when an officer in a golf cart stopped me on my walk home, telling me to hop on and steering the cart toward that unit. When he got me through the gate and multiple security doors, I found two officers giving CPR to an inmate on the floor in his cell. At that moment, I heard someone coming up the stairs hard. It was my nurse with the AED and a trauma bag. Due to the officers' quick response, we were able to resuscitate the inmate and he made a full recovery. It was the only code I had ever been involved in that turned out well, and he had those officers to thank for another chance at life.

That's what every human wants, when they are facing the end of their existence. They want a second chance, just like so many of the men behind these walls.

What does it take for an inmate to make good on a second chance? It depends on the inmate, but they first have to want it and be willing to do the work it takes to give themselves the greatest chance for success. For some, that may mean addressing and healing the issues and emotions that put them at risk for addiction. For some, it may mean taking responsibility, experiencing empathy, and understanding the impact their crime had on the victim and his or her family. I knew that there were other states doing what was called "restorative justice" through victim impact boards. It had helped a number of victims and their families, when they could interact with the person who had caused them harm and understand them as a person.

I thought back to what happened to me when I was taken hostage and raped. *How much of my ability to forgive Moth was because I knew of the demons he battled from the Vietnam war, and could empathize with his anger and hopelessness?*

There is no greater gift a victim of a crime can give themselves than forgiving the perpetrator, I thought. *A weight comes off, and you can get on with your life instead of being bound to the past. I am grateful that I was able to move on and continue doing my life's work.*

A few sparrows flew toward the fence and perched between the coils of barbed wire. I thought about the thin, young, blond inmate, on that small yard for the first time, who had panicked and scrambled over the barbed wire fence. Bleeding and screaming, he was kicking the door of the medical facility to let him in. He ended up with a few lacerations that needed suturing. *He was fortunate to have a warden who assessed the situation and did not charge him with escaping.*

A few steps later, I turned right at the corner unit. Memories surfaced: being called over to that unit to assess a stiff, cold middle-aged inmate hanging from a doorknob. I shuddered, thinking how committed you had to be to make a rope out of a torn-up t-shirt, tie it to a doorknob, and sit on the floor letting it cut off your air. *The decision to kill yourself, to fight back every cell in*

366

your body that wants oxygen to keep on living.

I thought about the stories I had read of Colonial ships that carried condemned prisoners and slaves across the seas. I remembered Coley telling me that the captains took better care of the slaves than the prisoners they transported, because the slaves had value. *I wonder how many of those people gave up and died or committed suicide because of how they were treated. How would a prison deal with the inmates differently, if they felt they were valuable when they returned to society?*

I turned my gaze to the right, looking through the fence that enclosed the field where the inmates played soccer and softball. The whole field had a dirt path encircling it where they could walk or jog. *How it has changed with disuse over the years, now that the inmates' movement is so restricted.* I remembered days when that field was used every day. I would see men getting exercise and discharging their pent-up energy in a healthy way. How different it was now: just an empty, barren patch of dirt.

I thought of one glorious afternoon when the warden had brought in a circus to perform on that field. I remembered the faces of the inmates, who stood shoulder to shoulder in their faded blue shirts, watching acrobats and horses cavort and show off their skills. The look on the crowd's faces that day reminded me of the joy on a child's face when they saw something new and beautiful for the first time. *Positive or negative experiences are intensified in closed systems,* I thought. Truly positive experiences create an environment where things run more smoothly, and the system is at less risk for strife and unrest.

As I rounded the last corner, I looked at the iron pile and the rust on the benches, weights, and bars. I had seen many heavily-muscled men over the years destroy their shoulders and backs competing with one another on that equipment. I had also seen it give them an outlet, discipline, and self-worth. *Every good leader knows that the people they are responsible for need not just an outlet, but a mission that gives them purpose and a sense of worth. When did this yard last have that?* Warehousing, looking for the worst in people, and dismantling education and programs had not only increased behavioral problems, complaints, and violence in the inmates; it had stunted and suffocated the staff as well.

The chapel was next on my path. I remembered hearing Mr. Cipher playing what sounded like a concerto to my untrained ears. After the service I asked him what the name of the piece was. He said he didn't know, couldn't read music, and had taught himself how to play the piano in the chapel by ear.

I was impressed with individuals who found their creative talent behind bars. It reminded me of all the drawings and paintings I had seen over the years, created by inmates who were almost all self-taught. I was glad I had been given one opportunity to showcase their art at a gallery for disadvantaged artists in the neighboring city. It had been serendipity: the gallery was looking for something new to showcase, and the prison director at that time trusted me to pull it off. Her only stipulations were that there would be nothing in the show that could be used against her, and that it had to benefit the prison and the community.

We had titled the show "Unlocked Treasures." I asked the prison director if one third of the revenue could go to the prison, one third to an organization working to end domestic violence, and one third to the inmates to cover their cost for supplies. I was very relieved when the show was well received. The director had taken a chance; she was one of the few directors I saw in the prison who believed in programs, education, and restitution enough to put her career on the line. She tended to strategically look for win-win situations.

How many leaders are willing to take a risk for something that could benefit all the players involved, but could also put them in danger if something goes wrong? Not many. Only the ones who look at the whole picture, and understand that there is little progress in any venture without some risk.

I smiled as I approached the visiting room. *I had happy memories there. Which impacted me the most?* Besides the graduations, I think the most powerful event was a ceremony by the Incarcerated Vietnam Vets. In the past they could collect cardboard and aluminum cans for recycling, and an officer

368

liaison handled the income they generated. When they reached $6,000, the group made the decision to give it to a grade school, to fund school supplies for disadvantaged children.

They sent letters to the principals of eight schools, and only one replied. I remembered the powerful emotion I had felt when she gave her acceptance speech, and felt the tears coming to my eyes again.

I took a deep breath in and let it out with force. *Come on, get a grip on yourself. Don't let this walk down memory lane get to you.* I returned to the thought of the prison as a ship on the sea. Self-contained, isolated, and at the mercy of the political winds and financial storms. Leaving the prison would feel odd, like returning to land after feeling the roll of the waves under your feet for years.

Last day on the yard, but it isn't over yet. The following week I had to go to a hearing, to be a witness for a caseworker who had a suit against the warden. *When mutiny raises its head, there is a reason—and that reason, more often than not, is abuse of power.*

The hearing was going to be held on the first day of spring. I wondered if that was an omen of things to come. The wind was already changing: the prison director had recently resigned. I hoped the governor would find a good replacement.

I rubbed my watery eyes and looked at the prison one final time. *All the stories, all the things I have heard and lived through all these years.* I felt a tiny smile start as I thought about my new project: writing down the stories from my journal and from the writings of the inmates that I had kept over the years.

Writing it down will be fitting. It will complete the circle. As a child, stories of doctors in the midst of adventure, intrigue, and danger had made me want to become a doctor myself, and that path had led me to prison.

Could my stories help bolster the wind to fill the sails, and send this ship in the right direction again? I hoped to see a day when a prison's mission was to return inmates to society: less dangerous, more empathetic, and with tools and support to help them be assets to society, not liabilities.

I will persevere and write that book. I will capture what I learned and the emotions I felt that might help readers understand why I stayed behind those bars for almost thirty years. In life, one can experience situations that bring out the best or worst in people. Prison is one of those unique 'situations.' It is a place of captors and captives hidden from public view where the potential for abuse of power is high. It is a place where one can lose one's faith in humanity or find it. It is a place where one can see people with hope and vision, or a place where people give up and die (figuratively and literally).

People over the years have asked me why I stayed in the prison system after I was taken hostage. Looking back, I realize that the prison brought out the best in me. It heightened my compassion for individuals that were damaged on a physical, emotional, psychological and spiritual level. I learned that they turned to illicit drugs and other criminal activity to cope and survive in a society where they did not have the skills or desire to fit into. Taking a stand against abuses of power when I saw them helped me become stronger and more resilient. Developing programs for the inmates as a volunteer helped me become a better teacher and speaker. Having to take care of illnesses like AIDS in the early days when no one else wanted to in a prison, made me realize that I could be a pioneer in areas that others didn't want to venture into. Watching inmates beat all the odds and succeed when they left prison rekindled my belief in the underdog. Watching custody and staff who stayed professional and sought to improve corrections gave me hope.

I couldn't have stayed in corrections and endured the things I did though if it wasn't for the love and support of my husband. Someone once told me that if his wife was taken hostage and raped on the job he'd never let her go back. Coley respected and trusted me enough to let me make the best decision for myself. He told me that he would support whatever decision I made and I will always love him for being my 'rock.' For me, the best decision was 'getting back on the horse' and not looking at myself as a victim.

It is my hope that there will be something in my memoir that will resonate with you and heighten your compassion for populations that you currently find difficult to understand. The experience of stepping out of your comfort zone and seeking proactive solutions for complex systemic problems is a challenge, but it can also bring out the best in you and others.

The Next Thirty Years

Karen Gedney, MD

My next act in life will not be one of retirement or retreat. The purpose of my memoir, "30 Years Behind Bars," is to offer a different perspective of prisons from that of an inmate or custody officer. I want the reader to experience the prison thru the compassionate eyes of a physician. One who is oriented and trained to ask questions in order to understand complex problems, and then help prevent and treat them.

My mission in the next thirty years is to act as a catalyst to help change the current paradigm of 'corrections' from one of punishment to one of prevention, healing and re-integration. Prisons were designed to keep individuals behind bars until they had finished their sentence. They were never designed as a system to address the complex societal problems that put individuals there in the first place nor help them re-integrate into society when they left.

The 'correctional world' and the 'medical world' suffer from the same problem. They both spend an inordinate amount of money, energy and time on the symptoms vs. the causes of the problem. What would it look like, if we as a society decided to shift that paradigm and try to identify the causes behind the problems and work together as an integrated system to fix them?

You might think that I'm crazy to ask that question, but I have a vision of what our society and world could look like if we became pro-active vs. reactive. As an example - When an individual commits a crime we react and punish them and put them behind bars. What does it look like, if one is pro-active instead of reactive?

We would try to understand what put that person at risk for doing the criminal activity and focus our attention and resources on that issue. Then we would analyze what we do in that area and what actually works in reducing criminality.

I am not alone in the correctional world for having that vision. I recently had a conversation with someone who had worked in corrections for thirty-seven years as a guard, an associate warden, a chief classification officer and a hearing officer for the parole board. He shared with me that he had lis-

373

tened to over 10,000 cases on the parole board and said, "You know with female offenders, I've come to realize that over 95% of the cases never had a chance. They were 'screwed' as children. They were either physically or sexually abused. Neglected or malnourished. Raised in dysfunctional families or dropped on their heads once too often."

I know there are individuals who have similar backgrounds that don't end up in prison, but my question to you is this. "Do you think that taking someone from that type of back ground and shaming and punishing them will actually change their behavior in a positive way?"

After decades observing and treating individuals like that, I can tell you the answer is, "No."

The greatest ability to affect human behavior is in childhood. If changing behavior is the goal, then that is where the energy and resources should be concentrated. The second greatest ability to affect human behavior is when an individual truly wants to change and they have access to the support and resources that enables them to make that change. That is where prisons and parole programs could play a part.

With age one hopes that one's experiences and insights can help the next generation. It is my hope that I can inspire people (especially my generation- the Baby Boomers) not to retreat and complain about the problems they see. I want to remind people that they can become a piece of the solution. Their life will be richer and more interesting when they are not sitting on the sidelines complaining.

If you consider yourself a compassionate person who wants to be proactive in life and is interested in doing something positive in your life, read on. I will use the example of 'corrections' in the United States which should come as no surprise to you by now. We have one of the highest incarceration rates per capita of any country in the world and that will only change if we approach it in a holistic, systematic way with a clear goal in mind. The goal is to reduce the amount of people we put behind bars by focusing on what society can do to prevent them from entering or re-entering prisons.

374

As an example, the 'War on Drugs' dramatically increased prison populations, violence and the power of drug cartels. As a policy, it has not decreased drug use nor made society safer. At the time of this writing, 2017, the United States is facing an 'opioid epidemic'. Instead of blaming the drug user and punishing them by putting them behind bars for years, society at least now is asking, "How and why did this happen and what are we going to do to help these people?" That is the same question I want society to ask about our high rate of incarceration.

I know it is a tough sell, but what if you align your interests and passions with a prison program that is a win-win. For example: If you love dogs there are programs where inmates train and socialize dogs in order to give them a second chance for adoption which the SPCA supports. The inmate learns a skill, responsibility and patience. They also have a sense of purpose which tends to reduce mental health problems and violence. That's a win-win for the people who love dogs and the people affected by incarceration.

What is your interest or passion? Is it children, mentoring, cats, dogs, wild mustangs, education, business, entrepreneurship, public speaking, art, music, religion, meditation, planned parenthood, law, justice, housing, jobs, addiction, etc.? I guarantee that you can find programs in all of those areas that can help prevent children at highest risk for becoming incarcerated – as well as healing and re-integrating the incarcerated back into society so they have less risk of returning to prison.

My question for you is this, "What will your legacy be?" Mine will be acting as the catalyst to change the prison paradigm from one of punishment to one of prevention, healing and re-integration. I want society to be more just and safe. "What do you want?"

When I first became a doctor, I did not envision that I would find my purpose or calling taking care of individuals that society chose to banish and punish for their behavior. My mindset as a physician was to first seek to understand, and then try to heal and make whole again. It is my hope that after reading this memoir, you will see individuals and systems that are broken in a new light and ask different questions.

375

Acknowledgments

Behind every book is an idea, an author and the people who help bring it into existence. The idea to write a book about my experience in prison as a doctor started when I heard people say, "God, what was that like? You've got to write a book." I did and have to thank my husband, Clifton Coley Maclin for encouraging me to do it. Sharing his thoughts and memories of the prison and what it was like for both of us was therapeutic.

When I finished the manuscript I fortunately ran into Christine Whitmarsh, the owner of the Ink Agency who took a look at it and saw that it had some worth. She turned me over to her editor, Jessica Reeder who was patient and pushed me to make it flow in a way the reader would not get lost. Both were very supportive of a naïve first-time author. (theinkagency.net)

Writing a book is one thing, but to publish and promote it is entirely another thing. I have to thank Cheri Hill with Sage Advertising & Marketing (www.SageAM.com) for introducing me to her creative team: Peter Padilla, Taylor Blake and Zack Marsh. Cheri and her team decided to take me on as a 'special project,' and their support and ideas helped me bring this book to print. They also were the ones who advised me to include images in the book which led me to Ismael Santillanes.

Ismael Santillanes experienced the prison as an inmate for decades. He was known for his poetry and art work, knew the characters in the book and was the best artist to capture the essence of the stories. He has been out of the system for years and is the author of, 'Indelicate Angels', a book on poetry. He is someone who ultimately benefitted from a second chance at life.

I'd also like to acknowledge Aric Bostick, who many years ago donated 50 of his books, 'Fired Up', to the Health-Related Recovery class in prison and is now one of the Nation's Leading Motivational Speakers and Trainers. You can find him at aricbostick.com.

Last but not least I want to thank my mother Eva for instilling in me resilience and my sister Joanie, for letting me be the big sister and always having my back.

Author | Speaker | Mentor

Karen Gedney, MD is board certified in Internal Medicine as well as Anti-Aging and Regenerative Medicine. Her memoir, '30 Years Behind Bars,' Trials of a Prison Doctor is her first debut as an author.

She is recognized in both the medical and correctional fields. She won the 'Heroes for Humanity Award,' in Nevada and was noted as 'One of the Best in the Business,' by the American Correctional Association.

Get In Touch With Karen Gedney, MD
www.DiscoverDrG.com

Like And Follow On Facebook
www.facebook.com/KarenGedneyMD

Made in the USA
Columbia, SC
13 April 2019